C000004907

HOUSE *by* *the* STREAM

BASED ON
A TRUE STORY

Gordon Channer's previous book, *Village by the Ford,* is a family story of leaving a big house and friends for loneliness of the wild Cornish valley to which they move - there to live under the most primitive conditions while struggling to survive, and to start a very special type of holiday retreat.

House by the Stream finds the family on the point of failure, but can they succeed after all? It is not a tale of violence, and crime, but danger does lie ahead. There is humour, how curiously people behave, problems to surmount, sadness and elation, a need to improvise - and the children, how do they manage? Could your own do better? This is a true story, but with just a sprinkling of fiction to bring out that sense of how things really were. The places and events are real, you can see for yourself, visit the village and the valley, for it did happen, always a risk, an adventure with no certainty of success - but wouldn't you love to do the same? If you dare!

i

To Katie and Jack
and to grandchildren everywhere.

Printed and bound in the UK
Cornish Books
First Published 1998
Reprinted 1999. Second impression 2003
© Gordon Channer 1998
IBSN 0-9537009-2-5

HOUSE *by* *the* STREAM

by

GORDON CHANNER

Valley of Dreams series

CORNISH BOOKS

5 Tregembo Hill
Penzance, Cornwall, TR20 9EP

Press Reviews
House by the Stream

Is this everyone's secret dream?   RADIO CORNWALL

Woven through with a rich vein of romance...will appeal
to readers of all ages... Nature plays an integral role...
happily devoid of crime & violence. THE CORNISHMAN

Written as fiction...the experiences are real
...an eye-opener   CARAVAN CLUB MAGAZINE

A heartwarming story of...improvisation...but most of all,
endurance...packed with interest   WEST BRITON

A gentle story of an idyllic life.
THREE PAGE ARTICLE - CARAVAN MAGAZINE

...pulls very few punches...told simply and effectively...
I'd recommend Gordon Channer's books to anybody...
how a real family made their dream come true. MMM

To anyone who enjoys a good easy family read this is the
book for you...full to overflowing with their adventures
...a book worth reading. CAMPING & CARAVANNING

Cornish dream became reality...a gentle book, packed with
incidents and a real unique feel for the Cornish landscape.
PAGE HEADLINE. WESTERN MORNING NEWS

Full of human colour...the reader is there willing them to
succeed. BH&HPA JOURNAL

It's a very good book with a great deal of humour about
real people and real situations. Once I have picked it up I
don't want to put it down. CARAVAN LIFE

**This series has now had 56 reviews including the
Daily Telegraph**

Contents

The Family at Relubbus

Gordon	Father
Jan	Mother
Christopher	Age nine (at start of book)
Sharon	Age seven
Stephen	Age four
Jim	Grandfather (Jan's father)
Audrey	Grandmother (Jan's mother)
Max	The big yellow excavator.

Period.   June 1970 - October 1972

Sketches and photos – see end of book.

Chapter 1

The St. Michael's Mouse

The caravan came on, slowing even more as it rounded a small bend to pause astride the bridge. The towing car's two occupants leaned over, gazing through open windows to watch the crystal water of the little stream flowing below, unaware they in turn were watched by other eyes; eyes staring from the concealment of deep shadow.

The couple were unsure, had seen the signs on the main road, half a mile back in the village of Relubbus and entered the stony track on impulse, not expecting it to be so long. Nor were they prepared for the wild uncultivated valley bottom through which the track led; but there had been no going back, no place to turn. Sitting centrally on the small arched bridge, its low parapets no more than a haphazardly-arranged row of granite blocks along each edge, it was easy to look directly down; even a few trout were visible against the gravely bed. Scanning in both directions along the remote Cornish valley, they turned to confer, heads together in deep discussion.

Jan, having watched the caravan's approach, stayed back in the shadow holding her breath. Would it sweep round in a big circle and drive off? She prayed it would not. After fourteen months of non-stop work, nothing in her life had seemed so important, so vital!

Waiting nervously, memories of the past year ran in a chaotic jumble through her mind; the family's first arrival in this wild lonely place, the work, the primitive conditions, and all aimed at one goal. She watched the couple intently. They *must* stay!

1

Her free hand shook slightly as the car rolled forward again, slowly, hesitantly. Would it stop? The vehicle steered towards her, a surge of hope; the throbbing pulse beat faster. She stepped through the doorway into the light, into view; wanting to do something with her hands but forced them to remain still, outwardly calm. It could yet be manoeuvring, to disappear in a sweeping turn.

The car drew to a halt.

A sigh of relief escaped Jan's lips. Standing on the top step, one hand now gripping the doorway of her own caravan home, she held back a moment longer, something within still whispering the word 'illusion'. Steeling herself she inhaled deeply, descending, feeling awkward - not shy exactly but unsure, like a first job or her first day at school all those years ago. How long was it since she had mixed with people? Ages! These were River Valley's first ever customers.

The new arrivals opened their doors and emerged as Jan swept up, shaking hands vigorously, an outward confidence struggling to mask those butterflies fluttering away inside. The Queen would have received no warmer greeting. No caravanner was ever so cosseted and fussed over, or received a more profusely sincere welcome.

Gordon appeared, hurrying towards them from beyond a clump of low bushes. In the quiet surroundings where no sounds penetrated but those made by themselves, the engine noise of a strange car had drawn him like a magnet from labours farther downstream. Asking their pardon for his working clothes, he guided them round, offering an over-whelming choice of pitches. Pushing open a door he proudly showed one sparkling toilet building then led them to the other, totally disregarding the quite obvious fact that both were identical in every respect.

And they did stay!

With the couple settled and comfortable, Gordon dashed back to Jan, leaping up three steps, straight through the doorway, lifting her in the air and swinging round with elation, hugging her close as they revolved in the confined space between cupboard, sink, and table.

This was it then! The site was on its way!

She placed the kettle on one of the gas rings that formed their only means of cooking, turning back with shining eyes. They kissed again with excitement. He fished in a pocket extracting two notes, depositing them on the table edge with a dramatic sweep of the arm, leaving them there and stepping back a pace, hand raised, palm upward as a cricketer might say, 'How's that?'

Reaching across, she touched with a certain reverence, lifting one up to the light. A pound! Glancing down, not relinquishing her hold, she scrutinised the other note; ten shillings!

"Three days!" he spoke with pride.

Long after the coffee was finished and he had returned to his work, Jan sat fingering the notes, deep in thought. Just over a year ago, early May in 1969, they had first arrived in a touring caravan with their three young children. At that time, tangled vegetation had covered the entire valley floor in a profusion of colourful blooms. Wild flowers of every description had sprouted from raised banks, sunken gullies and partially flat areas of tall grasses, all dominated by the brilliant yellow of densely-packed gorse patches. No clear space existed, not even enough for their tiny caravan home. There had been no piped water, they carried it in containers from the village half a mile away, or more often drew water from the river. An outside chemical bucket had provided the only toilet; truly outside, its user exposed to the elements and for a time clearly visible from the riverbank and surrounding hills.

How things had changed! She looked around at the slightly bigger caravan in which they now lived. Still just the one room, no electric and only two gas rings; but main's water ran from the single sink tap. Instead of that old chemical bucket, they now had no less than twenty flush toilets at their disposal in the toilet buildings not too far away, and sixteen basins all with hot and cold water at which to wash. The old ritual, which the children had detested, of taking a regular bath under the bridge in the clear but decidedly chilly river, had also been replaced. Now there were eight hot showers to choose between.

She crinkled the notes in her fingers again, looking out through a tiny window at the larger caravan a short distance away, the only other habitation as far as the eye could see. Enchanted with the beauty of this remote valley, her retired parents had sold their London house, coming to live nearby. Jim and Audrey were out shopping at the moment, taking Stephen with them. Stephen, her youngest at four, fair-haired, quiet, sometimes rebellious and often in trouble, would start school in September, three months away; until then he roamed the semi-wilderness at will. Reckless of personal safety and happy in his own company he talked little, seldom demanding attention; so different in character from his older brother and sister.

Sharon, competent in the home, inquisitively nosy but liked by everyone she met, acquiring friends so easily, would be eight in August.

"What can I do special for her birthday?" Jan wondered. Christopher, their oldest child at nine, would wait until December for his next birthday.

Gazing unseeing through the window, she drew in a deep breath of satisfaction, then glanced down at the notes moving backwards and forwards between her fingers.

"Pity not to frame them, hang them on the wall, but we need the money too much." She rose to start lunch, plain food as usual, the cheapest available. No meat today, it would be omelette, done at the last minute; but the potatoes must be started, they formed the main mass of every meal. She looked down yet again at the money.

"Perhaps I'll buy chicken later this week?"

* * *

The mouse was a surprise, one could almost say a sensation. Both older children now caught a bus to Marazion school. Christopher was progressing steadily after the unsettling effect of moving from the big house. He had handled the change to solitude and basic living conditions well, carrying water from the stream in buckets for most of the previous year, until his father had eventually received permission to dig the half-mile trench and lay a three-inch pipe for mains water. It was only one of the lad's many jobs; all the children had their chores. Life in the first small caravan, though good, had been arduous and cramped.

Christopher's talents were more physical than mental. While good at Maths, English and the Sciences, he had not the burning interest in learning that led to academic brilliance, though might well develop it later. He was good with his hands, no doubt from assisting in construction of the toilet buildings, good at sport and strong on common sense. Not that he displayed it on every occasion, and there was still his tendency to exaggerate. Like the rest of the family he had become increasingly interested in natural history. That may well have accounted for the mouse.

The school had visited St Michael's Mount one afternoon at the invitation of His Lordship, a local custom that the children all enjoyed. At some time during the tour of castle or grounds, Christopher found his mouse. How he managed to catch it, let alone persuaded the small creature to remain in his pocket, he could never explain. Arriving home that evening, he didn't even reveal its presence, until at tea it crept stealthily from hiding.

Eating arrangements were similar to those in many caravans. The table converted to a double bed at night, taking up the entire narrow width of one end. In the daytime it hinged to the wall, with a bench seat on either side. Jan and Gordon liked to sit opposite each other but sometimes the confined space dictated otherwise, for instance when all three children were present and a hot meal was being served.

So it was on this evening. The two parents sat one side of the table, the three children close together on the other. As the bench seats were fixed to the caravan walls, they could only be entered from one end; the person sitting in the corner must enter first. Gordon sat in one corner since

Jan, serving the food, would sit down last. On the other side Stephen entered first, then Sharon in the middle and Christopher on the outside. Squeezed on the small table were five cups of coffee and five steaming plates of beans on toast.

As they ate, the mouse crept from its pocket and crossed unseen from Christopher to Sharon; by what route no one would ever know. It first appeared on the front of her white cardigan, climbing towards the shoulder. Jan, from across the table, saw it first. Her eyes grew wide; she stared, frozen, fork half-raised, mouth opening to speak but no words issued forth.

Everyone turned to follow the direction of her gaze. The mouse was hidden from Stephen, but Dad and Christopher saw it almost simultaneously. Sharon however, caught a movement from the corner of her eye and acted quicker.

"Eekk!" She jumped back in stark terror, hitting the table hard with one knee. Two coffee cups went over and much of the rest spilled, but all eyes were on the mouse.

Christopher made a lunge, but Sharon was faster, flicking the thing (she had no idea what it was) away with the back of one hand, a shudder passing through her whole body as she touched it.

The mouse landed straddling toast on her plate, little feet scrabbling, disappearing, submerged in the hot mixture, one furry side liberally coated in tomato sauce. Squeaking loudly, it jumped clear scattering beans as it went, skating and slipping across the wet surface.

"Mouse!" Stephen now saw it too, shouting in delight, the one word comment typically short, an impish grin on his young face, light brown hair awry as he tried to push forward.

The caravan was in uproar! Jan swivelled sideways to avoid coffee running off the table edge. Gordon held his plate in the air but too late, the damage already done as liquid washed around the toast and dripped off the under-side. The children were in a tangle, pushing in opposite directions, Christopher trying to reach his pet, Sharon straining to back away, and Stephen pinned back by his sister's greater weight, attempting to free himself and move forwards. As they struggled, the mouse continued to skate around the puddled surface, hither and thither hunting a refuge from the pool retained by a shallow plastic lip that ran round the table's edge.

Christopher lunged again, trapping the small rodent between his hands and, quick as a flash, restored it to his blazer pocket then looked round with an innocent expression as if nothing had happened.

A stillness descended from the chaos. Four pairs of eyes bore down in his direction.

"Get orf!" Stephen's yell momentarily distracted attention as Sharon squashed against him in a vain attempt to recoil away from Christopher and the now hidden mouse. Her mask of alarm contrasted strongly with the roguish grin of anticipation still on young Stephen's face as he struggled to push past her and nearer the action. Gordon, across the table, was trying not to laugh, seeing the accusation on Jan's face as she issued an order.

"Own up. Where did you get it, and what is it doing in my caravan? Show!"

Christopher's hand moved reluctantly to his side, reappearing complete with mouse, now almost clean again, the greater part of its savoury coating residing, no doubt, inside the school blazer pocket. As his palm flattened it sat up, looked round and unconcerned by the havoc caused, contentedly commenced to lick remnants of baked bean from a paw. Stephen, having succeeded in pushing past Sharon into the middle position, held out a hand. Christopher looked doubtfully at his mother's accusing expression and detecting a slight nod, placed his hand next to Stephen's, tipping it sideways until the little feet slid down onto the flatter surface.

Picking up knife and fork, Gordon again attacked the beans on toast, now barely warm, coffee-flavoured, and very damp. He ate automatically, attention still on the tiny newcomer.

Sharon eased forward tentatively. A wave of deep panic

had assailed her when first sighting the unknown 'thing' clinging to her body, but that had passed now the nature of the intruder was clear. Nevertheless she remained unsure, apprehensive, not yet ready for close contact.

Stephen turned, watching her silently, young face inscrutable, perhaps with a hint of mischief; like a cat might watch a bird as it waited to pounce. The mouse still sat unconcerned on his palm, a palm that slowly retracted, arm bending as if in preparation.

For what?

Sharon recoiled sharply, trapped in the corner and unsure of her younger brother's intention; alarm in her face she looked quickly towards Dad. Gordon threw a warning glance at Stephen, anticipating his intention to toss the little rodent into his sister's lap, or worse into her hair, just to see her jump again.

Having pre-empted any such move by stern expression alone, he turned to Sharon.

"Think of it as a very tiny rabbit. Put out your hand if you want to hold it."

She raised her arm slightly, looking doubtfully at the empty palm, then reached slowly forward. At a nod from Dad, Stephen eased the tiny creature alongside. The mouse, seeming to know what was needed or preferring the cleaner palm, hopped across. Nervously at first she retracted the arm, gazing at the small ball and reaching hesitantly with the other hand to touch. The muzzle twitched, sensing perhaps the possibility of food, a movement very similar to the pair of baby rabbits she had nursed earlier that year. The young girl smiled and leant back, relaxing into the couch, stroking the short fur and inspecting it more closely.

Presently she stretched out an arm, past Stephen and towards the waiting hand of Christopher, who accepted the mouse but in swivelling round to offer it to Mum, nudged the table. A small tidal wave washed across the surface, some swilling over the edge.

Jan reached for a tea towel to mop up coffee still retained by the raised plastic rim. Leaving it to soak up the liquid, she looked round for some bread, and not seeing any, pulled free a well-saturated corner of toast from under the beans on her plate. Leaning over, she placed the damp offering on Christopher's hand. The mouse sniffed all round this sodden crumb, then stood on hind legs and shook its little head vigorously from side to side, perhaps to dry its whiskers.

"There you are," Gordon declared. "He doesn't like your toast either. Sensible fellow!"

Having reached unconsciously for the cloth to resume mopping up spilled liquid and loose beans from the table top, Jan turned, glancing down at his empty plate, a fierce expression failing to mask her underlying smile.

"Can't be that bad, you've eaten all yours."

"Yes. Well, it was cold, tasted funny, soggy all over, but then, that's the way it usually is. I'm used to it."

He ducked, not entirely escaping the thrown, coffee-soaked tea towel; it stuck to the wall behind before dropping, glancing off the bench edge onto the floor. While he wiped the wetness from one side of his face with a handkerchief, Jan reached for the mouse, which Christopher had drawn back close to his chest, protectively shielding it with his other hand when the cloth flew.

Everyone was laughing, the spoiled meal proving after all to be a great success!

Their little rodent became very popular, not seeming to care much who held it. A friendly chap, quite unafraid. It would stay on a hand or one of the big square cushions which formed the seat backs, sitting upright on its rear legs, munching various scraps that were offered, small furry cheeks rounded outwards as it chomped happily away.

Fortunately a mouse should be a most economical pet, provided there was only one, thwarting a natural tendency to multiply at alarming speed. Although women traditionally jump on chairs at the sight of mice, neither Jan nor Sharon now worried about this particular mouse. It was accepted and all agreed that, with certain restrictions, the little creature could live in their home.

The visiting caravan booked on for two extra days, another pound note, before leaving. This first arrival had failed to presage any massive influx, far from it. Empty disheartening days passed before the next appeared, then odd ones and twos at intervals over the next few weeks.

The financial situation began to look very serious. Never, so far, had the number of visitors exceeded the size of the family, which was now six, including the mouse, but that too disappeared later in the week.

"Leaving the sinking ship?" Gordon wondered briefly, pushing the idea away quickly, searching for less depressing reasons. The call of the wild maybe? He couldn't remember Jack London ever writing about mice. Perhaps it went off to model for some church restorer?

The few visitors that did find the site were mostly out during the day, but often in the evening they wandered to the bridge, fascinated by the clearness of water flowing below, and by fish plainly visible beneath its surface. Jan and Gordon usually walked over together to talk to them; it lay less than twenty paces from the makeshift steps descending from their own single doorway.

Questions were always asked about the river; why was it so clear, why did it flow away from the sea? Few realised just how close the sea lay in either direction, Atlantic to the north, the Channel to the south. Engine-houses, pubs, footpaths, fishing, a whole range of diverse subjects came under discussion. Offering advice and chatting with their meagre number of guests was so different from the previous year's total isolation. Gradually Jan began to feel more at ease with people, but was never entirely comfortable.

Sitting in the caravan one evening, she watched two couples who arrived separately but had quickly become friends. That was only to be expected, for at present no other visitors graced the park and people naturally tend to seek company. They strolled along the riverbank, pausing here and there to point down into the water, presumably at the trout.

"They're walking towards the bridge. Let's go over and chat to them." Gordon stood, holding out a hand but Jan hung back, not taking it.

"Let's not."

She had spoken quietly, with reluctance, almost sadly.

"What's the matter?"

"Look at them. I feel it with all the visitors but with those four in particular. Look at them," she urged again, pausing while he bent to peer through the window, then back at her with a blank expression.

She sighed, not really wanting to explain but seeing no other way.

"Men are just insensitive beasts!" She reached for his hand, pulling hard, forcing him back down onto the bench seat beside her. "They're coming closer. See their clothes, everything new, not a thread or a stitch out of place. The two leading; his trousers. Sharp? I could peel potatoes with creases like that! And what about her blouse? Crisp, perfect, might have been unpacked this evening. And that skirt. What do you think I look like next to visitors who can afford anything they want! I've nothing new, can't even iron anything. All creased and worn. How do you think I feel, standing out there talking to them?"

Gordon looked at her. She had said nothing before and he had never given it a thought. There was an intensity of voice, a brightness in her eyes that threatened to spill over. He cursed himself. She was right, men were callous beasts; he ought to have realised. She still held his hand, gripping it tightly. Leaning over he slid his right arm round, pulling her closer, pulling her head onto his shoulder. After a few moments he eased away just far enough to kiss her lips gently, then leaned forwards to whisper in one ear.

"I wouldn't care if you were wrapped in old cement bags, you're what Christopher would call fantastic!"

They sat for a while, hugging and watching the visitors, seeing but not so easily seen, knowing it was more difficult to look into the relatively dim interior of the caravan with its small windows.

After a while Jan leaned her head back, brushing his lips softly with her own.

"Thanks."

He noticed a stain down one cheek and wanted to say something, feeling a great tenderness, but unable to find the proper words, only squeezed her tighter. The silence lengthened again, the visitors wandering off down river leaving them still sitting, comfortable in each other's arms. Both glanced up when Stephen's little head popped through the doorway, but satisfied nothing interesting was going on, he disappeared again. The two older children were round the site somewhere, playing with a friend from school.

"What would *you* call me?" Jan asked quietly.

"Pardon?" Chances like that didn't come up very often; he was taken aback.

"If fantastic is Christopher's word, what would you say?"

"Ah well..." He saw a hint of a smile, she looked great when she smiled. He thought for a moment. "I'm more conservative, more honest..."

A little fist banged lightly on his ribs, he caught the flash of white teeth. It was good to see her laughing again. They used to laugh a lot but she had been more sombre lately. Small wonder with so few visitors and no clear way ahead. He reached for a towel, gently wiping the stain from her cheek, then leaned back shaking his head slightly.

"Yes, I'm more honest, but you're OK. Bit wrinkled as you say," he spoke doubtfully, pretending to look her up and down. "A good hydraulic press might do wonders." He saw the fist raise again, and rushed on. "Anyway, you're special."

"Special?"

"Yes - such a comfortable woman to live wi..."

He never finished the sentence, she pushed him off the end of the bench, falling on top in the effort. The fight was short, neither could do much for laughing. She rose gazing down at him, her melancholy mood lifted.

"You don't cut that great a figure yourself. There's not the faintest sign of a crease in those trousers. Couldn't you

12

sleep with them under the mattress?"

He glanced at the trousers. She was right again, they hung limply baggy, but her suggestion would never work.

"No chance. It's not a proper mattress remember, only four cushions off the bench seats, laid flat."

"Just have to put up with you then." She shook her head, offering a hand. "Come on, the visitors are returning up the bank, we'll go and chat if you want."

* * *

Penzance was not a big town, but rambling enough when hoping to locate something not quite run of the mill. Jan walked up the high street with Stephen, knowing what she wanted, but not where to find it. Ostensibly she had come for supplies, parking free in a side street at the bottom end of town and now walked upwards, towards the figure of Humphry Davy, inventor of the miner's lamp. The statue stood dwarfed by Lloyd's dome but she didn't intend to go that far. On her right lay Wilton & Nicholls, the ironmongers, its old-fashioned window frames painted pillar-box red. Entering, she approached one of the several counters.

"I want an iron?"

The assistant's face said 'No', his eyes flicking towards an electrical shop across the street, but she stopped him before he could speak.

"Not an electric iron, the old-fashioned type for heating on a range."

It took longer than expected. The ironmonger's directions were to a small side-street shop, and from there the quest led to others, but eventually an iron was located. Two pounds had been asked.

"Some people collect them," the man suggested.

It sounded absurd. She had paid a pound in the end, and thought that expensive. Now back at home with Stephen off playing outside, the iron sat above a lighted gas ring and a blanket lay spread across the table. Alongside, on the bench seat, a collection of blouses skirts and trousers awaited attention, many belonging to the children.

Was the iron ready? No even heat this, not like the top of a hot kitchen range. Sitting directly over a gas flame was less predictable. A few liquid droplets sizzled strongly when flicked at the chunky tool. Fine, should be about right, best not leave it too long, might scorch the material. Reaching out, Jan lifted the handle.

"Agh!"

Dropping it clumsily back on the flame, burned fingers were plunged into a bowl on the worktop nearby, the hand waving around in cool water, joints flexing. It was more than lucky chance; the bowl stood there every day, keeping any remaining part-bottle of milk cool, for they had no fridge.

Looking more closely, the cause became clear. Little tongues of fire licked out around the iron's base; not to any great extent, the blue flame scarcely visible, but that heat was rising. Like a finger held over a lighted candle, the handle was unbearably hot! An oven glove thickened with a yellow duster overcame the problem. She worked quickly, using a damp cloth, leaving the gas on for re-heating at frequent intervals.

That evening, with the children playing outside, and having sent Gordon on an unnecessary task in the toilet building, she slipped into a freshly-ironed skirt and blouse. The children arrived back first. She had not expected the boys to notice but was disappointed when Sharon failed to comment.

Gordon walked in shortly after, spoke to her and turned away, then swung sharply back. Though he passed no remark, the long lingering glance said everything.

Strolling to the bridge that evening, chatting again with the visitors, she felt better, more confident, no longer so second class. Only the scarcity of holidaymakers prevented her feeling really good.

That night after the children were asleep, she prepared

for bed, folding her blouse, bending over to lay it carefully on the floor. A rough hand reached from behind, pulling down the zip and popping open the stud at her waist.

"No!" She jumped back with a whisper of alarm, grasping the skirt to stop it falling, and was on the point of warning "Don't crease it," but stopped, suddenly remembering the garment could now be re-ironed at any time. Smiling, she let it fall and stepped forward.

* * *

June passed with only sporadic improvement. By early July caravan numbers had still failed to rise. They were desperately disappointed. Having done so much to make people happy when they arrived, the possibility of visitors not finding River Valley at all had never been seriously anticipated.

How could more be attracted? They sat together again, as so often before, hunting for a way. Why had the carefully placed advertisements not worked? Both knew in their hearts it was a case of too little too late, but lack of money had precluded more. In any case, neither had any clear idea of the best way to advertise.

"What do we have that people want?" Jan asked aloud but mostly to herself, chin resting on the supporting triangle of hands and arms, with elbows spread apart on the table.

"It has to be the countryside," Gordon rubbed his chin thoughtfully. "We've the cleanest river in England, this beautiful valley and quietness like most people have never experienced; what more can they want? But it isn't that. It isn't that they don't like it; they're just not finding it – not even passing the entrance. On the coast road everyone would drive by, but inland we need an advert to make them come looking, something eye-catching, otters in the river or an osprey, but we can't - it isn't true."

"We've badgers in Christopher's sand heaps. Might they have young by now?" Jan frowned, uncertain.

Gordon knew where she meant, the heaps had been

Christopher's since the lad discovered them the previous autumn, the residue from washing for tin a century ago. Young badgers?

"We've no more money to advertise, but a photo...?" He pondered the possibility, working it through in his mind. "We could send it to various caravan magazines hoping for free publicity. The young are always attractive, particularly nocturnal ones. Pretty slim chance though; don't see adult badgers often - and I've never seen their cubs." He paused again. "But I have to try! Must get close, use a flash; one shot is all, and they'll be gone. I'll need moonlight just to find them."

Eleven o'clock; an almost full moon shone from the eastern sky. Two figures, both dressed in dark clothes, emerged from the caravan. White faces shone palely in the cold light, to disappear as they turned off northwesterly, downstream. One large one small shadow preceded them, leaning diagonally to their left along the riverbank. The smaller figure glanced back once towards the warm, friendly glow of gaslight penetrating thin curtains at the caravan windows.

As the cleared areas were left behind, Christopher stayed close to his father. Though he had ventured in the dark often enough, it had usually been no more than to cross to the toilet buildings, or before they were built, to locate the old chemical bucket hidden in a pile of concrete blocks. Then too, noise had not mattered; now they were moving stealthily. Quietness bred its own uncertainty; what else was creeping furtively nearby? Peering into the deeper blackness as they passed an opening in the bushes, a recess beyond the moon's penetration, the young lad glanced quickly up at the taller figure beside him for reassurance.

Leaving the river, the sand heaps were approached and a vantage point located; two gorse bushes with a narrow gap between, not too far from an entrance hole to the badger setts. Here they squatted, listening, watching and waiting. Gordon tried to check the holes were not downwind but no detectable breeze offered an indication as to which direction that might be. They crouched unmoving.

On one occasion a small cloud hid the moon casting deeper shadows, otherwise visibility remained good, detail disappearing with distance but general outlines clear right across the valley. Ten minutes passed, Christopher stirred restlessly, dropping one knee to the ground, sliding the foot backwards with a slight rustle. How could his father keep so still? He wanted to turn, to look behind, to check...

More time passed; a night flying moth fluttered close, causing him to breathe in sharply then ease his neck slowly round, peering behind again. Minutes stretched to twenty, then half an hour; long minutes with a landscape still devoid of movement. Imperceptibly, shadow positions were changing as the moon tracked fractionally westward, the process slow - undetected by the waiting pair.

In the end they withdrew, heading back, Christopher for bed, his father intending to try later, the sound of their own careful steps loud in the silence.

Towards the river progress became easier. An area of poor soil supported mainly low growing heathers with occasional patches of sparse grass. Halfway across, Gordon stopped as a rabbit raced towards a gorse thicket fifty yards away. Christopher, a dozen paces in the lead, hurrying on, anxious for the security of the caravan, quickly halted, watching the rabbit disappear, then turned to look back at his father.

They stood momentarily, silent and waiting; springy vegetation flexing slightly as they twisted, feet unmoving, to scan in other directions. Between them a break in the heather, a large ellipse of almost barren ground. This amphitheatre in miniature lay highlighted in the moonlight, crossed by a few twiggy shadows from nearby trees and flecked with patches of low growing hardy grass, but nothing more.

Suddenly, from the heather under Gordon's boots, a dark shape slithered at speed onto the bare ground, heading directly towards Christopher. For long moments both stared, fascinated by the sinister form of a large adder squirming its way rapidly across the opening.

"Look out!"

The lad failed to react, his eyes riveted, paralysed... hypnotised almost, by the snake heading straight for his feet. Moonlight magnified the sinuous outline against the lighter grass, a uniformly black body and its own dark shadow moulding into one broader form. Disturbing even in daylight, here in the dappled darkness the creature took on malevolent shape, its writhing motions the epitome of evil, commanding the eye, numbing the mind!

And still the boy stood, unmoving. Already more than half the distance had been covered.

"Move! Now!" The urgent command, shouted like two bullets, burst through his trance.

Christopher stirred, acted, leapt aside! A heavy pulse drummed in his ears; he was breathing deeply, shaken and unsure! The sinister reptile, no more than six inches from his feet as he jumped, now slid on to disappear under heather in the direction of the stream.

Father and son looked at each other. Somewhere between themselves and the riverbank, the most direct way back to the caravan, lay the snake!

"Well?" Gordon looked down at his son who had stepped back quickly to stand close. "Do we go the long way round, or take a run and hope our feet are moving fast enough if we tread on it?"

Christopher stared towards the river no more than fifty yards away, then in the opposite direction, to the longer route through a tangle of taller trees and bushes; undergrowth in which the children regularly played. It seemed different tonight, full of deep shadows. He turned back to where the snake must lie, paused for only a moment then raced across the heather, lifting his feet like a dressage horse.

CHAPTER 2

Red Brick

Sharon opened her eyes; it was light. She had slept badly, assailed by uneasy dreams, nameless worries the meaning of which eluded her but which would not go away. Last night when her parents were talking she had lain awake like many times before, eavesdropping, keeping quite still, trying to hear what was said. Often in the small single room where everyone slept and lived, she would feign sleep, struggling to stay alert after her brothers dropped off, anxious not to miss the private conversations between her parents. What they said last night had not been clear, they had spoken guardedly, in low tones, worried anxious tones. It had been this rather than the actual words, this and several references to leaving, to going somewhere, that caused the foreboding. The voices had made clear this was something neither mother nor father wanted. Why should they have to go anyway? What would make them? And where? True they had moved before, but this valley was great. She wanted to stay. All her new friends lived in this area now! Did it mean anything or had they been talking about someone else, a visitor maybe?

She could never ask, was not supposed to be listening; could not even talk to the boys, they would question Mum. Best forget it. Turning carefully over, she looked towards the window.

Daylight filtered easily through the thin caravan curtains. That was normal in July, giving little indication of the time; the midsummer sun rose by five o'clock, an hour before any of the family. How different from winter mornings, when only a gentle hiss from the single gas light and heat from the log-burning boiler had kept their small home warm and cosy.

She lifted her head carefully, half surprised to find her parents still asleep in the convertible bed across the room. It must not yet be six o'clock. Snuggling back, trying to lie comfortably, she dreamed idly about her eighth birthday in a month's time but the uneasy thoughts resurfaced making her restless again, unable to settle; besides she needed a toilet. Sitting up carefully, Sharon eased herself away from her younger brother who slept head to toe on the same bench seat, covered by the same blankets. Pulling knees to chin brought both feet clear of the bedclothes, allowing her legs to swing out and noiselessly to the floor. Gathering a towel, sponge bag and small pink flannel, she reached down for the dressing gown that lay folded on top of her pile of clothes. Garments in use were always stored on the floor overnight, for lack of space elsewhere.

It felt warm in the caravan, she hesitated, took three silent steps, easing back a curtain from the tiny window in the door's top section and peeped out. The sky was clear. An idea formed in her mind. Putting the gown to one side, she lifted the pile of clothes, being careful not to disturb neat folds created by meticulous placement the previous evening, unlike two other crumpled heaps thrown down by the boys. Stealthily she made for the door, trying not to wake the family.

Habitually she had returned to don her clothes after washing, not wishing to carry them and let visitors see that she dressed in the toilet building; but she did not really like dressing in the caravan any more either, with brothers and parents in the same room. This morning she was so early, surely no other person would be about. Slipping through and closing the door quietly, she ran erratically across the stony yard, clutching the clothes, hastily transferring her weight to counter small pebbles under bare feet. The activity helped brush away more of the morbid thoughts, probably just a bad dream anyway.

The boys often washed at the single tap in the caravan. If Mum was using the sink, they sometimes dashed to the stream, splashing cold river water over faces then wiping it off with a towel, freshening the skin rather than cleaning it. Sharon however, loved the hot water available only in the toilet building. Leaving a cubicle, she crossed to the basins, filled one with water almost too hot to bear, stood on a footstool then dipped in the flannel and wiped it round her face with a deep sigh of contentment. Dipping again, she rubbed it with soap and washed thoroughly, rinsing off twice in the soft feeling warm water; then again from sheer pleasure.

Popping into a shower compartment the young girl slid the door bolt, stripped off and hurriedly dressed, then back to the row of sinks, standing again on a footstool to see in the mirrors and comb long tresses, pleased not a soul had yet appeared. Brushing shoulders for hairs and carefully straightening her collar, she made sure the basin was not left dirty before returning to the caravan feeling much better. Both parents had risen and were about to go cleaning.

"Wake the boys and prepare breakfast," her mother whispered, laying a hand on Sharon's arm, then reached into a cupboard and extracted five eggs, placing them on the tiny working top beside the sink. "Time it for twenty minutes; with hardly any visitors, cleaning won't take long."

As her mother stepped to the doorway, Sharon nodded acknowledgement, smiling at the prospect of cooking. She knew in advance the boys would grumble about the meal however good, and frowned, believing they should show more appreciation and gratitude. Never mind, it would give her chance to order them about. The final uneasy thoughts had disappeared.

* * *

The depressingly slack days dragged on, school holidays began, and still numbers failed to respond. The outlook was bleak. They sat together over morning coffee in that last week of July, despondent, few smiles, the radio filling that gap more usually taken up by conversation. Both were withdrawn in their own sombre contemplations, neither with a desire to talk - at a loss for words that would help. The news was on but neither was really listening when suddenly both sat bolt upright, attention rigidly fixed, disbelieving. The announcer had been speaking of traffic jams and went on to claim that all sites in Cornwall were full!

"People who make these sweeping statements without taking the trouble to check their facts, ought to be shot!" Gordon voiced his resentment with feeling, switching off the set sharply as he spoke.

"No!" Jan uttered the single word forcefully, her features tight with anger, "Even hanging's too good for them, they should be barbecued over a slow fire!"

These barbarous, out of character suggestions from a couple who normally thought in more sanguine terms, resulted from an explosion of pent-up frustrations, raised to boiling point by the irresponsible radio statement. None of the children were in; neither parent would have allowed their feelings, their depression, to show so clearly otherwise.

"Why do researchers ring up the most well-established, easy-to-find site they can think of, right on the beach, and assume all others are the same?" asked Jan in despair.

"Maybe they don't," Gordon frowned, deeply resentful. "Probably they ring one after another until somebody says he's full. The radio man conveniently forgets those who still have space - *that* isn't news! He only wants the sensational answer, never mind who suffers as a result!"

"That's probably exactly what happened!" Jan paused. To say she was annoyed would be the understatement of the year.

They sat for a while, the gloom deepening before she spoke again.

"It still means some sites have lots of people. Why do they all head for the coast?"

Inland sites in her opinion, apart from generally

22

attracting a quieter class of customer than those right on the sea shore, offered not only better value but less crowding and as a bonus, more shelter when the wind blew.

It would be wrong to say they were downhearted. They were desperate!

"You must be right. No good pretending visitors are staying at home any more, the election's over now. Did you know John Nott lives farther down the valley, between us and St. Erth?"

"Someone mentioned it in the shop," Jan nodded.

"It seems almost unavoidable that we'll go broke," Gordon spoke quietly, looking disconsolately across the table at her, "but there must be a way, must be something we can do?"

It was no new sentiment, further efforts to find badger cubs had failed, as had all other ideas for free publicity, and there was no spare cash to pay for any. Jan's Dad might have lent them money for more advertising but he needed it himself. With his worsening leg, living in a caravan was difficult, he must build a bungalow, the cost of which was uncertain. In any case the advertising taken so far had been ineffectual, obviously done in the wrong place or the wrong format, and it was already too late, people were on their way!

Both Gordon and Jan had believed for many weeks that the outcome was almost inevitable, but this announcement made it so much worse; like dying of thirst within sight of water.

She reached out, touching his hand before speaking.

"I know things look bad but it's been a good year. Better we made the attempt and failed than to think back in years to come, always regretting we didn't have the courage to try. The children have loved it; been good for them, too. You couldn't have done more." She smiled and leaned forward, kissing him gently in an effort to lift his sombre mood.

He responded, placidly, without fire, then leaned back to look at her and smiled, a tired half-hearted smile. He

23

couldn't shake from his mind all the work, the long hours, poor food, cramped conditions. True, it had been fun, hard to be sure, but so different; stimulating, a challenge! Would it really be for nothing? They wouldn't even recover much by selling up. Who would want toilets with no one to use them?

Defeat stared them in the face; they both knew it. Only having each other and the children remained a light, shining in their gloom. Had they risked all, given all, and still lost?

"What can we do?" Gordon asked grimly, spreading the fingers of his outstretched hand on the table in a despairing gesture. "A trip up the A30 to Bodmin might at least tell us the number of caravans on the road."

They set off straight away, not waiting for Jan's parents to return from Penzance. A scribbled note left on the caravan door said, "Park anywhere - back later" though they doubted anyone would arrive. Sharon and Christopher were somewhere in the valley but the caravan door was never locked and they would see the note. Stephen, who had been playing by the bridge, came with them, refusing Jan's lap to kneel behind the little van's seats. It was action born of desperation, not with hopes of any achievement, for even if they did see caravans, what could they do? But anything had to be better than sitting in a deepening gloom, drowning in their own sorrow.

They hurried away, Townsend, Leedstown, Praze-an-Beeble and on towards Camborne, nearly ten miles with minimal traffic and no caravans. Jan sighed as Gordon glanced at her in resignation, returning his eyes quickly to the way ahead.

It was on entering the main road at Camborne that the first caravans appeared, then one every minute and a half on average, drove by; all heading into West Cornwall. Twenty flashed past in the next half-hour as the little van followed the A30 towards Bodmin. Traffic intensified at Indian Queens, much of it now turning for Newquay. There seemed little point in continuing. Turning in a side road, they joined the stream and drove back, Stephen climbing between the seats to sleep on his mother's lap during the return journey.

How could these caravans be contacted? Once home, a pile of leaflets produced earlier in the year for responding to telephone calls, was extracted from the bottom of a cupboard.

"What about lunch?" Jan asked, glancing at her watch to find it had already gone one o'clock, but neither could face eating. While she stayed on site, without much hope but ready for action, Gordon shot off to a rather difficult junction on the A30 at Scorrier. A long line of vehicles waited bumper to bumper, snaking off into the distance.

Bouncing up the ragged road edging, he parked on the grass verge nearby, jumping quickly from the vehicle, running down the line of traffic and offering a leaflet to each caravan. They were accepted. Sitting prisoners in the slow-moving queue, windows open against the stifling heat, these caravanners took the brochures, glancing through from sheer boredom if nothing else.

Standing in the caravan doorway, Jan had watched Gordon carry the bundle of leaflets, jump in the mini and disappear up the track. "Too fast," she thought seeing a cloud that all but hid the vehicle. As the dust settled, she turned to look across the site at two caravans on the grassy area near the river, the only ones staying at present. Even those were empty, the visitors out for the day.

"Will there be two more here by evening?" Her head shook doubtfully; probably not and certainly nothing could happen for an hour, it would be forty minutes before he parked the mini-van. The sound of voices drew her attention, Sharon and Christopher appeared, walking across the yard; they would need a meal. As the pair ascended the caravan steps, Stephen greeted them in the doorway. Jan stepped quickly over putting arms round all three, hugging them close, squeezing them to her, eyes closed, swallowing a lump in her throat, face turned away to hide a deep concern for their future.

Only Sharon remained when a caravan appeared up the road; she had helped with the washing-up while her brothers went off somewhere together. Stephen had mentioned the trip towards Bodmin as they ate but he had no idea of its significance and Mum had made light of the matter. Nor had she revealed what their father was now doing. The family were always pleased when a caravan arrived but Sharon wondered why her mother seemed more keyed-up as this one approached. It rolled across the bridge and drew slowly to a stop. A man emerged, stretched, arched his back, and looked round. Sharon, peeping carefully through the front window, saw her mother walk over with a greeting, then drew in her breath sharply. Three children sat in the back seat, one was a girl of about her own age.

"Welcome to River Valley!" Jan, as always, felt slightly awkward greeting strangers, people had been so few over the last year.

"Hello. Some bloke gave me a leaflet. Is this the place?" he waved a copy of the site brochure.

"Yes, come and have a look round."

"Can I book for two weeks?"

For a moment Jan was unable to reply. Two weeks! No one had ever booked for two weeks. "Yes!"

"Good. How much?"

"Um... just a minute, I need my pad." She raced back into the caravan, snatched pad and a pencil, scribbling figures while descending the steps to the waiting customer. "That's ten shillings a night for the two adults and one shilling each for the children, thirteen shillings multiplied by fourteen nights. Just a minute while I work it out."

Silently she put the figures down, "Wish Gordon were here, let's see, ten times thirteen is a hundred and thirty, plus four times, that's a pack of cards, fifty-two." The figures were written down, one below the other and added up; one hundred and eighty-two shillings... "That's nine pounds and two shillings please."

Having taken the money, the caravan was led off to a pitch, and shortly after another appeared along the track.

Back at Scorrier, Gordon continued to give out leaflets, having no idea whether any would be effective. Later in the afternoon the queue dwindled. By six o'clock the supply of incoming visitors appeared to dry up and the mini-van headed home.

On returning to Relubbus, there were twelve caravans, and one jubilant wife waiting. A 600% improvement! Jan hugged him, bounced up and down with enthusiasm and wanted to do something madly extravagant like opening a pot of salmon paste for tea! She knew there was one, unopened, bought in a rash moment and hidden in the far corner of her food cupboard, just waiting for such an occasion.

The children too, were affected, for Jan had explained the importance of customers. It had been a mild explanation, understating the probable outcome but sufficient at least, to make them aware that more visitors meant better food. In any case, over the past weeks they would have known something was amiss; it was difficult in a small caravan to keep anything secret. Any attempt to conceal entirely the facts, would have been counterproductive. They would have sensed her anxiety. Even so, both parents had been careful that none of the three youngsters should recognise the full gravity of their situation, the abyss of failure that threatened.

Similarly, her own contagiously joyous mood was now more responsible for their present happiness than any real knowledge of just how significant this extra income was to their own future.

Leafleting continued. In four days, numbers rose to forty, but two days later dropped to the low thirties. The following week, the beginning of August, the combined total of caravans and one solitary tent surged above the magic fifty!

This transformation, the change from being practically alone to having people everywhere, affected the family deeply. Suddenly being the centre of attention, the focal point, was flattering, exhilarating - but the constant demands were hard to cope with. It called for a different outlook. Whereas before it had been concentration and endurance on single tasks, suddenly stamina of another kind was needed. All manner of things required dealing with in quick succession, instant answers, snap decisions, juggling several matters at once. An early casualty was the system of recording how long people had paid for. Writing down *'John Smith, fifteen nights'* no longer worked. With the numbers now involved it became too time-consuming and prone to error to go back through a host of entries trying to find when any particular caravan was due to leave. Several times Gordon approached people a day early, apologising profusely and feeling stupid when, with the aid of their receipt and days counted on a calendar, the visitor proved they were not yet due to pay again! A new system must be devised, something simple and quick, they hardly had time to eat, let alone browse through accounts. When a customer came to book more nights an answer was needed immediately, at one's fingertips, before the phone rang or yet another caravan arrived.

And as if that was not enough, yet more problems required a solution! People wanted gas bottles, expecting to find them on site and were unhappy to have to go searching elsewhere. They expected and asked for information on a panoply of subjects, wanted help with awnings that refused to fit, left odd items of clothing in the toilet buildings and came hunting for them later. Some were unable to back their caravans into position and wanted help pushing, one man asked to cash a cheque but Gordon refused, not daring to risk money which might just allow them to survive; the list was endless - and suddenly Jim needed Help!

* * *

Plans, plans, and more plans! Jim and Audrey, Jan's parents, wanted a bungalow on the pocket of land half a mile away in Relubbus, a plot included in the original purchase. The building's appearance was important, since it lay centrally in the small hamlet where the stone track to the site branched off the B3280. Details had been redrawn many times during the previous winter and spring. Planning permission first sought from the Council over six months before, had been dogged by setbacks. How many times had Gordon carefully extricated his only suit from the tiny, tightly-packed caravan wardrobe, to attend a meeting with Council Officers? All had not gone well.

On the very first occasion an initial, as yet incomplete drawing had been presented to ascertain that there were no fundamental objections. The question of finishes had arisen. It was an informal meeting, three Council men looking at the sketches, passing comments on this and that, offering advice, asking questions.

"What external finishes did you have in mind?" one officer enquired as the other two discussed together the general appearance of the building.

"A good quality red brick?" Gordon had replied, offering Jim's preference more as an idea than a certainty.

A sudden silence engulfed the room! The three officials turned to stare with distaste.

What had happened? He glanced quickly downwards, checking his trousers; no, the flies were not undone. What then? Measles?

The senior officer was speaking again, in a cold severe voice. "We don't have bricks in Cornwall, certainly not red ones. Conflicts with nature!"

A further silence followed before another man, in a more friendly tone, explained. "There are no brick clays in the county, we use concrete blocks then cement render to produce a weatherproof surface, usually finished with white or cream paint."

"Red bricks are Devon." The first officer cut in, his comment tinged with contempt.

Though similar matters of detail cropped up from time to time, the main delay arose from a desire on the Council's part for a house in preference to a bungalow. However, Jim's arthritis made a single-storey building essential; he could never manage a flight of stairs. In the end, Mr Race of the Architects Department at County Hall, sketched several external changes that he considered would make the building acceptable. His ideas gave a well-balanced pleasing effect and were gladly incorporated in yet another drawing, in high hopes that this time permission would be forthcoming. Gordon was grateful for the help, and for assistance from Mr Lanyon, Mr Rolf, Mr Collins and many others both at County and at District; all had added in some measure to the pleasing appearance of the site. Perhaps the long delay was worthwhile after all, though it had really upset Audrey as the weeks slid by.

Waiting for the postman one Friday, she stood with Jim by the bridge, talking to an elderly couple who expressed surprise at their retirement to live on the site, and asked how they found it.

Telling of their plans to build, Audrey explained, "A caravan is all very well while you're young and fit, but at our age you get pains in muscles you didn't know you had! We want to enjoy our bungalow while we still have time."

She was sixty-one, borne in the spring of 1908 in Three Bridges, Sussex, and having lived through two world wars, figured they could do without more hard times. The postman arrived as they chatted, but the vital letter still failed to appear.

"There! Another week wasted," Audrey protested in disappointment. "The last thing I need is some stupid council wasting years of my life because they can't make a decision!"

"Kept you waiting?" The elderly man asked Jim quietly.

"You wouldn't believe how long. Pity they weren't in China back in the 1920's. They'd have made decisions quick enough then; made them or died!"

As the two women wandered off along the riverbank, Jim took a few stiff paces but decided against following and stayed on the more level ground.

"What was China like, then?" his new friend asked, waiting with him.

"Hard," Jim said. "The Guards, that was our mob. We moved a lot, but one place I remember clearly. Constant danger, bad food, and our Corporal - raving mad. The Chinese people were nice enough, particularly the older ones, they have a special sort of dignity you know, the old people - looked up to in China. Conditions were bad, we'd rats in the billet, more like a pillbox, everyone slept hands on rifles, bayonets fixed, always ready for action. One day a rat ran across the floor, our Corporal after it with his bayonet. Everyone jumped clear, he wasn't safe, see - utterly insane. That rat ran right across my boot; that's where he got it. Spiked it straight through, rat, boot, foot, everything. Fixed the lot to that dirt floor! Pity it wasn't those damn council blokes, teach 'em to think quicker, like I should have done!"

Jim spoke with bloodthirsty sincerity, he hated anything that upset Audrey. The couple had married in 1932, when she was a shop assistant at Bourne and Hollinsworth in Oxford Street, and he a young Constable in the Met, having transferred directly from Guards to Police.

Happily however, a few days later the revised drawings arrived, stamped with Council approval. Work could start!

Great! But why now, when they were so busy? Why not a month or more earlier when visitors were few? Such is life! Making those drawings, mostly late in the evenings when other work had ceased for the day, had been a problem in itself. Instability of the caravan, which rocked slightly when anyone moved, had added to the difficulty. Jan was delighted with the news, knowing the big drawing-board could in future remain stored in the toilet building loft.

Both she and Gordon were now fully occupied, rising at six each morning to clean the site's facilities, then one driving off with leaflets while the other attended to visitor's needs, usually until quite late each day. They would be unable to help much with the building work for many weeks yet, though Gordon did trundle down in 'Max', the excavator, on a couple of evenings to dig the foundations. He also left Christopher and Sharon in charge of the site for two hours when the concrete arrived a few days later.

31

Audrey however, although pleased to have started, remained impatient. She persuaded Jim to hire Percy and Charles, the father-and-son local builders who the previous year had helped apply cement finishes to the toilet buildings. Jim readily agreed. He found increasing difficulty with his legs; confined spaces in the caravan and the many steps on entering or leaving, were aggravating his condition. Paying wages to get the blockwork under way was preferable to waiting until the season quietened down.

* * *

"Leafleting *has* been successful." Jan repeated, happily gazing out over the field of little lights as nightfall softened the outline of the many units now with them. She drew the flimsy curtains closed. "They're a bit crowded; if I send in many more, what will you do with them? It was busy today, I like the busy periods. Sitting at the roadside on slack days, or towards evening when few caravans are travelling is not so good."

Gordon listened and watched her, it was past eleven, they were preparing to turn in for the night. She had arrived back for a late tea and since then had been restless, spirited outbursts gushing forth at intervals, talking, animated, alive, like bubbles from champagne. She had reason! Those little lights dotted in such profusion across the small usable area of site, embodied more than success - they represented survival!

"You're right." He agreed, smiling at the renewed outburst. "We do need extra space. I'll work on more pitches next winter, try to double the area available. Not just for caravans, we must reach more tents and each one should be farther apart."

"You think there will be a next winter then? We are going to make it, take enough to see us through?"

"Not yet we haven't, not by a long way, but it does seem promising. Isn't it a great feeling, snatching victory? Well, having a chance to anyway, after the way things looked.

32

Life's funny you know."

"Why?" Jan asked.

"What would you say were the two worst things that have happened this year - No let me tell you. That radio announcement about all sites being full, for one. The continual delay of Jim's bungalow plans for the other. Do you agree?"

"I suppose. Stephen's back injury was worst of all but that was last year. Yes I'd agree, those probably were the worst things, but what's funny about them? I would never call either funny and Audrey certainly wouldn't."

"It was the radio that made us go checking for caravans, without that we might never have started leafleting, just sat here hoping, then failing without a clue what to do. And that planning permission, if it had arrived a month earlier we should have been helping Jim build; probably have missed that 'all sites are full' announcement altogether. Those two things which we hated so much, may have been our salvation!"

They looked at each other, smiles broadening as a hand reached out, found another and squeezed. They hugged with a deep feeling of vitality and elation, Jan breaking away in a little pirouette, clenching her fists, arms giving a little inwards jerk of exuberance as she spoke.

"I think I love naughty radio men and indecisive Councillors!"

A traffic warden had been introduced at the junction, with whom first Gordon and later Jan developed a very happy relationship. They became so friendly that Jan felt he was actively helping by stopping the queue at exactly the places that suited her best, but he never mentioned it. When she hinted to him, trying to offer thanks, he just winked and brushed her thanks aside, so she still couldn't be sure. He was good company if the traffic became sparse, and as days passed he never took anyone's number, only really becoming annoyed once with an abusive motorist who well deserved to be clobbered.

Life was very full. Any one of a variety of tasks constantly demanded attention, often several together. New arrivals, existing customer's needs, dustbins, cleaning, running down lines of traffic with leaflets, mowing, trimming brambles that seemed to re-grow by magic, helping occasionally with special tasks on Jim's bungalow - and everything done at the double. Meals were consumed with incredible speed, and prepared nearly as fast, often by Sharon at weekends. Life was a blur; but vastly enjoyable. They slept like logs!

Running the park however, though fun, was not without difficulties. Gordon had naively assumed that any problem would come through malfunction of some toilet facility, on which he had lavished so much care and attention. Blocklaying, carpentry and plumbing had all been done meticulously, with help from the whole family. He hoped that quality of work would see the season pass without real troubles. Indeed, apart from a small problem with shower taps getting bent downwards where they emerged from the wall, caused probably by young children swinging on them, the workmanship proved most satisfactory. However, not all was sweetness and light!

"How wrong can you be?" he asked himself, when it was not equipment but people and his inexperience in dealing with them that caused the main headaches.

One evening a gentleman, casually attired but neat, his hair well brushed, probably in his fifties, came to complain that a ball had hit his caravan several times. He bristled with indignation. His wife was not happy either.

"What are you going to do about it?" he demanded, expecting an instant and permanent solution. The gent had no children, his caravan a classy one; it was easy to understand how a ball would be annoying.

Gordon trudged off to see for himself, to find a group of children and their dads playing football with a large beach ball, never the best game in the world next to caravans. "Ideally we need a separate area," he reflected, watching the sport; but no such area yet existed. Time would have prevented the preparation of one, even had anyone thought one would be needed so soon, which they had not! Bowls, badminton and swing-ball had been played quietly in various corners since opening, without causing anyone concern. No one realised football might cause problems.

Discussing the matter with the players, a promise was obtained to avoid this particular caravan, but as they pointed out, the ball was light and soft, and parents expected to play with their children on holiday. As no separate area was yet available, this also seemed reasonable. What to do when both sides are right?

He offered to provide an alternative pitch for the couple who had complained.

"*We* are the innocent party, the others should move," the elderly gent replied stiffly.

"How," Gordon asked himself, "can I make them all satisfied? Is this how a referee feels?"

The little dispute was never truly resolved and neither party left completely happy.

Talking to Jan later that evening, discussing the incident, he put the idea forward. "I really should prepare a special area soon for the more robust games."

She nodded thoughtfully. "We'll have lots of separate areas eventually, won't we? Can't some be just for retired people who prefer quietness?"

CHAPTER 3

Stella

Christopher and Sharon's only problems were ones of choice. Though having to help with the work in all sorts of ways, usually taking turns on alternate days, they had come to expect it and took these various tasks in their stride. They even answered telephone calls and greeted arriving caravans during those periods when both parents were absent, Mum leafleting and Dad showing the previous new visitor to a pitch.

This influx of people, mostly families with children during August, posed for them the question, "Which new friends shall I play with today?"

They were enjoying the best summer of their lives, a mixture of fun and responsibility, of doing an almost adult job *and* finding an unending supply of companions; what could do more for any youngster's confidence. Knowing the area and having parents who owned the park gave them a special status; made them in demand. Christopher in particular became a leader in his own age group. Even some of the older boys turned to him for information. Apart from knowing the best ways into the site's more remote regions, he knew which of the many local beaches were sandy, when tides would be in or out, where to get fish and chips and a hundred other useful things. He had become the friend to have on site for boys near his age, and took full advantage of it. Other bigger boys sometimes joined the band, a few looked like taking the lead away from him and did for a while. But Christopher knew when to speak and when to keep quiet. His opinion or advice, once given, usually turned out to be true and reliable, if occasionally a little exaggerated. A reputation for 'knowing the score' on many subjects maintained his position; when he spoke, others generally listened.

One snappily-dressed young lad, a year or so older and several inches taller, appeared with a large new fishing rod complete with expensive reel and a bag full of weights, floats, flies and other gear. He waved the rod around a good deal, talking to the other boys before setting off for the river. Without exception they followed him. Christopher nipped into the caravan, put something in his pocket and tailed on behind. The lad with the rod produced a folding stool, set himself up on the bank and while busily preparing his gear, held forth on the best fishing techniques. He cast out and reeled in, happy to be the centre of attention. The group around noisily showed their appreciation, asking his advice, which he dispensed loudly and with pleasure. After a while without success, the newcomer turned to his followers, voicing criticism of the fishery's quality. "More fish in our local pond! This river is rubbish, not looked after properly!"

Having stood for some time in the background, Christopher had edged quietly forward to stand nearby and now ventured an opinion. "You're probably right. They seem very difficult but I'd like to try. I've only a hand line, do you think I stand a chance?"

The bigger boy, noticing everyone was listening, swung round to them with a broad grin and spoke loudly.

"What have we here? Bet the fishes, if there are any, are shaking in their boots now!" With that he turned back to the river casting out his line fiercely. The other boys crowded the water's edge, shouting encouragement and approval.

Christopher smiled to himself; he had never pretended to be a great fisherman but he knew these small brown trout well. Moving casually so as not to attract attention, he strolled off downstream, choosing a place where the smooth surface indicated deeper water below. It was well within sight of the other boys but far enough away that the fish would not be frightened by their noise. Taking the line from his pocket, he approached the river with stealth and in silence. The other lad would never catch anything; no self-respecting trout would go anywhere near that din. Nor would they go for a line with weights on, these trout were seldom bottom feeders; and another thing, that hook was too big.

Kneeling down he selected something smaller, a number ten with a few small dull brown feather clippings, one he had tied recently and had coated slightly to help it stay afloat. Even that might be too big; a fourteen perhaps? No, stick with a ten. Lowering the end gently, he watched the current take it, paying out more line. The trick was to let the hook float a good way down river but not far enough to snag on the weeds below and get caught up. A glance upstream confirmed they were still busy, crowding the water's edge. Deciding the line had floated down sufficiently, Christopher started to haul in; not in one continuous movement but in a series of controlled tugs, letting the fly rest a few seconds between, like a live fly might do. About the sixth tug he felt a bite and jerked the line tight. Less than a minute had passed since casting out. A trout of perhaps ten inches, bigger than expected for the small stream, fought gamely while being pulled in, hand over hand.

When the line was raised so the fish hung clearly visible, a series of shouts arose from upstream. Lowering it back into the water, he waited, pretending to search for something in a pocket. Within seconds the horde was upon him. He looked up in apparent surprise, catching a glimpse of a solitary figure farther upstream, still sitting on a folding stool.

"Will you take it home to cook?" a voice enquired from the group now gathered closely round.

Lifting his trout from the water, Christopher removed the hook carefully, holding the fish in a manner to display its size, but without making the move appear intentional. Turning to reply, he regarded the group of lads, and not sure who had asked the question, addressed them all.

"One this size? Not likely!" He slid the fish back into the water, hiding his reluctance to lose such a good catch.

As the trout floated towards the surface then darted away, he rose to leave. "No, we don't cook the tiddlers, pity to catch them that size really. Think I'll give it up for the day. See you later?"

They nodded, their eyes following him as he walked away.

Sharon made friends even more quickly. Her easy, likeable nature ensured she was asked out constantly, had tea in various caravans and was seldom seen with less than three other girls in her company. She listened well too, and spoke at breakfast of her new friends' interests, and just recently, particularly of ponies. Mostly however, it was they who sought information and turned to Sharon to supply it. She could speak with equal authority about the area, about beaches and even the buzzards that wheeled overhead. The rigours of life on site over the past year had made her, as with her brothers, self reliant and capable beyond her years.

When they were alone in the caravan one morning, Jan told Gordon what she had overheard through the open doorway. Sharon had been relating to a small group, details of the primitive conditions under which they had lived through the previous year. In particular she spoke of walking alone in the dark of night across the lonely valley and into the creepy blackness of an unfinished building where the chemical toilet bucket had stood.

"They couldn't see me," Jan continued, "mostly hidden, my face in shadow. You should have seen the looks of incredulity and envy on the young faces of those listening girls."

Stephen, still four, his fifth birthday due in little more than a month's time, was not yet allowed out with other people in their cars, but it made no difference to his enjoyment. Those children too young to mix with either Christopher or Sharon's groups were often to be found together with Stephen in their midst. Sometimes he led the games, quiet but confident in his own environment, though just as frequently he followed someone else's lead, usually happier to do the listening than the talking. While walking round the site, leading new arrivals to a pitch, Gordon often noticed these younger children. They played in a group, sometimes on the waste heaps on the valley's western side, spoil from Wheal Virgin, the ancient tin and copper mine. As some of this stony material had been removed using the big excavator over the past winter, the leading edge, the face, had tended to fall from time to time, creating small landslides. Such a slide late in spring, had left the surface sloping less precipitously and therefore safe for the summer. On more than one occasion as Gordon walked by with a caravan trailing behind, little Stephen could be seen leading his band up this moderately steep and uneven slope, all searching on the ground. On one occasion, a young figure bent to pick something up, holding it high over his head with a shout. Other children rushed to gather round, forming a closely packed ring. What had they found?

"I know what they're hunting for," Jan replied when Gordon mentioned the incident. "Bits of metallic mineral, the yellow glittery stuff, fool's gold. Souvenirs to take home, like they collect pebbles from the beach between Marazion and Penzance."

Tea, when Mum had returned from leafleting, was still the favourite meal; the one the whole family ate together, except when either Christopher or Sharon were away from the site with friends. Breakfast too saw the family gathered, but pressure of jobs allowed little time for idle conversation in the early morning. Even tea seldom passed without some person seeking advice, or a gas bottle, or the occasional late arrival. These interruptions were viewed with pleasure rather than annoyance, for mostly the faces at the door were happy ones, bringing with them the prospect of a little more cash, much needed for the long winter to come! At times, bets were placed as to the number of minutes before another tap on the caravan door, the children betting purely for the prize of being right, or occasionally with their chores but never with money.

As at all meals, everyone ate fast. Several times Jan thought she should try to instil some sense of dignity to the family's dining habits. However, seeing the happy faces, chatting and munching simultaneously, almost gobbling the food, she sighed, saying nothing, knowing that eating at a sedate pace was entirely impractical in their present circumstances.

Within ten minutes the food would be gone, but usually they sat talking until the children spotted a friend outside, or some other event demanded attention.

"Jim's bungalow walls had reached bottom of window height when I came back this evening. That Delabole slate looks good." Jan mentioned. "And I saw children playing on the old horse drawn mower again as I drove across the bridge. We must find a way to keep them off; those blades are dangerous. With the tall vegetation cleared from those flat areas, it's hardly ever used. Can't you find somewhere to hide it?"

Sharon was speaking wistfully of some ponies she had passed when out in a friend's car, but a caravan drew across the bridge and the conversation broke up.

Another thing quickly learned was how devastating ground sheets could be. The grass everywhere fell far short of that luxuriant turf so prized by golf courses and more zealous home owners. Two acres nearest the bridge had, on first arrival, bloomed with a chaotic mixture of meadow flowers, long tough grasses and gorse stems. This turf still retained much of that original wild mixture, rich in weeds. Many of the taller varieties were intolerant of being cut short and had disappeared but the lower-growing forms persisted. Among the green lay such curiosities as little yellow four-petalled Tormentil, and the pinky-red specks of Dovesfoot Cranesbill, a miniature wild geranium with its elongated seed pods. These attractive weeds thrived, along with a collection of others able to tolerate regular mowing.

41

In other places, sections had been laboriously filled and levelled by months of hard work, then covered with imported topsoil and seeded. This newly-set grass, germinated only that spring, still remained open-textured and vulnerable. However, new or old, all areas were evenly cut and freshly green. It may have been a groundsman's nightmare but the tourists loved it.

These broad green sweeps were accentuated by untamed strips around the edges, bursting with foxgloves, purple knapweed, valerian, St John's wort, and a host of other wild flowers, changing with the season, many now drooping and brown in the summer sun, seeds ready to scatter. This, together with the valley's remoteness, not another sign of habitation visible whichever direction the visitor looked; pocket-sized fields on distant slopes, clusters of willow bushes, the odd copse of taller trees dotted here and there - a million miles from the city environments around which many visitors lived.

One caravan with a ground sheet in its awning stayed for over two weeks. It departed late one afternoon. Gordon waved farewell as he pushed the mower, preparing to trim grass that always grew tall in the shade under longer staying caravans. On reaching the vacated pitch, he signalled Jan to join him, pointing to where the awning had rested.

"Look at that, not a blade of grass left, just a brown earth scar. Will it recover do you think?"

It was destined never to do so and would later need re-seeding. The porous soils of the valley were good at draining water but not so hot at re-growing grass. They began to understand why the Caravan Club asked members to lift their groundsheets each day. Tents however were a different proposition, a way to prevent them damaging the turf would not be so easy; a tougher species of grass seed perhaps, and maybe improving the condition of the underlying soil over the years - who knows? They were still novices at running a park but each little incident contributed that extra fraction of knowledge.

The third week in August had almost ticked away.

Caravans, though beginning to decrease, were still numerous and Jim's bungalow reached roof level. Unable to help in the daytime, Gordon marked the impregnated timbers late one evening, leaving Jim to cut merrily away over the following few days, reminding him to check that all cut ends were properly treated. Jim and Audrey now spent most of their time at the bungalow, and being right near the site entrance could observe with pleasure the daily quota of arriving caravans. They were, however, much more excited at prospects of the roof being raised.

Leaving the site long enough to erect these roof timbers posed a real problem with Jan still away for most of each day. However, knowing how upset Audrey would be if work came temporarily to a halt, Gordon felt forced to make time somehow. Having grabbed a sandwich with Jan after she returned from her roadside vigil, he had just pitched the first four rafters one evening when a caravanner walked up from the site to offer assistance. Gordon readily accepted. The holiday-maker turned out to be a first-class chap, an experienced carpenter, it was good to have someone who knew about building to chat with as they worked, clambering about the roof.

The joists, those horizontal timbers to which the ceiling would later be fixed, were already firmly in position. Sixteen-inch gaps on either side of each beam allowed a clear view of the concrete floor, eight feet below. It was on the narrow two-inch-wide tops of these widely-spaced timbers that they cautiously walked. Much time had passed since Gordon last discussed technical points and compared techniques with an experienced craftsman; the chance was relaxing - too relaxing! He slipped!

Whether caused by outright tiredness, from rising before six and seldom being able to retire until eleven, or just carelessness as they chatted, who can tell? He was hoisting the next rafter, a stout timber nearly twenty feet long, hauling it up from Jim below. Suddenly a projecting knot snagged against the blockwork, causing his foot to slip. The timber's far end rose, snatched from Jim's grasp by

43

the upward force, Gordon reeling, hanging on to his end as it pivoted like a seesaw, marginally slowing his fall but not preventing it.

"I mustn't let go! It will land on Jim's head. With that bad leg he will never get clear in time!" The urgent thought flashed through his mind as he slewed sideways, scraping skin from his calf as he fell, the other leg still supported but stretched out so far in front as to give no chance of recovering balance. A second later he fetched up with a thump, lying crosswise above the open joistwork; bruised, winded and somewhat dazed. One hand still clung doggedly to the loose rafter which had followed him down, glancing off his head to strike one shoulder heavily. It was several seconds before he could move; his new friend now kneeling alongside, prized the rafter from his grip.

A short time later, they were back on the ground having shakily descended the ladder. Nothing seemed broken, and even the scraped leg was not bleeding, though small globules of clear liquid seeped through the grazed skin. They sat together, the three of them on Audrey's garden seat. The carpenter looked past Gordon, speaking to Jim at the other end of the bench.

"He nearly fell through. Good job it wasn't a tall building."

"Have you worked on many tall ones," Jim enquired. It was small talk, filling the time, giving chance for recovery.

"Not personally, I tend to avoid them but an old chap I used to know told a story about his father. Said he worked on the original Forth Bridge, you know, where the painters never stop work; takes so long to get from one end to the other, when they finish it's time to start again." He turned to Gordon, "You feeling all right?"

"Yes. Give me a little longer and I'll be ready again."

The carpenter nodded and resumed his tale.

"I don't know whether he worked on the actual construction or on maintenance afterwards, but times were hard then and bosses were harder. The men worked up there on that bridge without much protection, a dangerous place, high up. My friend's father was foreman, had to keep the men in order or lose his own job. Couldn't afford to lose a job then, no unemployment pay in those days.

"One morning a shout floated up from the water, a young girl was drowning, calling for help. One of the men dived off the bridge! The other chaps could hardly believe it, the water could break your bones at that height if you hit it wrong, or knock you unconscious and drown you. This man, courageous or mad, no one could say, but he rescued the girl - became quite famous in the district. The foreman, my friend's father, wrote off to head office suggesting a reward. A letter came back a few days later. It said, 'We do not give rewards to men leaving their post. As he jumped in rather than falling, he left work voluntarily. You are ordered to stop this man's pay from the moment he left the bridge!' Some bosses would still like to do that, if they didn't fear the publicity."

The story finished, they rose, crossing to the ladder. Two caravans turned into the entrance, obviously travelling together.

"I expect you want to see them in," the carpenter suggested, "Jim will stay with me and pass up the rafters. Leave this to us if you like."

Gordon did like! He scuttled off before the man changed his mind. Apart from still feeling sore, it was difficult not being on call in the evenings. One of the children usually helped in the daytime but were invariably all allowed to play after tea when their friends arrived back from the beaches. Even with numbers beginning to fall, Jan could hardly cope single handed with existing visitors, new arrivals, gas bottles and requests for advice on diverse subjects ranging from beaches, to eating places, to car repairs. The volunteer roofer erected the remaining timbers without a hitch, calling in at the caravan to report, 'job complete'. In the whirl of activity, there was little time to express more than a few thankful words of gratitude before someone else demanded attention. Nevertheless, Gordon did return next evening, working late for the rest of the week, felting, battening and tiling; making the building waterproof.

Audrey, like so many people, imagined the bungalow almost ready for occupation once the roof was on. News of just how much work remained took her aback.

"There's the plastering, plumbing and glazing, all the electrical work, floor finishes, the joinery, decoration, and a dozen other small jobs still to complete," Gordon told her, adding a warning: "I won't be free to help much for some time; the site is still busy, it was difficult enough finding time to tile the roof. In any case, glazing and plastering must come first, not my jobs, they can go straight ahead. I'll pop up tomorrow evening to fix the internal door liners and Jim can knock chases for the electric conduits if I mark them out."

* * *

A return to school lay some way off but Jan viewed this impending event with mixed feelings. She regretted of course, that income would reduce to a trickle. Like squirrels hiding nuts in autumn, they had been tucking away the income in the bank, stingily spending the minimum possible, hoping it would see them through the coming winter. She consoled herself however with two prime advantages. Firstly, the end of leafleting, or at least its drastic reduction, would shortly follow; they would be at home together much more often. Secondly, early morning cleaning could be postponed, done that little bit later. Over one hundred consecutive days had passed unbroken since either had been in bed after six o'clock. Even in the early season when caravans had been so few, never had this vital task been neglected. In perhaps as little as two more weeks, or maybe three, cleaning before breakfast could cease; they would eat first and attend to the toilets half an hour later.

Often, at meals, the children led the conversation, talking among themselves, sometimes asking the opinion of one or other parent about some visiting youngster of their own age.

"How many more days is he staying?" was a frequent question. Sometimes it was she rather than he, usually a friend but occasionally someone they hoped would leave soon. In contrast to winter and spring, the three children no longer played with each other, meeting mainly at meal times. Sharon often criticised her brothers' friends, only to have her own ridiculed in turn. Jan looked at Gordon with a knowing smile. Christopher's friends were exclusively boys and Sharon's all girls. In a few years, instead of running down each other's playmates they would be asking for introductions. Time would solve the problem; with age they would become aware of the opposite sex in a completely new way.

Stephen still mixed with anyone of his own age group, only putting up a pretence of bias against girls in his big brother's presence. Less talkative at meals, he was, none the less, not prepared to be pushed around by the older two. In fact, Stephen had little regard for authority in any form, using his size to wriggle out of many jobs and quite often doing things he had specifically been told not to do.

One evening just after tea, the sound of an approaching engine caused Jan to bend and glance through the caravan window. Having checked this was not a new arrival, she made to turn away but a group of young children caught her eye. They clustered around something close to the river, some kneeling, others standing, the young bodies obscuring her view. As she watched, several boys stood up; five or six perhaps, it was difficult to see exact numbers with the others crowded nearby. They rose slowly, hoisting a large boulder. Stephen, lifting on the far side, glanced anxiously towards the caravan.

Though it was unlikely anyone could see in through the small windows, Jan instinctively stepped back from sight, then standing well away from the glass, peered out again. The children were taking their load towards the bridge. At first it appeared they would carry it up and round onto the

47

parapet. She should stop them but curiosity held her back. What was their intention?

The bridge formed an arch spanning onto granite abutments. A ledge ran along these abutments at about half height, say three feet above river level - like a narrow horizontal shelf. Often enough youngsters clambered up and walked along for it extended right to the water's edge, so they could stand looking directly down into the stream. It was here that the children placed the boulder, struggling a short way up the bank first to gain some height, sensibly avoiding any need to hoist the heavy stone above waist level. It rested now perhaps ten feet from the river.

At this point most youngsters raced off to stand looking down from the parapet above. Only three remained below, heaving the stone along the granite ledge, end over end, pausing at intervals from their exertions, rolling it nearer and nearer to the river. Stephen seemed to direct the operation. When the boulder rested, balanced on the very edge, two of these children ran up to join their friends above. Stephen stayed behind, flattening himself against the wall as if trying to hide, both arms outstretched, hands clamped on the precariously perched stone.

Jan knew she should stop him, he had specifically been told not to throw stones in the stream, and particularly not the ones his father had dragged from the river-bed the year before to support and protect the bank. Intrigue stayed her hand; she could scold him later, but what was he trying to do? At the moment the purpose of this little enterprise was still very much a mystery. A large splash perhaps, but why had all the other children hurried to be on top. To avoid getting wet? The girls possibly, but why the boys? Generally, little boys revelled in the chance of a wetting. She was suspicious. Stephen would tell nothing if she challenged him now, she knew him too well to expect otherwise. He would clam up, go silent on her. So she waited.

Several of the boys above started to throw bread on the water; a trout rose, and another. Why were they only throwing pieces on this side of the stream close to where the big stone was balanced? Some were signalling to Stephen, she could see arms waving but heard no voices; they were obviously trying to be quiet. Suddenly the little lad's shoulders braced and he heaved the boulder forwards. It fell with a great splash, deluging him in a sheet of water and spray. Then, all the others were streaming down to where the rock had fallen. Some leaned out, others lay down, their bodies extending over the water, all scouring the bottom looking for something. After a while they ceased searching, obviously disappointed.

"Must get him a fishing net," Jan thought, grinning to herself and deciding not to mention the incident to Gordon. Stephen was naughty, she knew that; a little devil sometimes, but this exploit had shown a certain imagination. She liked the idea, the optimism. His father could be severe about anything that caused more work, and might deliberately think up extra jobs for idle little hands.

Earlier in the year, the two older children had break-fasted, done their chores, then left for school. Once the holidays started, they had originally expected to lie in, since few other children on site rose early. In that however, they had been sadly disillusioned. The one roomed caravan was also the office, Jan turfed them all out to wash directly she and Gordon returned from cleaning, normally soon after six-thirty.

Talking on the bridge one evening, Jan was approached by an attractive lady of perhaps thirty years, with a two year old girl holding onto one hand. The woman introduced herself as Stella and they fell into conversation, moving over to sit side-saddle on the downstream parapet so the child could watch the water, amused by occasionally jumping trout.

After a while Stella stopped chatting and became somewhat pensive. Following an awkward pause, she twice attempted to speak, stopping after a few words, obviously embarrassed. Finally, with a deep breath, she commenced.

"I hope you don't mind my asking but I have an eight

year old daughter and she's acting very strangely this holiday. I know you have one about the same age; I wonder, can you tell me what's going on?"

Stella paused, looking questioningly at Jan, as if unsure whether to say more. Jan nodded encouragingly, showing interest but not interrupting, and Stella continued.

"First, she's the world's worst person for getting up, I practically have to drag her from bed at home. Here, she's suddenly taken to rising regularly at six-thirty and disappearing to the toilet building with her washing bag shortly afterwards. Yesterday she returned with her hair done differently, announcing she intends to grow it long. She's always hated long hair before." Stella paused, shaking her head, then ran on again.

"Another thing, cooking has never been of the slightest interest, I've tried several times to get her in the kitchen at home but she doesn't want to know. Now she's suddenly talking about pastry. We've an oven in the caravan and she wants to bake Cornish Pasties - seems to know exactly how to make them too. I've tried to find out what's behind all these changes, but she won't tell me. Says it's secret. I'm mystified. Mind you, I don't care. It's wonderful really!"

Jan smothered a smile, making a 'who knows' gesture with her hands and being at a loss to know what to say, grabbed the first thing that came to mind.

"Didn't say anything about baths under the bridge did she?"

Stella stiffened, shooting out a hand to steady herself on the parapet, eyes opening wide to stare in amazement.

"How did you know? I avoided mentioning that. It sounded too ridiculous."

Jan hadn't intended to say anything, the baths bit had just slipped out. The reaction was unexpected; clearly she could no longer pretend ignorance. Stella was waiting.

"I suppose your daughter isn't interested in horses is she?"

"Madly." Stella again looked confused.

"My Sharon also washes every morning before seven,

she's been talking about horses quite a bit lately. I think our daughters are meeting and playing together. Those baths, the river was the only place we had that first year; I overheard Sharon talking about it to some of the girls, guess your daughter was with them. And Cornish Pasties - I suppose she told you they can be made in a biscuit tin on the gas ring?"

"She mentioned that," Stella nodded. "Can they really? She said something about making holes so they didn't blow up?"

"Ours did!" Jan smiled. "Terrified me."

The baby, tired of sitting, struggled to get down. Stella rose stretching, turning to smile back at Jan as she prepared to leave.

"Don't discourage them, I think your Sharon is good for my Gill. What a strange life she's led though!"

CHAPTER 4

Loot

September loomed, just a few days away. Life was changing again, not the daily routine but the intensity, the pressure, was falling. Numbers had continued to reduce and by nine o'clock, with the early chores complete, both parents could relax. Interruptions of various kinds still occurred, but without the constant stream of demands that characterised the peak period.

This morning, Sharon stayed with them, chatting while making the coffee. Her friend Gill had left the previous day and no other young girls remained at the moment.

"She's got her own pony, kept in a field near her house. She has colour television too." Sharon said sadly, lifting the kettle from a gas ring and filling three cups.

"I'm sorry, there's no chance of you having either; not for a very long while at any rate," Jan looked sympathetically at her daughter.

Sharon nodded, knowing in advance there had been little point in asking. Being used to doing without, she gave a little shrug, put two coffees on the table, reaching back to lift her own cup from a small worktop beside the stove.

A car drove by on its way out, the occupants waved as Jan stretched to peer through the small caravan window. She lifted an arm in acknowledgement, and remembering something, turned to Gordon.

"Those dust clouds that have followed cars up and down the road all summer, they're causing potholes again, or something is. When things get quieter they'll need filling. And don't forget you've to hide that old horse drawn mower somehow; children still keep playing on it - it's dangerous."

They sat for a while, idly finishing the coffee, before Jan departed for the days leafleting. It was usually Jan who went now, since the day a small plumbing problem had arisen, which she had been unable to fix. Her morning departure time, dependant on the likely caravan numbers travelling that day, was always earlier on Saturdays. She set off in the mini-van with sandwiches and a flask to last until mid-afternoon. Falling traffic levels made it seldom worthwhile to stay after three o'clock, leaving her able to cook the evening meal.

Unlike the peak weeks, the children's help was now seldom needed, though Sharon often prepared a midday snack, eggs or beans or something equally quick and easy, for any of the family who happened to be around; otherwise some form of sandwich generally sufficed.

Gordon, remaining home, cleaned the toilets again at midday and booked in new arrivals, taking their cash, or more usually cheques. He could even experience the strange luxury of indulging in a certain idleness, his presence necessary at unpredictable intervals, with a good deal of free time between. Occasional flurries of activity and the odd human problems still arose, but with time between to ponder, to muse on the season's successes and failures.

Failures had been frequent, due sometimes to difficult or surly customers, but most were down to his own inexperience. This power to make decisions with no higher authority to countermand them, represented a drastic change in life. Formerly, work had been submitted for approval, to a boss, or a client, always someone else making the ultimate choice. Now he had not just the right to decide, but the absolute necessity. There was nobody from whom to seek advice, to discuss matters as he would have done previously with colleagues. No one would assist with sudden problems, technical or human; though technical ones tended to be few. Those, at least, he could fix! On human problems he could always seek Jan's opinion, provided she was available and circumstances permitted. Events however, seldom did allow the luxury of time to think! Immediate decisions were required; no option existed other than to jump in with an instant ruling. This authority over other people, the power to make or spoil someone's holiday, worried him sometimes.

"Have I been fair? Could I have handled that better?" he often asked himself, and after a clumsy confrontation that went totally wrong, a despairing, "Will I ever improve?"

All such feelings must be carefully hidden from visitors, and an outward confidence maintained. That was for self defence, a facade, a hard exterior masking inner sentiments, but necessary if some sort of order and standards were to be maintained. He had heard often enough the derogatory remarks from caravanners about sites where anything was allowed, dogs running wild, loud music, people tearing around at dangerous speeds. Most visitors wanted the peace of mind that only a well-controlled site could offer, but exercising that control was not easy. Fortunately, elation was the more frequent emotion, when things went right, when a tricky situation ended with everyone happily shaking hands.

He remembered with particular pleasure the dispute one evening between a very rough diamond from Newcastle and a stockbroker type from one of the London suburbs. This pair were sited next to each other and had fallen out. Nobody in particular was actually in the wrong, just a general antagonism between two very different types of person. Gordon had tried to sort the matter out but it seemed insoluble until he was exaggeratedly polite to the working-class chap, and downright rude to the toff in a friendly way, looking from one to the other and smiling as he spoke. Everyone ended up laughing. They were to remain friends all through the holiday, even sharing a barbecue.

"I can't think what made me believe I could get away with it," he told Jan, on returning to the caravan. "It was absolutely against all common sense, but it just felt right. Among other things I called the rough one 'Sir' and told the toff he had, 'Clorf ears, with very little between them'. It worked like a dream." He smiled, squeezing her hand.

"That little success did more for me than half a pint of Scotch would for a drinking man. I could jump over the caravan, I'm so high on something."

"Well it's not Scotch, your eyes are shining, not your nose!" Jan stepped closer, slipping a hand round his waist. "I don't think you ought to try jumping over the caravan but it does seem a pity to waste all that energy." She paused, brushed her body gently against his and asked innocently, "Is there something I can do to help?"

* * *

Children of school age reduced rapidly as weeks went on, but more couples arrived. Stephen still had one young friend left, a boy of his own age; the two spent much time together. In addition to playing in the river and on the big waste heaps, Jan was delighted that Stephen popped back to the caravan on several evenings for pencils and paper. Watching the two youngsters sit on the riverbank drawing, she asked, "Does he do that in the daytime as well, when I'm away? Did you know he can write several words? His letters are still a bit scratchy."

One evening after tea, Stephen had gone off with his young friend to play and Jan sat reading, when Christopher appeared, furtively beckoning to his father from the caravan doorway. Gordon's reaction, straightening up and looking towards his son in surprise, caught the eye of both Sharon and Mum. It was obvious from Christopher's expression that he had not intended either of them to see; something which immediately piqued Sharon's natural nosy curiosity.

Realising that he had inadvertently drawn attention to something meant to be private, Gordon rose and walked casually towards the door, but stopped as Jan spoke.

"What's going on?"

"Just something I wanted to show Dad," Christopher replied looking uncomfortable but not giving the slightest indication of what that something might be.

His mother regarded the lad for a moment, suspecting

55

mischief lay afoot, but decided she must be wrong if he wanted to show Dad. "Just don't get those clothes in a mess. The last lot I washed are not dry yet."

The two males made to leave, but Sharon was up and after them. That her brother should want to show something only to Dad was unprecedented. What could it possibly be? Entirely unable to bear the thought of being left behind, of missing out, she dashed forward. They might never tell her afterwards!

"Sharon's not coming!" Chris's forceful objection held antagonism and perhaps a touch of alarm.

"Why? What are you up to?" Jan voiced her suspicion.

"Yes, why can't I?"

Christopher was in a dilemma. To block his sister's presence meant Mum might insist on knowing, but Sharon could be a nuisance. Standing outside the caravan, only his head inside, he looked from one to the other.

"OK. You can come. But don't interfere."

His head disappeared before Mum could ask more. Sharon dashed forward, fearful her brother would run off, keeping his secret secure. Dad, still standing near the door, turned to Jan with a shrug of the shoulders then followed at the rear.

Christopher made for the bridge, crossing it, but instead of heading up the road in the normal direction, turned downstream on the far bank, a place they seldom went. Sharon was right on his heels, keeping close, unsure what they were hunting for, but determined not to be last. After a while overhanging trees and other vegetation made the going more difficult. Sharon began to grumble about her clothes. Looking west across the river, they were now well below the areas so far levelled for caravans. Pushing on, it was necessary to force a way past gorse and other woody growth. Sharon's complaints became stronger but she refused to follow Christopher's advice when more than once he suggested hopefully, "You don't have to come."

Dad followed silently behind, intrigued but saying nothing. No doubt some discovery had been made; all would be revealed in good time. Eventually they stopped atop a steeply sloping but not too high section of bank.

"Probably all for nothing! Must be an easier route for anyone with sense enough to find it." Sharon remarked sarcastically, catching her breath.

Christopher pointed downwards at the river and waited. Seeing no sign of understanding in the watching faces, he pointed again. "Look, the brick path. See - where the gravel has partly washed away."

"Is that what we've come all this way for, got stung and scratched for a silly brick!"

"You could never have found it."

"Who'd want to? *You're* more stupid than the bricks."

"Shut up!"

"I shan't shut up. You can't make me!"

"Can't I?" Christopher gave her a shove but she grabbed him and clung on, fighting back. A cough nearby as Dad pretended to clear his throat brought them both to a stop.

"Before you tear each other apart, don't you think we should find out if it *is* anything interesting?"

Sharon made to object, but Dad's raised hand stopped her. "Isn't it strange that some kind of a brick path should appear on the riverbed? How old could it be, what was its purpose, who put it there? Bricks are rare in Cornwall, I'm curious if you're not." Christopher's grin of pride and triumph as he gloated over Sharon's discomfort made Gordon realise he had taken sides and ought perhaps to redress the balance. "And you, Christopher; don't tell young ladies to 'Shut up'. Not only is it impolite but you'll find they seldom comply. There are much better ways of making them silent; ways of saying 'Shut up' without actually uttering those words. Remember that when you grow up."

The two children looked at each other and back at Dad, signs of disbelief evident in their expressions, but he decided against trying to explain and changed the subject. "Now let's see if we can find out what this is. I don't want to get these shoes wet, should have worn wellys but the water's shallow. I can roll my sleeves up and slide down the bank hands first. It's a bit steep, can you both hold my feet?"

He lay on the bank and as they took an ankle each, slithered down to the water's edge, plunging in both arms to well above elbow level, fingers brushing away at the gravely covering before calling up over one shoulder, "Seems something around two foot wide, but I can't find where it ends, can you ease me farther down. Yes, that's it; think I can reach now... no, bit more..."

Suddenly a section at the top of the bank gave way and Christopher shot downwards, hitting his father without warning. Sharon abandoned her grip, throwing herself aside as both males fell straight in the river, lost in a flurry of water and falling soil. Gordon staggered up quickly, grabbed an arm, pulling his son to the bank. Both were saturated. Sharon, brushing her dress with one hand, looked down at them, trying to hide her mirth, but a grin spread across her face defying all attempts to prevent it.

Gordon, seeing Christopher's crestfallen expression, asked, "Should we throw her in too?" Immediately the boy's face lit up. As they made to start up the bank. Sharon emitted a shriek and turned to run. Dad's hand reached out, holding the lad back and they stood together watching as she threw a fleeting glance over one shoulder and went headlong.

Rising up and seeing not only no pursuit, but her father and brother laughing, she realised they had no intention of getting her wet. Returning, she stood angry and indignant, staring down.

"Hm. Wait 'til Mum sees. She'll be mad! Serves you right. Now you can try telling *her* to shut up and see how far you get!"

At Sharon's words, all antagonism between the children seemed to melt and they regarded Dad with new interest, wondering just how bad a tongue-lashing he would get.

"OK, you two little terrors. I can read you like a book. Come on, let's go back and face the music."

After making their way back to the caravan, the two males squelching at every step, Jan met them at the door.

"What an earth...?"

The children, following up the concrete steps, waited for the outburst, but saw Dad reach for their mother's hand, raise it to his lips, kiss gently, and looking into her eyes say, "Thank goodness."

Jan, mouth still open, stared back at the three, at a loss what to make of the situation, and felt herself guided gently into the caravan and over to the sink by Gordon's firm hand. She was about to speak again when he continued.

"The riverbank gave way under Christopher, he fell in the water. I went in after him, pulled him out."

"What...?"

Gordon's finger moved to her lip, stopping the intended flurry of words. "No, don't say a word, let me look at you." He gazed at her face, giving a little sigh before continuing. "Christopher had found this special flower, magnificent, never seen one like it before, but it lay at the bottom of this steep bank. I wanted it for you." He stopped again, gazing deep into her eyes, moving closer. She opened her mouth to speak, but again he stopped her.

"No! I just want to look at you. Wait. I'm all wet, I'll change. Stay exactly where you are, don't move a muscle, don't speak - let me remember you exactly like this. Wait for me, I'll be back."

He opened the cupboard, grabbed a handful of dry clothes and was off. Jan moved to the open doorway, a dreamy gaze on her face as she watched him go. Only when the running form disappeared round the toilet building did she turn back and notice the two children - they were looking at each other as if strawberries and cream had just been invented, round-eyed with excitement.

"What's the matter."

Christopher turned evasively away at his mother's question, glancing at Sharon, but unable to contain himself, the words burst out. "He did it!"

"Did what?"

The lad shook his head slightly, studying the floor, grinning from ear to ear. Sharon, her face a picture of mixed

59

emotions, torn between amusement, surprise and indignation, made to speak, changed her mind, hesitated then declared, "That wasn't fair!"

Mum looked at her daughter, not understanding but seeing the girl still undecided, waited patiently. After a short pause, when she several times glanced to her brother for some cue or hint as to whether she should speak, Sharon attempted to explain.

"Christopher and I were arguing, he told me to shut up, and we started to fight. Dad stopped us, told Christopher he was using the wrong technique. Said if you wanted a woman to shut up, you could do it without her even knowing. I said 'bet you can't do that when Mum sees your clothes'."

"But he did!" Christopher chipped in, facing his mother, punching one fist into the open palm of his other hand in involuntary zest. "He said to you, 'Don't say a word', that's *shut up*, isn't it; and you did!"

Jan looked at her son, a black thunderous look, but he only smiled more broadly, chuckling and glancing again towards Sharon who watched her mother with intense curiosity.

"And the flower?" Jan turned to her daughter.

"There was no flower, just some old brick path in the river, that's how they both fell in, they weren't thinking of you at all! Dad invented it!"

"Did he?" Mum's head was nodding. "Right!"
A thoughtful smile spread gradually across her face. She reached under the sink for a bucket and commenced filling it from the tap with a jug, the sink being too small to fill it directly. Lifting the now full bucket to a position near the open door, Jan turned to the children, kneeling down and putting an arm round each, but withdrawing it quickly from Christopher who was still quite damp. "I do hope your father won't be too long. I miss him, don't you?" There was a touch of that 'we'll see who laughs last' about her smile as she looked at the two faces, asking, "Just as he's coming up the steps, don't you think?"

Sharon drew in her breath deeply, the intention dawning,

and turned to Christopher, the two children nodding eager agreement. Their mother nodded with them, "Would you like to say the words with me afterwards: *Don't move, don't say anything, we want to remember you always like this*!"

Later that evening, darkness fallen and everyone finally dried off, they sat around the table listening while Sharon and Christopher, vying for the juiciest bits, revealed to Stephen those earlier events. The parents sat close together, holding hands, smiling at each other, glowing with the recent tussle at which neither had triumphed, but both emerged with some success.

"What exactly are those bricks, and what makes them so interesting?" Jan asked in a lull.

The family looked to Dad for an explanation.

"Well, they cross the river in a diagonal line, about seventeen yards from the lower site boundary and some two feet wide. Could be some sort of crossing, a kind of path, but I don't think so. The top is curved, falls away about three inches at each edge. I think it's probably some pipe or underground tunnel - here, pass me that paper and pencil." Gordon sketched the brick formation and putting some figures on the drawing, scribbled a quick calculation.

"From what we see of the top, I figure that the tunnel, if that's what it is, must be at least four feet in diameter, assuming a perfect circle. Almost big enough to walk inside. Very strange."

"How can you tell those sizes?" Christopher asked.

"Measured them before you fell on me."

"I saw no tape measure."

Sharon nodded agreement, turning to Jan. "He never had one Mum, he's telling lies again, like the flower. He shouldn't tell lies. We're not allowed!" She looked intently at Dad, accusation in her face.

"We'll talk about the flower later. Let me deal with the bricks first. You don't need a tape to measure. Look!" He placed one hand flat on some paper, with the thumb tight to the forefinger, then made a pencil mark each side of the knuckles. "That's the width of my hand, four inches. If I stretch the hand out and mark by the thumb and little finger, that's eight inches." He made two further marks and passed the paper to Sharon. "You've a ruler, check them."

Sharon found to her disappointment that both were correct to within a quarter inch.

"You see, I did take measurements. But it's still a mystery. What could a big pipe like that be for? A drain maybe, but where from, and where to? Why put a drain so deep, below river level? Maybe it really is a path, one that's arched up to run water off, not a pipe at all, but who would build a path below water? Mermaids perhaps? Anyway, historically, back in the days of sail, the water was very much deeper. A secret passage then? What do you think?"

"Break in and see?" Christopher shrugged.

"Better not. It comes from Gurlyn direction, at least seems to. If it was a drain from the old Gurlyn mine, the water might be toxic, kill all the trout. Let's leave well alone."

Dad made to rise and leave, but Sharon lifted an arm to point, "What about the flower. You told Mum a fib. We get in trouble for that!"

"Quite right, Sharon," Jan offered support. "He did promise to explain. Let him try, I should like to hear! All this talk about pipes was just to make us forget."

Gordon shook his head in denial. "OK. But you children tell lies too."

"We don't!" Three cries echoed simultaneously.

"I'll prove it. Now Sharon, you know Christopher always criticises your cooking, doesn't he, even when it's good?"

"It's always good. Yes he does, and yes that is a lie; but I don't tell any."

"What about when a school friend shows you her new dress, or a new hair style that you don't really like, you tell her it's smashing anyway?"

"Yes - sometimes. Mostly I suppose. But it's not the same."

"It is a lie though, but I agree it's not the same. My story of a flower was very similar, it made Mum happy for a while, until she found out. Little fibs sometimes make the world run smoother but never let it get out of hand. Lying for politeness may be OK, even occasionally for a jest - like Mum's flower, but make sure it never hurts anyone else."

Jan nodded, the opportunity to discuss such things with the children in an easy way was unusual; she offered a suggestion. "Some people lie to cover up bad things they've done. Try not to do bad things in the first place, then you won't be tempted. You'll live a lot happier."

* * *

Life for the parents became easier, intervals of idleness lengthening, both during leafleting by the roadside and back at the site, for development work had not yet been restarted. In the day when Jan was out, someone must be at the caravan to receive incoming visitors and telephone enquires, few as they might be. Late afternoons and evenings when Jan was home and able to do these tasks, leaving Gordon free to work, it quickly became obvious that anything which made noise or required old clothes, was counterproductive. Once or twice he went the half-mile upstream Jim's bungalow, only to be called back to help a customer. In the end they accepted the forced inactivity as a bonus. It offered the continuing chance to sit for varying intervals, indulging in a measure of indolence, enjoying the luxury of relaxing together; they might as well - this transitional period would be short!

Little feelings of guilt were pushed aside. These few lost weeks might cause some small decrease in the number of new pitches ready for next season, but the whole winter lay ahead, surely there would still be ample time to prepare? In any case, survival depended on something else - taking money! That remained priority number one; sufficient at least for another year! Neither was avaricious by nature, but by circumstance had become careful; a Scotsman might call it canny. Keeping visitors happy was a vital part of that, as well as being pleasing for its own sake. The great hope was, not only that each customer would book on for a few more days, but that they would enjoy the site enough to re-visit Relubbus next season!

* * *

"Would you like to know how much we've taken?"

Jan looked up. They were sitting in the caravan, shortly after tea. She had finished washing up and now worked with a needle, repairing a rent in Stephen's trousers; torn, she supposed, on brambles as he pushed a way through to some hidden corner. Gordon sat opposite, the ledger in his hands.

There was something smug about the way he spoke, a smile lurked which he tried to mask with a serious expression. It presaged well. Self-satisfaction oozed from him; she could tell he expected to impress her. An impish impulse triggered her reply.

"No, not particularly."

His face changed, taken aback, mouth slightly open, uncertain what to say. He breathed in, lips closing to form a word. Watching, she knew it would be 'but'.

"But..." He didn't finish, at a loss.

She cut in, smiling broadly, mentally notching up the success, "Of course I want to know. You'll tell me anyway, whether I do or not, so get on with it!"

He smiled back, realising now that she teased, aware he'd been slow, should have guessed.

"Over two thousand pounds!"

"*Really*?" In spite of expectations she was surprised, but recovered quickly. "Let's go to town, you can buy me a new dress!"

"If you truly want one, I'll buy it for you, you know that." He reached over and squeezed her hand across the table.

For a while they sat, facing each other. She knew he

would; sensed also there was more he wanted to say, it was in his voice; but she was content, wouldn't destroy the moment by asking.

After a while he continued quietly.

"There's more you should consider. First, this money is takings, not profit. Think of the toilet rolls, disinfectant and soaps, gas for hot showers, the insurance, water rates, council rates; everything spent on the site. And don't forget we've been living off it already. I don't suppose, after everything's paid, we'll have a thousand, maybe quite a bit less, to last until next season. Say eight months, you can't count March or April for much - about twenty five pounds a week."

"A whole lot more than we've been living on. I can manage well on that much!" She looked happy.

"If we want to build a house in a few seasons, we shouldn't spend it all."

Turning pensively to stare through the window, Jan nodded, weighing the long term against the short, gazing absently at foliage on the valley slopes. The colours were changing. Earlier in summer, blue skies largely devoid of cloud, broken unexpectedly by rare days of rain, had given a rich brilliance to vegetation on the valley floor. Colourful blooms had dotted wild verges surrounding closely cut green areas.

By mid-season, gradually increasing heat had shimmered hazily above grass that looked distinctly brown, smelt of hay and rustled crisply under foot. True green survived only on the leaves of deeper-rooted trees and in a narrow band along the very edges of the clear, slightly shallower river.

She focused absently on the scene before her. Now, just into September, shorter though still warm days with heavier morning dews were slowly reversing the picture again. Grassy areas grew steadily greener but trees and bushes had begun to fade. With the onset of autumn, many species were showing the first signs of browning at leaf edges but not yet the golds and yellows they would later display.

Summers always seemed a little longer in the far southwest.

Jan sighed and turned back.

"I'll do without the dress."

It was a simple statement, no undertones of protest; her own decision, there had been no pressure to forgo. She yawned and stretched.

"Laziness is an autumn feeling." Gordon spoke as he watched her. She nodded agreement, realising it was true. Another week had passed, they still had enough visitors to prevent the starting of any serious site work, but insufficient for a full time job. They remained on call rather than working. Anything could need doing at any time, a blocked drain, a new arrival to book in, the telephone ringing; and yet, between these events they had time on their hands.

A further week passed, caravan numbers continuing to dwindle. Leafleting sessions shortened and were eventually abandoned, no longer worth the petrol used, but a few visitors continued to appear, adding a tiny measure of cash, still most welcome. Their chats over coffee had often turned to money. Site expenditure in the coming winter should not be large, since ninety-nine percent of expected progress entailed working with Max, the excavator. However, there could always be unforeseen expenses. No further building was planned at least until after the following summer; not from lack of need - just an absence of funds.

Jan viewed the final figure with satisfaction rather than elation, but after fears of failure early in the year, the result certainly came as a relief.

"How much does a house cost? I don't mind economising again now it's clear we can take enough to live on. Next year *will* be better." She emphasised the *will,* trying to convince herself, pausing thoughtfully before explaining. "People who stayed this year must talk about it to other caravanners and campers. Next season is bound to show an improvement?"

Her voice held a mixture of doubt and hope, more question than conviction.

Late September, and still the odd visitor trickled in,

but the 1970 season, their first, was drawing to a close. Numbers had fallen so low that Jan could easily manage the site alone.

The children were back at school, including Stephen, who having turned five had started his first school year. He departed one morning with Christopher and Sharon, taking this major stepping-stone in life as if nothing new was happening. At breakfast he showed no signs of nervousness or anticipation, at least none an outsider could have detected. While the other two chatted avidly about the return to classes and meeting old friends, he sat quietly, saying very little, face almost expressionless. His way of dealing with problems, the quietness, the reserve - and off they went!

Jim and Audrey were decorating inside their bungalow, the glazing and plastering long since finished. Gordon had installed the central heating to speed up drying out, although the splendid weather had almost achieved that anyway. Each morning he helped with the remaining jobs needed before occupation, but as neither of Jan's parents rose early, some site work was always possible first. At the bungalow, doors remained to be hung, curtain rails put up and floor tiles put down, but he delayed these until Jim and Audrey finished decorating each room. This precaution was a wise one, recognising Jim's tendency to throw paint liberally at places other than the surface being decorated. Mornings, with just the occasional afternoon, were quite sufficient not to fall behind for the older couple were really enjoying themselves. Walls of various rooms appeared in such colours as dark green, blue, and magnolia.

"Have you seen the colour they're painting the kitchen?" Gordon asked as they relaxed after lunch one day.

"Yes. Nappy yellow I'd call it. Disgusting!" Jan nodded with a grimace. "Unusual though, makes you look twice. I popped up yesterday to collect the papers. There's an item in *The Cornishman* about exceptionally low tides. Three chaps walked from Tresco to St Marys in the Scillies, first time it's ever been done. The water was up to their chins. A woman tried too, but turned back; a few inches too short."

Afternoons Gordon spent back on the site, easing his way into the main tasks that would become so tediously repetitive that winter. The excavator's use for that vital job of levelling new pitches was restricted to those hours when the site was almost empty. Even though numbers were very low, such visitors as were present had come for the quietness and the picturesque country setting, not to hear the continuous sound of Max's engine. As people started to trickle back about teatime, quieter types of work were undertaken, tasks done by hand, building stone walls, grubbing out roots, transplanting odd saplings.

Occasionally one of the caravanners, for none of the remaining visitors were campers, wandered over to chat as he worked. They asked after good pub food, or a bird seen but not identified, or of ruins with big chimneys; these were the old mine houses, common only in Cornwall. Gordon wondered about the lack of tents and mentioned it to Jan during after-lunch coffee.

"Worried it might rain, I suppose. Don't realise how mild our weather is in autumn. People live such careful, risk free, lives - well some people do!" She emphasised the last words, grinning.

Gordon, sitting on the opposite bench, looked back at her wistfully across the little table. Chin on hands, he moved slightly to gaze vacantly at the wall, speaking as if thinking aloud.

"*I've* always been a risk taker. I once spent seven shillings and six pence on..." He didn't finish, ducking and raising arms in defence as the content of her cup was thrown towards him.

It was not the first time he had referred to the cost of the marriage licence. She laughed, holding up the cup to reveal it had been empty, and pointing a finger.

"Chicken. Anyway I was worth every penny. Where else would you get an unpaid slave to follow you into the wilderness? And remember, my Dad paid the seven and

68

sixpence!"

"A bribe for me to take you off his hands. And that was only the deposit, he didn't warn me about crippling payments for life!"

She came round the table, squeezing into the bench next to him and pummelled his chest, but gently, laughing, ending clasped in his embrace, a hug of pleasure at each other's company, two deep friends, who just happened to love each other madly. Gordon walked back to work, happy and with a light step.

Returning to the area being cleared, he noticed the visitors' cars were all missing, it would be another afternoon alone, like so many afternoons now. He could start the excavator but decided against it. The whole winter lay ahead. Five entire lonely months at least, probably more like seven; March certainly would see few visitors, nor April and most of May probably. This winter would be even more solitary, working farther from the caravan and with Stephen at school. He thought back to the previous year when they had struggled non-stop to be ready, working every daylight hour, his only companions for much of that time a robin and a blackbird, both almost constantly at his side. Over hours, weeks, and months, as their association grew, he had talked to them as equals. Robin fell easily into the role of a brash cockney, but the black feathers of his other companion had suggested something more reserved. A vicar perhaps or maybe an undertaker? In the end he had plumped for philosopher - with ancestors from ancient Greece? The choice had been subconscious but it pushed away all limits to discussion.

Always interested in any aspect of nature, a new plant, a strange insect, he had come to know the habits of these two birds so well. On more than one occasion he had imagined Robin's reply to his questions with such vividness that he thought the bird had spoken. A trick of the lonely mind, he realised; but never mentioned it to Jan. She might think, well...? He couldn't bring himself to admit what she might think. But she had overheard him anyway, once or twice when bringing coffee.

Robin, because of its cheek in perching on the half-open stable doors of caravans, had found easy living off the visitors that summer. As a result they somewhat lost contact for a time but had reunited now departure of most tourists forced the bird to fend for itself again.

"So, I'm only good enough for you when there's no one else." Gordon remarked as Robin perched nearby. The mental reply was immediate.

"Not my fault if you're idle all summer. No digging, no worms. A bird's got to live."

Autumn also heralded a return of blackberries to the diet, and toiling on steadily through the undergrowth an apple tree was uncovered. Unexpectedly, the weather changed; overcast skies, a belt of rain and a fall in temperatures caused the caravan to feel less cosy.

"Light the stove again, Mum," Sharon urged.

"You can do it, you know how. Ask Stephen to crawl under the caravan and find some dry logs. You'll need lighting wood too."

Jan screwed up a newspaper into tight rings, placed them in the bottom and let Sharon manage the rest. The stove had remained unlit most of the summer, a blazing sun on the caravan's metal shell combated by leaving the single door permanently fixed aside and each small window open wide. Nights, with the door closed, had been more than warm enough, often excessively so as they slept under sheets, the single blankets mostly discarded. This change to cooler weather came as a surprise.

By evening, with the fire rekindled, the caravan felt better.

"It was more the damp feel than actual coldness," Jan suggested, closing some windows, adding their own blanket to the one for covering Sharon and Stephen, and extricating another for Christopher from the bottom of a locker under one bench seat. From the same locker she produced an old duvet for themselves, one discarded by her mother.

70

The temperature rose again during the night, making her wish the stove had been let out rather than banked and turned low. She tossed and turned restlessly, thinking of opening more windows but not wishing to wake the recumbent figure beside her. Eventually sleep came, and she slept on, well after daylight.

Waking first, Gordon lay still, knowing her to be a light sleeper but on raising his head, noticed the duvet had slipped halfway across the bed. Instead of crumpling to the floor as the blanket always had, it extended more stiffly, its end within an inch of the boiler, within an inch of disaster! There was no protecting guard to the hot steel casing, and little space to install one without great difficulty. They must be more careful. Fortunately, this would not be their home for much longer. Jan's parents' bungalow was nearing completion. Jim and Audrey had arranged to move on 21 October; after that the bigger caravan would be available.

* * *

The big removal van with Jim's stored furniture reached Relubbus, turned onto the stone track leading to the caravan site and slowed to a crawl.

"That's the one." The driver's mate looked across as the headlights illuminated a crude sign painted on a board in front of the now finished bungalow. He directed a small torch back down at the sheath of papers on his knee, "Yes, Riverside. We're here!"

Darkness reigned, not a light showed anywhere from the handful of houses that made up the village. Travelling through the night, the lorry had arrived shortly after five o'clock.

"Could be here ages. Might as well get some kip while we can." The small man in the driving seat, past middle age and slightly balding, spoke with a coarseness mingled with resignation. "Better back off the track, else some idiot'l wake us at first light."

He shifted the gear, eased his foot on the clutch and the

lorry moved backwards, steering onto a flat bank beside the river. It had just cleared the track when everything tilted, one rear wheel sinking in soft ground near to the river's edge.

"Damn!" He engaged first gear, trying to move forwards onto the road again but felt the wheel spinning. They both climbed out to look.

"We'll be able to unload and carry the stuff to the bungalow when someone arrives. It's not far. Might get her out when the weight's off?" The mate didn't sound too hopeful.

"Unload! Don't be so damn stupid. Don't they teach you nothin'! Once the stuff's off, who'll care about us? Leave it aboard; they'll find a way to pull us out! Come on, get some sleep."

On being informed later that morning, Gordon trundled Max up the road. The old excavator, purchased and rebuilt the preceding summer, should have no difficulty easing the lorry back onto firm ground. Unfortunately, neither he nor the removal driver had a chain. Never mind, Stanley Thomas, at his workshop a quarter mile upstream, could probably provide something.

Stanley did more than find one, he brought the heavy chain down himself with one of his workmen, and stayed to help fix it. Bravely, but unwisely, he stepped between digger and lorry to make the connections as the digger was still manoeuvring to its final position.

Gordon was driving in forwards, so the chain could be hooked round the front bucket. That way the excavator's big rear wheels, the ones that would do all the pulling, remained on the hard stony surface of the track. As he inched towards the lorry, lowering the bucket at the same time, one front wheel dropped into a small hole concealed by the long grass. The machine pitched, throwing his weight forward, jerking both his accelerator foot and the hand controlling the lever.

The bucket shot suddenly downwards and simultaneously

the excavator jumped forward. Both stopped in time, but only just! For a split second it was a toss up whether Stanley would be flattened by the bucket, or pulverised between vehicles.

"I could have killed him!" Gordon thought, heart racing as he stretched over to lean through the cab doorway.

Someone else thought so too! He could see Stanley preparing to let rip, saw him take a deep breath and gather his words. Old Stanley had a very good turn of phrase when upset, enough to make your hair curl. Gordon however, adrenaline coursing in his veins after the almost fatal slip, reacted like lightning.

"Don't you ever get in front of me when I'm driving! You ought to have more sense! 'Bout time you knew these old machines are difficult to control!"

For moments they looked at each other, eyes locked. Stanley, forestalled in delivering his own rebuke, hesitated.

"OK, Gordon," was all he eventually said.

Concealing a sigh of relief, turning it into a snort of indignation, Gordon quickly withdrew into the cab. He never normally raised his voice, felt it seldom did much good, but this time it had really worked.

"That's just about the mildest thing Stanley ever said to me," he pondered while waiting. "Especially considering it was probably my fault in the first place. The only time I ever came out on top. He'll never let me do it again!"

The heavy chain was hauled into position and connected up. The slack tightened as the big machine moved backwards, pulling hard on the chain. With Stanley directing, the lorry eased gradually towards the road until all its wheels rested on the stone surface. Another fifty yards under its own steam, and it stood right outside Jim's gate.

Audrey, who watched the whole procedure with concern, was really grateful. She walked over to express her profuse thanks. Few people ever succeeded in making Stanley uncomfortable, but waving away the lavish praise he looked distinctly embarrassed. The man who had come with him from the workshop rubbed his hands in relish and turned to speak to Audrey, unable to suppress a gleeful grin, casting sly glances at Stanley as he spoke.

"Don't worry missus, you did us all a good turn; kept him out of mischief for at least ten minutes. More than we could ever do!"

CHAPTER 5

All Change

Jan looked round their caravan home. It was small; not as small as the tourer had been, true, but cramped for a family of five; cramped and old! So much was clear at the time of purchase but it had been cheap, all they could afford and it contained that essential extra, a stove to beat winter condensation. The wind-down steadies that supported all four corners could only be seen from outside but she knew they were well rusted. The chassis creaked and the single room moved fractionally when anyone crossed the floor. Her slow gaze took in the bench seats on the far side, benches on which the children somehow managed to sleep; that short length of worktop and two gas rings was where she, or sometimes Sharon, prepared the meals. A single quarter-sized wardrobe stretched from tattered carpet to roof, while cupboards hung from the ceiling in every possible place; each one packed to overflowing but each so tiny as to be wholly inadequate. The log-burning stove that had kept them cosy last winter sat unlit, midway along the floor; adjoining it, the sink with its single cold tap lay half hidden under lunchtime's crockery and saucepans which still awaited her attention.

She sighed, "I shall miss it, for all its drawbacks. A year we've lived here, Stephen was only just four when we first moved from that tiny tourer. How old are they now? Sharon is eight already, Christopher will be ten this winter. I wonder how they'll like Jim's caravan?"

She rose, picking up some clothes, sorted while checking through cupboards in preparation for the move; Stephen's younger garments now too small to wear. They must be hidden in a dustbin while Gordon worked, otherwise he would insist they be kept, 'Just in case!'

"Much as I love them, three is enough. I've absolutely no intention of having another. That possibility is out!" A nod of certainty accompanied the thought but her mind ran on, visualising a young baby in her arms again. It could happen, the best-laid plans were apt to go awry. Where would it sleep? Another thought struck. It, or they? Suppose there were two? How would they manage? Would she be suckling each in turn with one hand, answering the phone with the other, serving gas bottles with... No, she only had two hands. Gordon would fix that! He'll rig up one of those things the Red Indians have, what were they called, to carry the baby on her back so she needn't stop working. He'd probably fix a pair, one for each and in front rather than behind, so the babies could suckle while she ran along lines of traffic offering leaflets!

Determinedly carrying the small heap outside, she placed them in an empty bin, tipping the contents of another on top. He would never find them there - best not give him ideas!

Several hours later, three children rushed headlong down the road, their speed indicating both awareness and approval of the changes impending at home. They paused to wave vigorously as Jim and Audrey drove across the bridge and off towards the village, seeking the relative opulence of their new bungalow. The little Hillman Imp, well loaded with final belongings, hurried up the track; a heap of clothes tossed somewhat untidily over other household articles obscured its rear window.

"Right," Jan waited as the children ran up, "You wanted it, now it's ours! You know it only has one bed, the one Jim and Audrey slept in. That's for me and your father, so where are you going to sleep? Off you go and investigate."

At these words, they raced to the now vacant caravan, laughing and tumbling exuberantly through the doorway, no concessions to youth or gender; Sharon second, Stephen last. All disappeared up the corridor towards the compartment that had once housed the chemical toilet, an object discarded immediately the first toilet building came into action. A week previously this small room had overflowed with various articles not required for everyday use; it offered the only possible space for extra beds.

Sharon reappeared first, her face filled with dismay.

"It's too small Mum! We'll never get three in there. It looked bigger before they took all the things out."

Jan, having followed slowly behind, knew Sharon was the one most impatient for the bigger caravan. Not only did she expect a bed to herself instead of sleeping as she did at present, on a narrow bench, head to toe beside her younger brother, but the kitchen had an oven! With her interest in preparing meals, that cooker had enormous appeal; but where could she sleep? The large bedroom was only large by name, it scarcely had room to walk round the existing bed. The separate lounge had armchairs, not benches like their own one roomed caravan. Armchairs could never be adapted to form beds!

The boys appeared in the doorway, Christopher looking over her head, Stephen shoving her elbow aside to peer out, his head level with her shoulder. All appeared unhappy.

Looking at them, Jan smiled. She knew what Gordon intended, but thought it better that he explained.

"Cheer up, Dad has a plan. Why don't you find him, and ask."

They dashed off, quickly locating their father.

"Mum says you can fix it so we all sleep in Jim's caravan. Can you?" Sharon asked sceptically.

"I think so."

"How?" She sounded disbelieving.

"Well, I could make one bed in the small room and let the two boys sleep outside under the stars, or under the caravan if it's raining."

"I'm littlest. Sharon should sleep outside." Stephen's objection was muted, muttered quietly, eyeing his sister with hostility, daring her to disagree.

"Don't worry." Gordon smiled at the mixed expressions. "Expect I can fix it. I'll try tomorrow while you're at school. Inspect it teatime; until then it's a secret."

Sharon pouted momentarily, disliking secrets unless they were her own, but all three went off happily enough. Dad seldom failed to fix something when he promised.

The necessary transformation took place the following day. Gordon collected timber from Harvey's of Hayle, then sawed and planed, drilled, screwed and sandpapered away, constructing a three-tier bunk of flat plywood sheets on a framework built exactly to size and fixed on three sides by screwing directly to the little room's walls.

While he worked, Jan nipped back to Hayle, to Pratt's market, a sort of army surplus store, to purchase bed-sized layers of foam rubber two inches thick, and on returning, stopped in at the new bungalow to pick up some old sheets from Audrey to use as covers. One sheet, rather crumpled and flecked with the odd paint stain, had obviously been used by Jim as a covering-up cloth. These would make the mattresses; thinner than normal, but thicker foam had been much dearer and space was at a premium. The low ceiling height and Jan's insistence on an air space below the bottom bunk would make sitting up in bed impossible. The children, except perhaps Stephen, must be satisfied with raising themselves on one elbow. Some discussion took place whether the bunks should be equally spaced or in accordance with the children's heights. Identical sizes were chosen, to avoid arguments and allow changing bunks should this become necessary for any reason, such as illness. The remaining floor space was small, they would need to dress and undress in relays, or more likely, nip into the main bedroom next door to change. No problem, they went to bed earlier and arose later than either parent.

Studying the finished work, Jan pointed to the tiny opening window. "It's more like a cupboard than a room; they could suffocate. This door should be propped open or removed. Can you fix it?"

Gordon knelt immediately, screwing it directly to the wall.

"Good." She nodded in satisfaction. "At least it's a separate room, I hope they'll like it."

Arriving home from school the children headed straight for the bigger caravan, Stephen running his fastest, trying to grab Sharon's skirt but she outdistanced him. Christopher, already a promising runner at school, raced ahead. Both parents watching from their own caravan doorway, saw the trio tumble through the entrance and disappear.

"Count ten," Jan said, counting aloud.

On fourteen they emerged from what had been Jim's caravan, racing each other across to where she awaited their verdict.

"Great!" "Super!" they panted speaking together, Stephen nodding as he trailed in the rear.

Another adventure! No longer the necessity to sleep in the same room with Mum and Dad. Terrific! Enthusiasm shone in their faces.

They liked it since they could lay talking for ages without being told to go to sleep, but funnily, most of all it was the impossibility of sitting upright that appealed.

"Like astronauts in a rocket." Christopher suggested. They would have to climb up and squeeze in. Moreover, no one they knew had ever slept in a three-tier bunk!

Jan had decided that Christopher should have the top bunk and for safety little Stephen would be on the bottom, but had nevertheless expected an argument. However before a word was spoken, Sharon asked for the middle bunk and the other two wanted exactly those bunks planned for them.

How easy! But she didn't say so. Life had to be fun for the children as well. It didn't hurt to let them appear to win sometimes.

"I think..." She paused, pretending to give it serious consideration, frowning, head shaking slightly as they waited anxiously for her decision. "Oh, all right then. If that's what you want!"

Gordon, knowing her original intention, watched and listened.

"Typically devious. Just like a woman!" The comment was silent. He smiled, seeing joy on the children's faces at being allowed unknowingly to have Jan's way. "She lets me have her way too, and thinks I don't realise it, but she's so special that mostly I pretend not to notice. She probably does it more than I know anyway."

Sharon, he saw, was particularly jubilant. At eight, she approached an age when her own bed, her own hair brush, and new clothes were becoming important parts of life. She already had the hair brush, and now the bed. Two out of three can't be bad!

"...try them?"

He realised Sharon was speaking, and looked up, not sure what had been said.

"Can we try them?" she asked again, the boys' expressions clearly indicating their own keen interest.

"They won't fall down, I can promise you that!" He turned to Jan for her approval.

She smiled broadly, knowing her husband's tendency to decide what size screw was needed, then to use ones twice as big and put in double the number actually required. It certainly would not fall down, she knew that; could never remember anything he built having failed. Probably stand forever!

"Yes. But take your shoes off before you climb on the new mattresses." Jan nodded, smiling, watching them race off again, Stephen as usual trailing behind.

She was pleased for herself as well; felt sure the larger caravan, when they moved in, would have great advantages. The separate lounge which was also a dining room, meant breakfast could be prepared before making beds. It would look so much better, less degrading when visitors came to the door. Jim had warned of one drawback; while the central heating delivered bags of warmth near the lounge boiler, very little heat reached the bedrooms at the far end, which could make bedding more difficult to keep aired. The better kitchen had to be a big improvement and the children would go to bed in their own room, leaving the two parents able to sit talking quietly and secretly together.

Jan knew none of the three would grow up out of touch with reality, for they had been too much part of the struggle all along, helping with the work, learning the value of money by its very shortage, expecting to have little jobs rather than little presents. When she or Gordon did manage to buy or make them a small gift they were always surprised and delighted!

"There is no reason," Jan thought, "to burden their minds with every risk. At such a young age they need love and security, not worry about the future. At least now we look likely to succeed. Still, it will be good to discuss some things privately in the evening instead of just at coffee breaks when they're at school."

She continued to watch and wait, slipping one hand into Gordon's. He moved closer but neither spoke, the quietness extending as a small cloud, wispy white, sped rapidly by overhead in the freshening wind, outlined against a deep blue sky.

Sudden activity and noise burst from the big caravan. Protesting shouts rose as Stephen, stealing a march on the others, ran barefoot, leading the way, shoes in hand. Sharon followed shortly, delayed slipping on her sandals but now catching up fast as he slowed to place feet with more care. Christopher, with laces to tie, lagged unusually in last place.

Stephen did arrive first, abandoning caution over the last twenty yards, but it was Sharon who gasped the question.

"Can we sleep in it tonight?"

Hearing the eagerness in that plea, her father shook his head. "Sorry, wrong place. You forgot the visitors; it's the office as well as our home."

"We don't..." Sharon tried to protest. Christopher, having caught up, opened his mouth to support her.

Dad raised a hand, stopping them both.

"No need to tell me. The office isn't necessary until next season. True, but it's empty now, I'll tow it before we transfer everything - less breakages! There's no school tomorrow, let's do it then. You can all help."

Disappointment that had shown at the delay, left their faces as the idea of helping, of missing nothing, dawned in their minds. During tea their keenness grew, dampened only slightly as the wind rose steadily through the evening, buffeting the caravan.

Shortly after the gas light was finally extinguished, heavy drops sounded, bouncing on the aluminium roof. Rain continued long into the night as the occupants, one by one, fell asleep to its constant drumming.

Saturday dawned bright and cloudless; the front had passed. Having whistled rain clouds rapidly in, the fierce wind had equally quickly blown them on their way and with their passing, had itself subsided leaving a pleasantly soft breeze. The children rose before Jan could call them, dressing quickly, rushing off to the toilet building to wash. The boys returned minutes later with little sign that water had touched their skin. Jan regarded them suspiciously but said nothing, continuing to prepare breakfast, which was still cooking when Sharon returned some time later looking fresh and neat. She edged onto the bench seat next to Stephen, with a grimace least her skirt get dirty against his grubby play trousers.

Gordon knew what they all expected and during the meal gazed through the window frowning doubtfully. Finishing, he left to investigate more closely outside, walking round the caravan then crossing to the bigger one.

"A pity it had to rain; first time in a fortnight. Almost as if done deliberately." He glanced skyward, regretting the irreverent thought, giving a little shrug of self-degradation, a motion of acquiescence to higher authority.

Lying in mud would be unpleasant; not too bad right underneath though it still looked somewhat moist. Elsewhere a wet stickiness prevailed, particularly surrounding the edges where rain running down metal sides had formed puddles, some now partially dried to a silty goo.

Thoughtfully, Jan watched him from inside, casting a sneaky eye over the waiting, unsuspecting children.

"A good husband ought not to mind a little mud to please his family," she muttered quietly, gazing back out through the window, speaking to no one in particular. A smile touched her lips as the children looked at each other in alarm, but she murmured a few more comments, just to be sure.

Gordon returned, walking back to climb the steps, removing muddy boots before re-entering the caravan.

"Ground's too wet. We'll do it tomorrow instead."

"No way!"

The chorus of disapproval was instant. They were not going to wait just because of a little mud. Above the general hubbub certain remarks could be heard relating to their father's character.

"Lazy!" said Stephen.

"A wimp," agreed Christopher nodding.

"Not very nice," pouted Sharon.

Jan just stood, smiling as if butter wouldn't melt in her mouth, gazing up at the ceiling, over towards the stove, out of the window again, anywhere, while the children voiced their indignation.

"You promised!" accused Sharon resentfully.

Jan, with Sharon's assistance, packed crockery and other breakables into cardboard cartons obtained late the previous evening from Sampson at the village shop. As each was filled, Christopher helped carry them safely clear, choosing a stony spot where the ground was relatively dry. Dad, having lost the argument, greased and refuelled Max, the excavator, parking it nearby. Clothes and other non-breakable items would be transferred later. They worked fast; water and gas must be disconnected from both caravans, making it highly desirable to complete the whole changeover in one day.

All caravans that stay in the same place for a long time are normally supported by jacking up until the wheels hang clear of the ground. Concrete blocks and offcuts of timber are commonly used as packings to support the axle, the jack being removed for use elsewhere. This makes the whole structure more solid underfoot and helps prevent tyres from perishing.

The smaller caravan in which they had been living must first be towed clear. Gordon fancied he could do this part without getting too muddy. The various services, including the telephone were disconnected and all four corner steadies wound up, leaving the entire weight resting on the single central axle, which was itself supported in the normal way, on concrete blocks. With the towing hitch connected, the excavator inched slowly forwards. The axle slid jerkily on its supporting packings, wheels still hanging clear of the ground. Abruptly, both supports tipped, the weight descending with a thump, bouncing slightly before steadying. Luckily nothing broke.

He intended much more care with the larger caravan. Lowering it gently would be slower and entail going underneath. This was unavoidable. The far greater size already meant more intense stress on the single axle. He didn't fancy his chances with the rest of the family if their new home fell in two parts before they even moved in!

The bigger caravan was constructed differently. Steel trusses supported the side walls, showing like an inverted trellis on both long elevations. The bottom of this steelwork terminated only inches clear of the ground, thus preventing direct access from the sides. To reach the centrally placed single axle it was necessary to enter near the caravan's end, then somehow crawl and slide some three body lengths along the shallow gap inside these trusses.

Gordon knelt down in the sticky ooze to peer underneath. Stephen, watching, slowly bent his knees then straightened suddenly with a little leap of joy. Christopher and Sharon looked at each other with broad grins. When Dad turned carefully over, flat on his back like a mechanic going under a car, and squirmed through an area of thick mud, their glee knew no bounds!

Jacking up, removing each block supporting the axles, then lowering the jack again, proved a messy business, but shortly the new home was ready for hauling away.

Although Max was the ideal towing vehicle, some difficulty arose when due to the ground's curvature both ends of the long caravan touched down, becoming stuck. Easing back clear of the obstruction, a double line of building blocks laid across the hollow, quickly formed two causeways. These raised the wheels an extra four inches and with a little scraping, the ends cleared. Thereafter it ran easily into place.

Positioning proved simple, a little skill perhaps but no real effort with Max's horsepower. Climbing off the excavator but leaving the hitch coupled to give stability during the physically more difficult jacking up operation, Dad turned to the watching children.

"Right, your turn now! This one's heavier, I'll need more of those concrete blocks."

He pointed at the two lines laid minutes before to extricate the caravan from the dip in the ground, shaking his head when Sharon made for the nearer pile that had formed the smaller caravan steps; those would be needed for the same purpose again. Turning to Stephen, he indicated several short chunks of wood haphazardly strewn on the ground where the caravan had previously rested.

"You can bring the wood packings."

Concrete blocks tended to split under the axle weight unless they had chunks of wood on top to spread the load.

Jacking up and packing solidly under both sides of the single axle, just inside the wheels, was going to be awkward. With chest just clearing the floor's underside, Gordon wriggled backwards again, shoulders sliding through soft, slightly wet earth that clung to an already soiled shirt. Cold dampness penetrated to the skin as each heel in turn was pushed into the moist ground, forcing his body backwards with some help from the lower arms. A frog jumped, or maybe a toad, seen only for an instant as it leapt past his left ear to a point somewhere ahead, beyond the scope of neck muscles to rotate. Taking a block from Christopher through a gap in the obstructing steel trellis, he struggled to turn and place it under the axle.

Sharon, unhappy with mud on her skirt, reached the caravan, lowered another block on the ground before her and stood waiting.

"Do you want to bring that one under yourself?"

Eyes opening wide, she looked down in alarm; a very soiled Dad was laughing up at her, dirt now also dotting his hair and shoulders. She stepped back, face twisted in distaste, partly from his appearance, partly with dislike at being teased. About to put hands on hips in a typical bossy mannerism that girls of eight are apt to pick up from their mothers, she realised those hands were covered with thick, partly dried mud. Looking frantically round for some way to clean them, her glance came to rest on the river. She had taken no more than three steps in that direction when Dad's voice reached her again.

"Don't."

She turned back, expression still annoyed but not understanding.

"Don't wash your hands in the river - not yet anyway. Water softens the skin. Get the other blocks first, two more each should be enough."

Lifting and supporting the axle on both sides to a sufficient height to raise the wheels clear of the ground, took considerable time. Had the jack slipped, the momentum of falling weight could easily have caused an injury.

Caked back and front in oozing mud, Gordon finally emerged, stood up and stretched. A gooey wetness had penetrated, sticking clothes uncomfortably to skin; chunks of wet soil adhered, mixed with hair where his head had lain on the ground. With the caravan now solidly supported, he moved to uncouple the excavator.

"I'll drive," Jan shouted, seeing him unhitch and about to climb aboard. "You covered the seat in mud last time. I've only just cleaned it off! Keep clear, leave this to me." Running across, she swung up into the big machine, started the engine, and drove away.

Christopher placed a concrete block under each corner to give the stabiliser feet a solid foundation, then wound down the end steadies while his father worked on the steps. It took minutes only, the blocks close at hand, tossed temporarily aside when the smaller caravan was dragged away. Quickly reconnecting the gas bottle, Gordon made to enter the caravan for a coffee.

"*You're* not coming inside!" Jan called down, standing in the doorway as he reached bottom step. "The state of you! Why can't men do little jobs without getting filthy?"

"What do you expect. You wanted it done today!" He glanced automatically down at the muddy clothes, and up again, surprised to find her laughing.

"Not me!" she protested, "The children were the ones who wanted it."

"You put them up to it! Don't think I don't know."

"You're still not coming in! A Hippo in a mud wallow would be cleaner!" She smiled down at him, waving the broom threateningly, muttering loudly the after-thought, "And probably more attractive."

About to protest, he glanced round for the children. Little faces projected beyond the caravan end, partially hidden at a safe distance from the developing argument, and he suspected, from his own somewhat disreputable condition.

"No good changing yet, not if you want water and telephone; the connections are right underneath this time. And I'm not doing it before coffee!"

"I'll bring you one out."

"Nowhere to sit, everything's wet. I'll have to come in." He took a step upwards.

"Go jump in the lake!" She looked encouragingly towards the river, pleased with herself, before slamming the door and sliding the bolt. In the end he sat on a big granite block behind the caravan.

"Good! Where no one can see you." Jan commented approaching carefully with coffee, holding it out at arm's length.

"How about a little kiss?" he rose as if to move forwards. She ran off smartly, cup left on the ground. Children's noses were pressed hard against the window, watching from inside the caravan.

The balcony, with its steps one side and French windows the other, now faced the bridge and incoming traffic. These were the steps visitors would use on arrival next season. Already levelled on its supports, less than an hour was needed to plumb in the water supply, check the gas connection again for safety, and re-fit the telephone.

Dad disappeared into the shower, Jan accompanying him with an armful of clean clothes, to quickly return empty handed.

"Do me a favour. Turn on the shower before you take your clothes off!" had been her parting words.

Under Jan's direction, the rest of the team commenced the transfer of armfuls of bed-linen and boxes of breakables to their new home, unpacking them into various cupboards. By midday, they were celebrating with their first snack in a lounge with no beds. It was just a sandwich, lunch would be very late. Dad, now clean and in fresh clothes, had become quite a likeable fellow after all.

As they ate, Sharon asked, "What did you mean about water softening the skin when I wanted to wash my hands in the river?"

"I'll tell you a story," Dad responded, pausing as the children settled back, smiling at each other and at their mother.

"There were five bricklayers working on a big building. One lived nearby, the others arrived by coach each morning, carrying bags slung over their shoulders with flasks of coffee and sandwiches for lunch." He paused again, looking round the children's faces, noticing that Jan was also listening. "After a week, one of the men, the one who lived nearby, had dreadfully sore hands. At tea break one morning, three of the others were ribbing him about being soft. The oldest bricklayer spoke little, but after a while he said quietly, 'I could cure you'.

"The four men turned, curious to know how this might be done. The old man nodded his head slowly, taking another unhurried swig of his hot drink before speaking directly to the one with painful fingers. 'Your own fault. Bring it on yourself. Go home for lunch don't you... wife makes you wash before the meal. That's the trouble. Bring sandwiches, eat with the rest of us, your hands will soon recover'." Gordon stopped, watching for a reaction in the little faces.

Sharon's expression displayed a certain resistance but the two boys nodded agreement, quite ready to believe.

"Don't encourage them," Jan objected. "They already think water is poisonous!"

Later that evening while the children played cards at the table, both parents sat on small armchairs rather than benches, comfortably sinking back in the relative luxury of thicker foam padding with a satiny finishing material. Jan rested her own book on one knee, idly looking across at Gordon reading in the chair opposite, her mind pondering silently over the change.

"It *is* better. Much better. But somehow I miss sitting opposite each other. I miss being able to put our elbows on that old collapsible table, gaze into each other's eyes, then lean forward slowly until our lips met. Why do I love him so? He's not dashing or chunky; more wiry really, persistent, lots of stamina, and he's kind, particularly to animals though he doesn't like to show it much. You certainly couldn't say I married him for his money, or the better life he could give me." The silent reflections paused for a moment before continuing. "It *is* a better life though. Maybe it's the risks and the insecurity I like, who knows?"

His book was on birds, she noticed. He preferred fact to fiction: birds, flora, self-sufficiency, the sciences. She knew he read novels occasionally, sometimes a mystery but more often prehistory, Stone Age or before. "Perhaps he was born five thousand years too late. He would have enjoyed those days, living off the land, journeying for weeks, just the two of us, without meeting another soul."

"Maybe," she thought with a flash of insight, "River Valley in winter is as near to that as you can get."

She glanced down at her own historical romance resting unread on one knee.

"Our tastes are so different but somehow our minds seem to blend."

Looking up, she found him watching her, saw his eyes run over her figure and he smiled questioningly. She smiled back and nodded; an almost imperceptible motion but he understood. It would be their first night in the new bed in the new caravan - no longer a collection of lumpy cushions joined together but a real mattress, albeit old and somewhat saggy.

CHAPTER 6

Stephen's Treasure

Jan stepped swiftly onto the balcony, waving vigorously as the last caravan headed for the bridge.

"See you next year," a voice, barely audible above the engine, drifted across; then the vehicle was past. She leaned against the handrail, watching it drive away, disappearing behind trees towards the village. Isolation again, the site closed today, its licence expired until next March. With a certain indefinable feeling, she continued to gaze southward, vacantly viewing the empty landscape. This winter would be quiet, particularly for herself. Stephen no longer ran wild in the valley, popping in and out at irregular intervals; he left for school with the others now. Jim and Audrey were gone too; she glanced to where her parents' caravan had once stood. Even the phone would likely remain silent, there would be no bookings at least until the new year.

Looking along the track again, conjured memories of a busy peak season, cars constantly coming and going, each followed by a miniature dust cloud. How long before another stranger came down that road? Her attention flicked to one corner of the tall heap of mine tailings.

"Wheal Virgin, whoever gave the old mine that name. For eight hours every day, I'm the only girl at Wheal Virgin!" She paused, thinking about it. "Would I go back, be pure again?" A picture of the children drifted lazily through her mind. She could never lose them to recover the intervening years. Her glance flicked back across the valley floor, remembering the fun her youngsters had found here. A smile crept over her face at the thought, the disconsolate humour dispersing.

From where she stood, trees all but obscured the waste heaps. Odd leaves were drifting down, bare sycamore branches already raked the sky. Not so much autumn colour this year. Other foliage was falling early too, crinkling brown rather than yellowing; a belated effect of searing summer heat and lack of rain? Bushy willows, always last to shed, still sported a full covering of green but had lost their freshness. Ash and Oak were both loosing leaves; any strong wind would send a host swirling down.

The change to being alone was more in her mind than real, so few had been the visitors in the last few weeks. A return to almost full time shifting of spoil from the ancient mining activities had resumed; one smallish new area already filled with the stony waste. Max, the big excavator, did most work; she drove at times but Gordon never let her use it near the waste heaps, professing it too dangerous. She found that hard to believe, he worked there himself for the greater part of *every* day. Nor could she manage the hand work; removing gorse roots required too much physical strength. Sometimes she did help, collecting piles of vegetation already dug from the ground, topping Max up with fuel, mowing the grass and even spreading topsoil; but mostly occupied herself around the caravan.

She moved to scan the river again; not so much visible now, with the reeds grown taller. A noise made her look up; nothing could be seen but the sound was familiar, the first bucketful of a new load echoing in the empty trailer.

"I'm glad he's working shorter hours, last year I hardly saw him during daylight. At least now he sits with me longer over coffee. It's nice when we walk round arm in arm, inspecting progress, discussing the next pitches. Didn't realise how much I would miss Stephen. Most days now I see no other person until the children come home."

Jan loved the valley, but sometimes... A solitary buzzard circling overhead caught her attention, breaking the train of thought. "It's lonely too. Won't find a mate until spring."

For Gordon also, the last visitor's departure deepened the solitude. At first he felt somewhat self-conscious talking again to his feathered companions, glancing over one shoulder now and then to check no guests had approached within hearing distance, forgetting sometimes that they had all gone. He realised talking to birds was odd, and took some satisfaction from that.

"I only need to worry when I don't mind other people overhearing," he muttered quietly. "When I start to think it's normal, that's when I need to worry."

Association with lots of people during the summer had exerted a restraining influence, reinforcing conventional values. However, as the lonely afternoons wore on these inhibitions fell away, and the harder the work and hotter the day, the more they chatted.

"Not quite eighteen months. Let's see, three more days, that's 544 days we've been here." Unconsciously he seized on the mental calculation, a throwback to those old days when life had been full of calculations, and people, and bosses to placate.

Now all that was gone. Physically the work was demanding, unreasonably demanding at times, but satisfying! He had no one to please but himself, no higher authority to say do it differently.

"Not quite," he suddenly realised, "remember those Council Building Inspectors!" Immediately a picture formed; a man in a bowler hat looking down a hole. Without realising it, he was humming that tune made famous by Bernard Cribbens.

A mind didn't go into hibernation just because it was alone. Ever since their arrival at Relubbus he had thought of birds, and now increasingly of bushes and flowers, as his new companions. He talked to them all, not necessarily expecting a reply, but half believing they understood.

"I'm sorry little hazel bush, you can't stay there, but don't worry, I'm going to replant you. You'll like the new place when your roots settle in."

He believed each plant had its own set of problems,

problems that affected where and how it grew. These ideas, together with wider considerations of life, religion, the planets and absolutely anything else whatsoever, became useful mind-fillers as he toiled on mechanically. They made the work smoother, less tiring, easier to sustain.

"I know," he mused "that gorse has those sharp little spines to protect it from being eaten by grazing animals, that's evolution. Gorse bushes with more prickles survive better than those with less. That's obvious. But why hasn't the same evolution given prickly leaves to all other green bushy vegetation?"

Having found a suitable problem, he would work on, happily mulling it over, even asking the willow bushes how they survived without barbs.

It was escapism, fantasy; he realised that, and wondered in more sober moments whether a few further years alone would find him totally mad. He considered discussing it with Jan, but again a mental response came unbidden.

"Don't worry about it, no one will ever notice the difference!"

November ran on. On rare occasions, maybe three times in a month if they were lucky, a load of topsoil would arrive; a driver from some building or council work wanting a place to tip. These lorries, few and far between, and the postman's van, were the only vehicles other than their own to enter the valley.

Working the big excavator continued constantly, a major part of every day, but had become somewhat perilous. Cornish mine waste in general, rested naturally at a steep angle. Composed of stone and finely broken slaty material, the ancient spoil at this particular mine had a tendency to stick itself together as if laced with weak cement. An old tale alleged that miners who left their barrows full over the Sabbath had to empty the contents with chisels on Monday. Moreover, this waste did not rise to a single point as some deposits do. Formed along one side of the valley, it had a series of peaks; the top flat in places, sloping in others.

When the family originally arrived, some of these heaps had already been partly removed. Rumour suggested it was taken for the construction of Culdrose Naval Air Station near Helston. In other places the heaps had swept smoothly to the valley floor below, having stood undisturbed over generations. Loading from these untouched sections had at first been easy, but as more stone was shifted, the working face became taller.

That, however, was not the main concern. The real worry was the cohesiveness of these heaps - making the material reluctant to fall. Max could stretch little higher than sixteen feet, and the working face was now some fifty feet or more in height. The top material towered far beyond reach; it had to be made to fall!

As Gordon worked, scooping up stone, the pile became progressively steeper until periodically, a wedge of material from above would collapse. Over the months it had happened several times, each fall bigger than the last as the height of the working face had grown. The first one took him by surprise but had fortunately been quite small. The problem was always the same, how to make it fall safely!

This property of cementing itself meant he must remove material from the very bottom, undercutting it, making a cavern like those formed naturally behind some waterfalls; a cavern no sane person would enter. But the excavator bucket did, regularly, twice in each minute for many hours every day - taking the flimsy cab right against that unstable cliff. There was no other way to continue.

Gordon drove Max carefully forward, watching for any sign. He knew only too well what to look for. Small stones rolled down almost continuously in a random pattern, singly or in little rivers of stone. These were merely a distraction, but not to be ignored. He dare not ignore them least they contain the code, the signal he needed yet feared! The vital indication occurred when two such small streams tumbled simultaneously from widely-spaced points in the face. Such a phenomenon required an immediate response. If he was slow to react, death would be swift. He knew that too!

As he drove forward, the top of the heap disappeared, towering above him, no longer visible through the tall cab window. The danger increased. In this zone he might miss the sign! Gordon hurried forward now, loading bucket nosing into the recess, undercutting that overhang yet more deeply, digging a cave as it scooped up material, still trying to induce the working face to fall. He wanted it to fall, needed it to fall; but please, not just at this instant. While filling the bucket he cast a glance upwards; to the hidden precipice above, or to heaven in a silent prayer? There was no time to think, the machine hurried back, not stopping until it stood a goodly distance off.

Tipping loaded bucket into waiting trailer, he lined up to move in again, as on countless times over the past months. Hesitating at first, watching the occasional falling stones carefully, he moved slowly closer, then reaching decision point, forced a foot down on the accelerator to hurry forward.

A great jolt shot through his body. Energy, adrenaline, fear - who knows? He had seen it! A small trickle of stone fell to the right; from the corner of his left eye, movement! He didn't turn to look, for a split second could do nothing, petrified, statue-like; then as if stung, spun into action!

Stamping on the brake, he thrust the gear into reverse, let the clutch out and applied full power! Above the roar of the excavator's great engine he could hear, or feel, his own heart pounding. The stone face started to recede, then for some inexplicable reason he was travelling towards it again.

No! The face was coming to him! Coming to get him; hundreds, thousands of tons, leaping at him with fantastic speed. Foot pressed to the boards, he could go no faster as boulders and rubble began to break and bounce.

"Come on!" He mentally urged the machine.

John Wayne might have said, "Let's get to hell out of here!"

The sentiment was identical!

Riveted eyes saw no sky above, no distant tree through a side window, only the crashing turbulent mass of rock dead ahead. Reaching desperately, blindly, for the lever, feeling for the knob, unable to detach his gaze, he raised the bucket in a vain, futile attempt to keep the avalanche at bay. Ten feet! Seven feet! Five; a bouncing rock smashed against the metalwork sending a shudder through the steering column.

And suddenly it was over; the face receding again, or appeared to be as excavator and driver continued to rush madly backwards, eyes still glued to the front. A huge dust-cloud was rising over the scene. Gordon drew a deep lung-full of air, slowed, and stopped. He was not sure, but believed he forgot to breathe during the crisis. Shaken but elated, a pulse literally hammered through his body; he could feel it pounding at his temple, up his arms and somewhere within the chest cavity.

Stepping down to lean against the front bucket which still sat in the defensive position four feet off the ground, he watched the dust spread, heavier particles already settling. One or two rocks rolled down the new surface; a sloping jumble of stone and crumbled slate that now extended forty or fifty feet in front of the previous working face.

Full power of Max's great engine was never normally applied, never necessary under ordinary conditions; but this was that old self-preservation reflex in action. Maybe it stretched the imagination a little, but Gordon always felt Max agreed with him at these moments.

The whole episode lasted six, maybe seven terrifying seconds; short as a flash, yet so very long while it happened. He watched the falling dust. Loading would be safer for a while now - until the next time. Another risk would come soon enough, he knew that too; but for those few seconds he had really been alive, tinglingly alive!

No white-knuckle ride in the world could do what that had just done for him. For those few seconds, death had been inches away; not make believe, the real thing! The culmination of several days pulling the tiger's tail, when it could have happened at any time, hour after hour.

For a while he continued to lean against the bucket, somehow disinclined to climb back and start again, unwilling to resume the mundanely unending task; like a child might avoid cleaning its teeth after a succulent ice-cream, reluctant to lose the flavour. But work beckoned, and must be done. What an anticlimax. Pity loading showed such tediously slow progress; he watched the loose material emerging from the dust cloud. Not so slow over the last couple of minutes perhaps!

A characteristic noise had accompanied the fall, as with its predecessors; not unlike a fierce approaching rain squall, a sound that made the hairs on the back of his neck stand on end each time he heard it, and would probably do so way into the future.

Once a large round boulder had rolled from the top after the main fall settled. Bouncing and leaping it rolled on, passing the end of the fallen material and heading at speed straight for the digger. Without time to run backwards, he had fielded the boulder in the machine's front bucket, otherwise it would certainly have smashed the engine. That little incident however, had rated very low on the excitement scale compared to the awesome sight of a whole hillside racing forward only feet away.

He looked up towards the new outline against the sky. A crack often developed across the top of the heap; six, eight, maybe a dozen feet or more back from the edge, invisible from where he now stood, but obvious above. There were times when a person could put an arm down these cracks without touching the bottom – if one should be feeling particularly brave at that moment.

Still gazing upwards he remembered an occasion when the top had coincided with a short flat section. Climbing up by a different route, tiptoeing across this flat top towards the sheer edge, trying not even to breathe too deeply, he had knelt gingerly down. Reaching into the fissure, attempting to feel the depth, it had been necessary to lay full length, sinking the arm almost to the shoulder joint. The bottom had not been reached, but the crack had reduced in size so the hand could be pushed no farther. Such cracks might be there for several days, increasing gradually in width and depth, or could disappear quite quickly, as unpredictable as the rock face itself.

Breathing in deeply, Gordon patted Max's bucket as if saying "Well done," smiling ruefully to himself as he realised the implication. Working alone, Max *was* his closest companion; Robin never bothered to come near unless he dug soil instead of stone. Invariably it was Max who caused the face to fall. Only once had it collapsed spontaneously, when by chance he was towing the trailer back directly towards the heap but still several hundred yards away. How different the event had appeared with personal safety not at stake. Even at that distance he had seen the twin rivers of stone that presaged the fall; tiny far off movements but some part of his mind always alert for them.

He shook himself, the present dust had all but settled. Time to climb aboard and start again; or would Max like a drink first? He checked the fuel gauge.

* * *

The family had been in the big caravan now for nearly a month. It was certainly better, so much more space for storage and for living, but as expected the bedrooms were less cosy. In the smaller one-roomed caravan, the free-standing central stove with its exposed metal flue rising straight through the roof had kept the whole home snug. Now the separate bedrooms were already decidedly chilly. A small price for all the other advantages, but should the weather turn really cold, condensation might again be a problem, though not on the scale of that first winter in the tiny tourer. Jan already took the children's mattresses outside to air each day, or into the lounge if it rained.

"It's not too bad at the moment, I do it more as a precaution. Things could deteriorate in December and January," Jan commented one Friday morning while the children were at school. "At least the milk is usually OK for breakfast now, not so often gone off like in summer."

Having no electric and therefore no fridge had continued to be a problem. Towards the end of August, a cheap cooler had been purchased, a porous pot with a lid, inside which a single bottle of milk would just fit. The pot was then topped up with water, which leaked, or rather sweated, slowly through the porous walls. Evaporation of this liquid from the outside surface kept the milk a few degrees cooler than surrounding air temperatures. It stood in the shade under the caravan. The system worked - usually. At one time a bucket of water had been kept outside for the same purpose, but after the milk top was interfered with, presumably by some animal, a bowl in the sink had served until the cooler arrived.

"Sharon looked good in her new skirt this morning, don't you think?" Jan asked, wondering if he had even noticed. Sharon invariably rose earliest, taking longer over her ablutions, not yet for the benefit of boys, but with that natural vanity which young girls fortunately acquire; whether from encouragement by her mother or in competition with school friends was never clear.

They were on the balcony, sipping hot coffee, Gordon having slipped back a little earlier than usual for his break. The morning being relatively warm for November, they sat in shirt sleeves and a blouse, sheltered from a light north-westerly breeze as they faced southward under a clear sky, idly watching the river and scanning the higher ground. It was quiet now, they only had each other, little likelihood of seeing anyone else, not even at a distance, until the children arrived home for tea. Though he had given only a vague grunt of acknowledgement, Jan continued to talk.

"I've been saving *The Cornishman* and Mum's paper." This was the daily newspaper still taken second hand from her mother as an economy. Jan waited, expecting him to ask why, but he continued to gaze across the valley with a vacant expression, his mind miles away, somewhere. It wasn't another woman, she knew who her rivals were - a tractor, the site, and that robin. Turning aside she mumbled, ostensibly to herself.

"No one listens to me, might as well speak to myself, no one else here worth talking to. Perhaps I should start chatting to robins, they're probably more intelligent anyway." She paused for breath, watching him from the corner of one eye. He was grinning. She turned, reaching out to dig his ribs but he caught her wrist lightly and she didn't want to pull the hand away for another try.

"You never listen to a word I say!" She accused him, trying to appear serious but unable to resist responding to the infectious grin.

"I hang on your every word." He said it softly and with feeling. She wanted to believe him, felt herself slipping as he leaned towards her. Suddenly she straightened.

"Oh no you don't! Smoothy! I know you weren't listening, I was watching you, your eyes were vacant; in another world."

"Your voice does that to me. Like a dream, I'm entranced, can't think of anything else." He clenched his jaw tight, attempting a look of adoration, but the smile still showed through.

"You liar. But don't ever change!" She leaned across and their lips met - just for the pleasure of being close. After a while, she sat back in contentment, looking at him, shaking her head, "I won't ask you what I said, I'll just tell you again..."

"No need. You're saving *The Cornishman* and your mother's daily papers. I would have asked what for, but I know you'll tell me eventually."

The way he could dredge up her words when his attention had been elsewhere and that touch of arrogance when he assumed she was bound to tell him why; it disconcerted her. She wanted to be angry but found it difficult not to laugh. It didn't help that she knew she *had* been about to explain, had *wanted* to tell him. Well not now! She made a lunge but he was off the chair, hand on the balcony handrail, leaping over the top onto the ground outside and stood just out of reach, his grin even broader.

Standing on the raised platform gave her the unusual advantage of looking down into his eyes, a reversal of rolls.

"Romeo, Romeo," she whispered, holding out one arm in a very feminine gesture, a soft look in her eyes.

As he took the extended fingers she drew him lovingly towards her, swinging the other hand suddenly to clout him round the ear; not too hard but sufficient to make the point.

"Next time you take the micky, I'll use a baseball bat!"

* * *

Large stones dotted the heap, they were mainly of two types, slate and quartz. The slate was of little use being poor quality, all those pieces projecting above the surface had over the years been split by frost. One visiting geology student had suggested, "Heat and pressure from intrusion of the granite batholith was less than that required to render a durable slate product."

No doubt a fully-trained geologist could give an even more obscure explanation.

For practical purposes such as wall building, this stone was not ideal, except maybe for riverbanks where it would remain underwater and therefore protected. Similar stone was sometimes used locally for building low hedges, since frost was relatively rare in Cornwall except on the high moors, but it would probably all crumble eventually. Slate from some Cornish locations might well be of better quality.

The other stone, mainly quartz with chlorite and several minor minerals, seemed an excellent material for permanent use. With this in mind, such stones had been saved by rolling them into the digger bucket and stockpiling in a convenient heap, not too far away.

Although working less excessive hours than the first year, Gordon continued to put in long periods of very physical effort. Progress was steady if not spectacular, and still on rare occasions reached the magic figure of twenty loads in a day. At intervals loading stopped while these large rocks were picked out before filling the next trailer.

The rock stockpile was growing but a vast number would be needed to make walls on all the intended terraces. Some boulders were heavy enough to cause injury if wrongly handled but remembering weight training days in the forces he schooled himself to follow the correct drill.

"Bend the knees, keep the back straight, a couple of chuffs," he ticked them off silently to himself, remembering that the quick deep intake and expulsion of air to feed extra oxygen to the muscle fibres was often referred to by weight trainers as a chuff.

"Cornish chuffs do still exist," The irrelevant thought came, distortedly filling the idle mind in a horrible pun on the Chough, the Cornish County bird, black with a red curved bill, sadly believed to be on the point of extinction in the far southwest.

"Shoulders back, lift with the thighs." He heaved himself complete with stone into the standing position and keeping a straight back, staggered towards the digger bucket. During the short traverse, the stone rested heavily, partly on hands, partly on abdomen. This type of work was murder on clothes; old donkey jackets in really horrible condition were saved specially for the task. Having reached the bucket he dumped it in, closing his eyes and bending aside. Quartz, a major constituent of these rocks, was hard enough to cut glass, very brittle and when dropped had a tendency to send tiny shards lancing through the air.

Turning for the next rock, a noise, a squeal appearing to come from above and beyond the waste heap, pulled his eyes quickly skyward. The shape of the working face changed as loading proceeded; several weeks had passed since the last fall and it was steep now, almost sheer for three-quarters of its height, curving away slightly near the bottom.

Perhaps a second passed before a rabbit suddenly appeared right at the top, some fifty feet up. What predator pursued it was unknown but the rabbit came into view at full speed. So terrified was the animal that its feet continued running several paces in mid-air before plunging downwards, bouncing on the slope and rolling over. Coming finally to rest at the bottom, it lay bewildered and unable to move.

Not wishing to alarm the creature further, Gordon stepped slowly forward, stretching out to pick it up. Reaching for a grip his hand touched fur when, with an unexpected explosion of energy, the rabbit was off! Brushing fingers aside, it shot almost vertically, straight up the face, stones flying in all directions as powerful hind legs strove to find purchase. Without a whisper of hesitation, it disappeared over the crest, a performance putting any human mountaineer to shame.

"I don't know what was after you," Gordon muttered, shaking his head, "but with an accomplishment like that you certainly deserve to escape. Good luck Mr Rabbit, or are you Mrs?"

He related the story to Jan, back at the caravan for the mid-afternoon break. She listened to his droll description, particularly amused by the vision of a rabbit running in thin air.

"Mad," she said, as they both relaxed into the armchairs facing towards the French windows and the view upstream across the site. It was pleasant to sit, as so often this autumn, side by side while the coffee cooled. Mostly they chatted, contentedly happy in each other's company - just as well for there was no one else to talk with. They seldom argued, but liked to spar orally, not particularly to win or lose, just for sheer fun and for the closeness it brought. Occasionally, like now, they sat back, each lost in their own thoughts.

The word *March* came to mind. "What," Jan wondered, "have rabbits got to do with March?"

"Mad as a March hare!" it came back to her. "Be lucky to get any visitors in March, even though we'll be open again, and that's nearly four months away." She noticed a ripple on the surface of the river, a trout probably. "We've been here more than eighteen months now. I hope we don't get frost. If we do, Gordon will want to drain out the toilet buildings and we'll lose our hot showers. I don't want to lose them. That little tin bath is so restricting, but using the cold river is much worse!" She gave a little shiver, pondering the possible loss.

"The locals say it's unlikely to freeze anyway. How can I convince him they're too good to miss? Perhaps we should share a shower regularly to save water? He might like that."

She imagined their two bodies covered in soap, close together in the small cubicle, the steam billowing round them...

"He might even think the occasional burst pipe a small price to pay!"

* * *

Stephen mounted the caravan steps warily. A strand of blond hair, bleached by the past summer's sun, hung down in a half curl on the five-year-old's forehead. He moved quietly, furtively, looking round, anxious neither Christopher nor Sharon should see him enter.

His parents were seated at the table, not discussing anything particular, just idle conversation, relaxing together, watching small white clouds scud across the evening sky. Jan had noticed Stephen's approach. Something about the way he moved caught her attention. Several times the little lad had glanced over one shoulder, keeping close to the bushes as if trying to approach in secret. His left hand was held close to the body, palm upward, fingers curled over concealing something from sight. Whatever the object might be, he held it with great care. Alive perhaps?

She waited, intrigued. The caravan door opened a crack, then swung aside. A little head peeped round, hesitating, checking inside. Seeing only his parents he entered, walking haltingly forward, pausing halfway as if unsure whether to proceed.

Coming slowly to the table edge, the hand raised and cautiously opened, revealing a stone, but one such as none of those present had ever seen. It glittered brightly, reflecting light from many silvery facets that covered the entire area of its shattered surface. Stephen said nothing, just stood there, hand outstretched, arm almost level with the table top, shining stone sitting snugly in the palm.

"May I?" Gordon reached out.

Stephen, his eyes full of wonder, nodded once.

As his father cautiously took the stone, weighing it in his hand, Jan watched Stephen's eyes follow the gleaming treasure.

"No sound, no shouting," she thought, "just like when he's hurt. Christopher or Sharon would have dashed in proclaiming such a find to everyone within earshot. But he knows it's special, is excited in his own way; just keeps it to himself, hidden inside. You have to know him to understand." She realised Gordon was speaking again and turned towards him.

"...heard about this before. You can tell partly by its heaviness. Galena is the name, at least I think that's what it's called, I'll check later in the book. Feel the weight." He passed her the stone before turning back to the young lad.

"A clever find, Stephen. If I'm right, it's made mainly of lead, that's why it's so heavy, but has some silver in it. Real silver, the precious metal, though not too much. Good sample, you should start a collection."

Jan placed the stone carefully back into Stephen's still upturned outstretched hand. Small fingers closed loosely, shielding the glitter; he glanced warily over one shoulder, checking the door.

"Can I keep it in the bedroom?" He spoke in a whisper, breaking his silence for the first time.

"Yes," Jan nodded, "For now. But there's not much room, try to think of somewhere else soon. We could find a small box, you could keep it together with any others you collect; in the service passage of the second toilet building would be good. If I find three boxes then Sharon and Christopher can start separate collections if they want, though I doubt they'll find a piece as nice as that."

Stephen nodded, almost smiled, and made for the small bedroom, still holding the stone in front like a delicate jewel.

Jan watched him go, knowing he would search for a

better place to hide it.

Other interesting minerals began to appear. That first sample did check out in the book to be Galena a shiny mixture of lead with a little silver. Over the following weeks they found many pieces of Chalcopyrite and Iron pyrite often known as fool's gold, composed of copper with sulphur, and iron with sulphur respectively. Arsenophyrite was also identified, appearing as tiny silvery flecks within other stones, fortunately an insoluble form of arsenic. It smelt of onions when hit with a hammer, or the smell may have been from the rock that contained it. Several others were identified by a passing enthusiast, including the speciality of Wheal Virgin, a pink mineral called Erethite, a cobalt secondary that their visitor claimed was much sought-after by collectors from all over the world.

It seemed the last fall of the working face had exposed more interesting rocks than previously seen, though probably some had always been present and were overlooked.

Collecting different stone specimens became a hobby for everyone. The pieces were stored in individual catches, mainly in the wider service passage of the second toilet building, but Stephen's galena never appeared with his other stones, nor did he ever reveal its whereabouts to anyone.

CHAPTER 7

Work unending

Jan sat in the caravan alone, the children en-route to school, Gordon working as always, the hour still early. Now that work consisted for the greater part in loading and tipping the trailer, there was less she could usefully do. Life was easier this year. Since the season's end, many days had been spent tidying those parts of the site where pitches were already levelled and grassed, but that was now complete and all the large dustbins had been thoroughly scoured and packed away. Even the grass had at last stopped growing. She still occasionally operated the big excavator, helping uproot gorse bushes, driving into position and lowering the bucket while a chain was wrapped round the stems, then raising the bucket again to yank them free of the ground. This however, only worked well where gorse grew tightly packed together or on bigger, older bushes. With small single stems the chain just slipped. In any case, Gordon found it quicker to uproot these with the pick and welcomed the change as a break from loading.

Today nothing in particular was planned. The two toilet buildings needed a repaint internally to freshen them for next season's visitors, but that was for February when winter's condensation had largely passed. Sometime that morning milk must be collected from the village shop and as on most days, a walk to see her parents would be pleasant; later was better, they seldom breakfasted early.

Looking through the window and seeing the ancient mower, its long wooden shaft projecting in front, recalled memories of that journey from Lelant, towing it behind the little mini-van, herself sitting astride the shaft covered in cement dust. Originally a horse-drawn model, it had cut fine behind the excavator, proving excellent for clearing long vegetation from flat surfaces. They never used it now, none of the remaining wild areas were remotely flat and it proved useless for cutting short grass. It had become dangerous, standing neglected in one corner, tempting to the visiting children and so difficult to prevent them playing on. Gordon had promised to hide or dispose of the old relic somehow. Dispose of it? Who would want such a curiosity?

It had been cold last night, pity the bedroom radiator refused to get hot. Lifting the boiler lid and finding it low, Jan poked in three more logs, last of a small stack stored in the hearth to dry, then picked up a bucket to collect more from a heap behind the caravan.

Turning the corner, approaching the logs, she noticed a small bird crouched in the lea of the stack and drew up short, expecting the little ball of feathers to dart away. It remained still, standing upright but unwilling or unable fly off. Moving closer and reaching out, her hand touched it gently without response. The drooping head remained hanging.

"What's happened to you, little sparrow?" The words came automatically, followed by a wry grimace. "Gordon's got me doing it now. I've caught him talking to that robin so often; I think it's catching!"

Logs forgotten, the tiny bundle was scooped up and whisked away to the warmth of the caravan. Inside, Jan pulled a chair with one hand, dragging it near the stove, sitting with the little bird cupped in the bowl-shaped hollow of her two palms, inches from the hot surface. After a while it eased the weight from one spindly foot to the other, turning its neck upward as if to inspect her but not moving the body and making no attempt to escape. Looking round for something to feed it, she stood, carefully freeing one hand to turn the tap, trickling water into a flora tub, adding tiny pieces of bread to float on the surface.

The bird made no attempt to feed from the tub held

under its beak. Feeling in the drawer again for something to help, a corkscrew came to hand; she dipped the twisted metal in water before holding it over the bird. A few drops fell onto feathers and ran down to drip off the bill; the small head tilted backwards, beak opening and closing as it drank.

By the time Gordon returned for coffee, the sparrow had taken some small pieces of bread and recovered but still clung to the finger. When he entered, it flew to the top of a cupboard. Reaching out, stroking the chest feathers gently, Jan coaxed the bird back onto a finger and carried it to the door. Well aware that Gordon was watching, she opened the top half, held her hand outside and commanded, "OK. Now fly away."

It did, aided by a twitch of the finger. They watched it disappear into a distant tree.

She turned to make the coffee, offering no explanation, smiling to herself while filling the cups, aware his eyes were watching her back, waiting. He didn't like asking, she knew that, just hinted most of the time, expecting her to anticipate his needs. Well, this time would be different. If he wanted to know he'd have to ask.

"Did work go well this morning?" she enquired blandly, transferring cups to the table.

He nodded. "Moderately. Four loads."

They sat on in silence, both aware; the duel well and truly joined.

"Pistols at dawn," she thought sipping her coffee with relish, at one point leaning over to pick an imaginary speck from the floor to conceal a smile, straightening to gaze through the window and up at the sky.

"So you talk to birds too!" He uttered the accusation quietly.

She let the smile surface.

A broad grin of response spread across his face; knowing her objective, knowing his own curiosity had been too great, that she had won. It had not been a question but they both knew the intention. He didn't mind; these little contests made life interesting. One or other usually gave way, not letting a will to win come between them like a barrier. They gazed at each other, eyes shining, but she hadn't finished with him yet.

"Yes, I talk to them, but there's a difference."

"What?"

"They do as I tell them!" There was a touch of triumph in her voice as she tilted her chin upward.

"Don't we all?" he rolled his eyes to heaven, the cynical reply salvaging what was possible from a lost battle. He rose, drained the cup and made to leave, not prepared to admit further defeat by asking for the full explanation, guessing the whole tale would come out to the children at tea.

She had crossed to the sink, still glowing with the small victory, ostensibly to wash the cups but knowing he must pass to reach the door and wanting the physical contact. He squeezed by as she stood facing him, longing to hug her but resisting the desire, turning in the doorway to look back, love almost tangible in the air between them.

* * *

Now that Jim and Audrey were well established in their bungalow, the three children usually called in on the way home. Disembarking the bus in the village centre, they raced towards the bungalow, stopping briefly at the bridge since the adjoining seat, a local meeting place for some older men, was unoccupied. The parapets here were taller than their own bridge but not by much, still less than two feet high; low enough for all three to lean over and scour the clear water below for fish. This stonework was broader, the copings along the top shaped to a smooth finish and reinforced with steel dogs, like massive masonry staples. Knowing that trout often hid in the shadows under bridge arches, Stephen heaved his body onto the parapet and hung, head down, feet off the ground in an effort to see farther beneath.

"Get Down!" Sharon ordered imperiously. "You'll fall!"

Stephen, wrinkling his nose in defiance, deliberately eased himself forward, hanging even farther out, right hand clinging to the stonework behind, left hand helping support his weight in front. The position, too precarious to hold for long, had him struggling shortly back to the ground, facing his older sister with an unrepentant stare.

A voice called from the bungalow garden; the trio turned to see Jim waving, and dashed off. They could no longer cross directly, a garden wall had been erected round the property, the nearer gateway blocked, its double metal gates locked together where some unknown vehicle had backed into them. Jim, unable to move the stones himself, had agreed a price with Stanley Allen, who lived in the adjoining row of cottages. This wall, constructed in the manner of a traditional Cornish hedge, two skins of dry-stonework some eighteen inches apart with soil between, now sported flowers and shrubs all along the top. Gordon had arranged for part of the wall be set back into the garden, preserving the turning place widened a year earlier. Even so, during the previous season the site entrance had become very congested early each day. Caravanners had visited the village shop in such numbers for their breakfast requirements that Sampson, the shop owner, arranged to deliver milk, papers and bread around the site every morning. This smart move solved the congestion but the turning area had been retained, still frequently used by people from the site who visited the shop later in the day.

Christopher and Sharon raced towards the open gateway at the far end. Young Stephen, unable to keep up, headed straight for the wall, grabbed the post of the Private sign that had been erected next to the widened area, heaved himself up and jumped down the other side, sprinting across the lawn to arrive first.

Having greeted Jim, the children usually hurried inside, but he signalled them in the opposite direction. They followed, glancing back towards the house doorway; Audrey always had something to offer, a cake, chocolate biscuit, fruit, often with cream, sometimes even a full meal. At Jim's, the quality and variety of food was definitely better, not necessarily nutritionally, but different, richer, more sweet and gooey, things Jan's budget failed to include. Staying to tea was infrequent but highly favoured, even though the price was often a request to help outside afterwards, or in today's case, beforehand.

This garden's appearance held importance for all the family. Being at the entrance it formed every new visitor's first impression, and thereby might either delay or bring forward the eventual building of their own house, a point of which all three youngsters were well aware. Certainly the bungalow and garden were starting to look good. Audrey liked to do things differently. Inside for instance, the kitchen door had been removed, replaced by an open archway, and certain walls sported a rough textured finish in white, like a villa they once visited in Spain. Outside, clusters of shrubs and various fruit trees appeared in little groups in the grass, creating a pleasing effect by hiding some of the lawn's undulations. Today it was Jim however, who needed help and led the young trio towards a large granite slab.

"Roll that into the far corner for me, by the big fir trees at the back."

Having rolled the stone away, arguing among themselves as to who was and who wasn't pushing hard enough, they followed Jim indoors, surprised to find Jan sitting with Audrey, the table set with a considerable feast. That was the great thing about eating at Jim's; no economies. Even so, this spread appeared exceptional; but why was Mum here?

Audrey answered their question without waiting to be asked, spreading her arms towards the table, palms upward in a gesture of invitation to indulge.

"Combined celebration; a housewarming for our new bungalow and twenty-fifth November, Jim's sixty-sixth birthday. Your Dad will come up later, he's still working. Bring those wicker chairs through from the sun room for your Mum and me, please. You can sit at the table with Jim."

Chairs carried in and everyone seated, the meal commenced. Jan and Audrey, plates of food on their laps, chatted quietly between themselves, leaving Jim to talk with the children.

"Are you enjoying it?" Audrey called over after a time.

"Yes!" Christopher nodded, swallowing hard. "Don't get food like this at our house - especially if Sharon cooks."

"You don't do so bad," Jim stepped in quickly, foreseeing an argument about to erupt. "Should have been in the army, eat anything then. Bad as being in prison in some places."

Sharon, still smarting from Christopher's comment, had hardly been listening, too busy thinking of her own response, but Stephen objected quietly.

"How do *you* know?"

"I've been in prison - a rougher prison than you'll ever see. Almost fifty years ago, in the early 1920s. I was in the Guards then, and fit, used to box for the regiment. We had a corporal, I always found trouble with corporals; first step on the ladder of command, see - power went to their heads. Never had any trouble with officers, just corporals. This particular one had it in for me. I didn't jump when he shouted like the others did, he couldn't stand that. One day he got really abusive - they could do that with two stripes on their arm, call you anything. He called me a nasty little ba..." Jim stopped abruptly at a sharp glance from Audrey.

Christopher and Stephen exchanged glances, puzzled at the sudden break in mid-sentence; it sharpened their interest. Sharon too, ceased eating and gazed towards her grandfather, worried something was being withheld. Jim looked at the three intent faces wondering how to resume the narrative.

"This corporal said something which, err, reflected badly on my parents."

Jan raised her eyebrows, surprised at the mild expression, the original blunt words far more in keeping with her father's way of saying things. Audrey nodded approval, smiling at the children as Jim continued.

"I wasn't prepared to listen to things like that and I

114

didn't like being called little, we were both big men and we stood facing each other. He passed another foul comment about my father, grinning as he said it. I wiped that grin off his face. Laid him out cold, a single blow, right on the point of his jaw - never saw it coming." Jim stopped, an expression of satisfaction on his face.

The boys waited, eyes shining with expectation. Sharon wore a slightly disapproving expression as if such talk was distasteful to her, but Jan noticed her daughter's full attention remained on Jim, willing him to say more.

"Did you get in trouble?" Christopher asked.

"Oh yes! They all stick together. That's how the army works. No one is allowed to step out of line. I was up before the Sergeant Major, then one of the senior officers. Thirty days in the glass-house, that's what they call the military prison. It's hard, food is horrible. They have you running round the square in full kit, hours on end, take it in turns to come and shout orders. Left Turn! Right Turn! At the Double! Always at the double - everything. Want to break you, see you collapse, plead for mercy. But I was strong, never said a word. A Sergeant with some papers on a clipboard came along, '*Follow me!*' he orders, and led off to some waste ground. '*I want a hole dug right here*' he said, '*dig down until only your head shows over the top. Watch him corporal, if he stops so long as to wipe the sweat off his brow, put him on a charge. I'll be back in a couple of hours.*' That sergeant marched smartly away, military-fashion, shiny boots sparkling in the sun."

Jim stopped, taking a swallow from a small glass of whisky at his side, liking a nip when his hip was painful. Audrey told the children it was medicine for his bad leg. Smiling at the still attentive faces of his three grandchildren, Jim resumed.

"He did come back, that sergeant, with another corporal in tow, all of two hours I should think - certainly seemed like it. My eyes were just about level with his ankles by that time; he stood at the edge of the hole, looked down, said '*Good*', and marched off. Afterwards, the first corporal walked towards me. '*I'm off for a long cold drink and a sit down in the shade,*' he said, '*but not you; you keep digging*'." Jim paused for another sip.

"It was very hot, he thought I'd beg for water but I said nothing, just kept working. That niggled him. '*Put some life in it or you'll do three more!*' he bellows, then after a while, '*Get out!*' The hole was really deep now. Had to dig my toes in the sides to climbed up, made a mess of my boot toe-caps; I'd spent hours getting that highly polished finish - cardinal sin in the army if your boots don't shine! It meant re-polishing that night however tired I was. He knew that! I'd like to have thrown them at him but never let it show, just stood to attention beside the hole. He walked over and looked down, then pulled a slip of paper from his pocket and threw it in. '*Bury that!*'

"I started shovelling back in and he turned, speaking to the other corporal, '*Watch him. When it's full, you know what to do.*' As he walked away, he swung back to smile at me; not a pleasant smile.

"Filling was easier, all downhill you might say. Even so, it took more than an hour. The earth finished in a great mound, not so tightly packed you see, wouldn't all go in. I stood back and the second corporal walked all round, checking it, then he turned to me, '*Now dig it out again!*'"

Jim eased his bad leg and took another sip from the glass. The little circle of faces watched him, waiting. Placing his hands on the chair arms, he lifted himself into a new position.

"Expected me to object, to plead maybe, at least to say something! With drilling on the parade ground they'd had me working for over four hours non-stop in that hot sun - no food, no drink; not right, against King's Regulations. But I said nothing, made up my mind, wouldn't give them the satisfaction. I dug it out quicker this time, already loose, see. Took well over another hour all the same. Wasn't surprised when he put the paper in his pocket and said, '*Now fill it in again*'.

"I'd just started when the sergeant came back; marched straight over, examined the hole and spoke sharply to the Corporal. *'What's taken so long?'* They walked away talking, I couldn't hear properly, just a word here and there but the sergeant was annoyed, tore that corporal off a strip, laid into him something horrible. He came back then and spoke to me. *'Cut along to the mess, get yourself a meal, tell them I sent you.'*

"I never did finish filling that hole. Perhaps he made the corporal do it. Hope so. They seemed to give up after that, or got cold feet. They was breaking the rules, see; not that I'd have any chance of proving it. Stick together they would, deny everything. I cleaned windows all over the camp for the rest of the thirty days, never seen so many windows. Someone said that's where the name came from - the glass-house."

The children stirred, thinking the tale finished, for he sat there, silent, with a far away look. Stephen was about to get down when Jim spoke again, not to them, but gazing into space.

"Afterwards they sent me back to my camp, to normal duties. That original corporal was after me again straight away. He repeated what he'd said before about my family, thinking himself safe, that I wouldn't dare touch him now. I hit him again, so hard it nearly broke his jaw. When he recovered, they posted him to some backwater. I heard someone had told the C.O., that's the Commanding Officer, the man in charge; told him what really happened. Don't know who, I never said a word. Didn't save me of course, back I went for another spell in the glass-house; army discipline you see."

The children having finished eating, temporarily at least, left the table seeming unusually quiet and thoughtful but the effect soon wore off.

Jan started back to the caravan shortly after; she would return again later when Gordon finished his work. The children stayed, still managing to eat the odd chocolate biscuit and slice of cake, washed down with more lemonade. Eventually they too started for home, dawdling down the entrance road alongside the river towards the caravan, playing and arguing as children will. Somehow Christopher kicked off a shoe towards Sharon. Smartly, she side-stepped. The shoe flew on, landing with a splash in the water.

How he came to kick it off, never became clear. Whether deliberately, thinking it would hit Sharon or she would catch it, or whether accidentally while kicking a stone, no one knew - or at least, no one was prepared to say. It might even have been connected with Jim's wish to throw his boots at the Corporal. Such possibilities remained a matter of conjecture. Whatever the cause, the shoe disappeared below the surface. It was nearly new; the loss would certainly not be helpful in eking out their resources, nor assist in attempts at saving some small part of the previous year's takings towards building a future house. Jan would not be pleased! This they all realised and having failed to find it, proceeded home more sombrely than was normal, Christopher's gait somewhat unbalanced as he walked, one foot shod, the other bare. At least he had common sense enough to remove the sock. Jan sensed something wrong immediately, alerted by the subdued manner in which they arrived at the caravan.

"What's happened?"

She had not expected Stephen to reply but it was his shifty glance at Christopher's bare foot that drew her attention to the missing shoe.

"How on earth did you manage that?"

Christopher looked at the other two, then back at Mum.

"It just sort of flew off," he muttered lamely.

Jan raised her eyebrows, turning to Sharon who shrugged, uncharacteristically passing no comment.

Fetching Dad, who had still been working, they returned to a place just past the old cottage to search again more thoroughly. Some argument arose over exactly where it had entered the river, three small fingers pointing to different spots. Gordon lowered himself in at the point farthest upstream, indicated by Stephen. Near the edge it scarcely covered his ankles, but shallow as the water was a search revealed nothing. He eased out to midstream, water washing coldly through his wet trousers, then walked down the river's centre, moving from side to side, searching under drooping reeds. As he probed, wading slowly in the direction of the caravan, the children on the bank showed little sign of remorse. Certainly Sharon and Stephen were delighted, running ahead to locate patches where the water ran deeper, then waiting.

"Ooh!" Sharon cooed as the water rose up his thighs. Stephen, bending over, straightened up with a little jump of pleasure. Only Christopher remained subdued, or at least appeared to. Once or twice when Gordon looked up, he suspected a quickly suppressed grin but was never sure.

The hunt continued right back to the caravan in case the shoe had floated on the current, only the short stretch between bridge and weir was left unchecked; it surely could never have floated that far. Sharon's contention that it might, made in hope of seeing her father enter the deeper water, was quickly reversed when he suggested that perhaps the children would like to scour this final area. Only Steven was keen to try. Climbing up the stone steps alongside the bridge, water streamed from Dad's trousers but the old rubber gardening clogs, though squelching at every step, would come to no harm.

Poor Christopher, not like him to lose things, quite out of character, normally the most careful and sensible of the three. But, that's life! It was back to the old pair for a while.

* * *

A Water Board representative arrived one afternoon. He parked in the yard, locked his car, then seeing Jan step through the French windows onto the caravan balcony, nodded and hurried off round the corner. Puzzled, she watched the retreating back, knowing who he was from a previous visit. No inspections were due. What went on?

Out of sight from the office the fellow altered course, veering to the right and striding on, guided by sound from the excavator. Eventually locating the machine, he stood waiting at a safe distance. Shortly the engine died, its driver swinging down and walking over to hear what the visitor had to say.

"Now I don't want you to be concerned," the man started quickly, "because nothing is certain yet, but we're considering the feasibility of building a dam on the lower reaches of the Hayle river. We don't have enough water storage capacity; something has to be done." The man looked at the ground then up at a tree, his eyes moving restlessly, as if ill at ease.

Watching and listening, Gordon was filled with a vague apprehension, "What has that to do with us?"

The man hesitated, "Well," he fiddled with his hands, "nothing's certain of course, but the reservoir behind the dam would need to stretch a long way - because the valley's quite shallow."

"A long way? How long?" The sense of unease was increasing, a deep foreboding descending like black storm clouds, some not quite definable feeling warning of catastrophe ahead.

"Well..." the Water board man hesitated, making as if to point, the motion fading to some evasive gesture... "We couldn't flood Relubbus of course, but it needs to be as deep as possible." The visitor hurried on, plunging into detail about average depth, submerged vegetation, algae growth, then somehow ran out of steam and dried up.

Gordon stared at him long and intensely, not wanting to put his thoughts into words. What was the old saying, don't give the devil credence by mentioning his name! In the end he had to.

"What you're trying to say is that you want to flood the site, our home? You can tell your boss this; he won't find it easy!"

"It's only a feasibility study, I was told to sound out your reaction, that's all. Shall I say you're against it?"

"Against it! I'll probably drown the person who dreamt it up in his own reservoir - hold him down with my bare hands!" The hands rose of their own volition, fingers flexing - the man stepped back a pace!

That small movement broke the tension. Gordon dropped his arms quickly, realising his emotions were showing.

"Sorry, didn't mean to shout. Not your fault - bit of a shock all the same." He paused, collecting himself. "What of the other houses down the valley? What if old shafts undermine your dam? If that dam breaks, what will it do to St Erth?" He paused again, looking for other reasons. "This depth of water you spoke of, couldn't you find a steeper valley?"

The Water Board man shrugged, having no answers, then departed, leaving Gordon to continue with the work; only he didn't feel too much like working now, and instead trudged back to the caravan.

Jan saw him coming and lit the gas. "You're early for coffee, what did the water man want? I saw him leave."

"To turn our site into a marina." He sank into a chair.

"What! What do you mean, a marina?"

"The Water Board are thinking of flooding the valley."

"How? They can't - can they?" Jan's indignation turned to concern.

"It is possible. People's homes have been flooded before. They're thinking of making a dam, downstream somewhere, he didn't say exactly but it would have to be above St.Erth. They're only thinking about it, seeing if it's feasible. Might not be, something to do with the average depth of water he said, mentioned algae and other things."

"Would it flood the whole site?" Jan asked.

"Probably not - no it couldn't; too expensive to flood Relubbus and that can't be many feet above us. That's a point, how far up the valley side could they come without affecting the village? Come on, bring the level, I'll fetch the tripod and staff. We'll find out." He rose to leave.

"Hold on. The children will be home."

"Not to worry, Sharon can get tea, or Christopher can

take over the staff, whatever?" With that he jumped through the doorway, leaving her standing, then ran across the yard towards the service passage and workbench.

Gordon set the tripod and instrument a short way up the road while Jan stood on the bridge with a staff, just a tall slender length of timber marked off in inches. Working along the track, they had progressed perhaps a quarter mile, with Jan some fifty metres nearer the village, when three children rounded the bend and ran to cluster about her, asking questions.

"I'll tell you later, we'll be..." looking to where Gordon stood by the instrument waiting for the staff to be held upright, she yelled, "How long?"

"Half an hour!" the shout came back.

"Tell you all about it then. Go start your homework," Jan turned to Sharon, "Boil the kettle for half an hour but don't start tea, you know things tend to take three times what Dad expects."

As the children disappeared, their parents worked on towards the village. Levels taken through the eyepiece at each point were carefully written in a notebook for calculation later. An Ordnance Survey Bench Mark on the old miner's cottage halfway up the road was checked and another on the ancient granite bridge in Relubbus.

"How much shall we tell the children?" Jan asked, as they walked back carrying instrument and staff.

"About the flooding?" he saw her nod, and frowned. "Nothing, I think. Why worry them. Time enough to talk if it becomes general knowledge. Perhaps only people living by the river have been consulted, to assess the cost."

"What will you do about working. Is it worth so much effort under the circumstances? You don't think the chap was having us on, do you?"

"Possible I suppose, they might have been upset; we wouldn't pay for that six-inch water main, remember. But no, wouldn't really think so; I believe it was genuine, they do need more water storage. We must carry on, definitely -

as if nothing had happened, probably never will anyway. Let me work the levels out, that should tell something."

While Jan and Sharon prepared the meal, he quickly calculated the levels and after they had eaten, revealed the results.

"Our bridge, the top of it, is two inches less than fifty feet above sea level, and the main road in the village is eight-feet-three-inches higher than that."

"How can you tell?" Christopher asked.

Sharon looked at her mother in alarm, then turned to Christopher with a frown of annoyance. "This will take hours, you shouldn't have asked!"

Jan, seeing Gordon's expression, grinned with amusement. "Serves you right. If someone asked how to get to Land's End you'd probably route them through New York, Sidney, Bombay, and St.Malo. You don't have to include every little detail!"

"People want a proper understanding. Anyway, the rest of you needn't listen. I'll tell Christopher."

"You mean we can talk among ourselves?" Jan asked.

"Some chance," Sharon whispered.

"Just be quiet and don't interfere."

The two females burst into broad smiles and nodded to each other as Dad began his explanation.

"The staff is marked in inches. Mum stood holding it on the bridge, I sighted through the eyepiece and read the level. She then moved up the road 150 metres, that's about as far as I can see through our old instrument, and I took another reading on the staff. Now the difference between those two readings showed how much higher the new place on the road was. We just kept doing that all the way to the village. Simple Eh?"

"Is that all," Sharon asked in surprise, "You aren't going to tell us a lot of complicated things about how the level works?"

"Would you understand if I did?"

"No."

"Just as well. Can't stand intelligent women."

Although his reply was to Sharon, Gordon looked directly at Jan during those final words. Stephen, who had been rather lost by the conversation, cheered up considerably when his mother's tongue come out and quickly disappeared in response.

"There is one thing," Dad continued. "The Ordnance Survey level marks on the cottage, and on Relubbus bridge don't agree. One of them is wrong, the bridge seems two inches lower than it should be. Settlement perhaps, from heavy lorries; or did we make a mistake, hurrying to get back for tea?"

Nothing more was discussed that night; they did not want to risk the children overhearing. The following morning readings were taken going down the river. They already had a set of levels somewhere; Christopher Rolfe, a local architect, had made a survey before completion of the purchase. In the chaos of that first year however, these figures had been mislaid. New figures revealed the top of the riverbank at the downstream boundary, to be nine-feet-eight-inches lower than the bridge.

"What do you think; can it be done?" Jan asked.

"They can't flood the whole site, that's for sure. Our bridge may be eight feet lower than the main road but the real difference is less than that - some houses in Relubbus start well below the road and they couldn't let the water rise to anywhere near that level; it might affect people's foundations. They could flood the lower half of the site but the fall is so gentle, the lake would be very shallow. I don't think water quality keeps good then. We're probably safe. Let's try to forget it."

CHAPTER 8

Thunder

Max, empty trailer still coupled behind, drew to a halt near the caravan after yet another morning loading stone.

Jan poked her head through the doorway but waited until Gordon climbed the steps and entered before asking, "How many?"

"Only eight. It's getting difficult again."

She nodded, pulling a double page from the newspaper, one containing the crossword, and passed it to him, tossing the rest on a corner cupboard with a flourish.

He looked at the growing pile, "You're still saving them?" It was neither statement nor question, but somewhere between; an invitation to say why.

Jan turned away towards the stove, smiling to herself, remembering when the intention to collect newspapers had first been announced. '*I would ask what for, but I know you'll tell me eventually,*' he had boasted. Well, she hadn't!

Regularly at lunchtime, another was thrown on the pile, piquing his curiosity. Tossing the paper aside, flaunting it, had become a ritual, another little game. The reason must come out sometime, that was inescapable, but until then he could wait - or ask! She smiled to herself again sneaking a sly glance. He concentrated on the crossword apparently, but a shadowy grin lingering around his lips.

Lunch was a type of thick stew, the beef cubed, sealed by preheating in a hot frying pan with sliced onions, then casseroled with carrots, various other vegetables and a packet of Batchelors Farmhouse Vegetable soup for flavour. It had simmered for much of the morning. Light dumplings, added during the last half-hour, each floated on the surface with the lid left off allowing the tops to bake crisp. Cheap but exceptionally tasty, it had only recently been possible, courtesy of the newly acquired oven, immediately becoming a top favourite of the entire family. Sitting opposite each other across the small table, the two ate with relish, hardly waiting for the meal to cool, rolling hot morsels around on the tongue, drawing in air to avoid scorching the palate. Hardly a dish that encouraged conversation, the savoury mixture diminished rapidly.

Without warning, a rumble like thunder vibrated through the caravan walls. Gordon felt his scalp tingle, recognising immediately that underlying characteristic sound, even though greater distance and being inside had in some way changed its quality. He rose quickly, dashing through the doorway. Jan, casting a single glance at the almost consumed meal, followed hurriedly; baffled but knowing it must be important. Food had not been left unfinished since the pump stopped when they built the septic tank. Even incoming customers had been asked to wait once a meal was started.

Glimpsing his back disappear behind the bushes, she chased after, rounding the trees to be confronted by a vast dust cloud hanging over the waste heaps. Faltering for a second, she ran quickly forward, instinctively sliding an arm round his waist as they stood together watching.

The cloud gradually drifted in the wind, unveiling a jumble of stone and rock, a slide of such impressive size as to banish all thoughts of the part-eaten meal. Gordon stepped closer to the uneven edge, then on impulse, raced up the broken surface in a burst of energy, leaping from crest to crest, coming to rest balanced near the summit fifty or more feet above.

Jan gazed up at the massive slide in awe, seeing him wave down in jubilation, momentarily wondering why, then realising the risks he took in trying to make the face fall.

"Is that what he meant by 'Getting difficult'? Thank goodness it happened during lunch, not while working close to the face; he might never have escaped far enough or fast

126

enough for this one." Another thought occurred, "That's why I'm not allowed to load! Is it flattering or insulting? He can take risks, why not me? Am I more precious than his own life or just considered less capable? Frightened I'll dent his precious machine probably. Max? Maxine more like, he cossets that tractor as if... What am I thinking!" She glared at the big yellow excavator. "I'll be glad when it's all gone and just the terraces are left."

This was the largest fall ever experienced at River Valley. Standing there, one at the bottom the other looking down from above, they knew it was big, but neither could guess it would take a full six weeks to clear, moving on average almost a hundred tons a day. Better than 4,000 tons of material had fallen in those few seconds of that one slide; an absolutely unstoppable force, flattening everything in its path!

* * *

Jan watched the road, bending at intervals to peer through the small kitchen window, stepping now and then a mere two paces into the adjoining lounge for a better view southward, upstream and along the track. The children were due but would visit a while at the bungalow with Audrey and Jim, making their homecoming uncertain. Besides, the bus might be late. Not too late she hoped, with darkness due shortly.

As the trio eventually appeared some three hundred yards up the road, she reached for a slice of stale bread saved in a plastic bag to keep soft, descended the caravan steps and walked slowly to the bridge. Three small figures approached at a run. Kneeling down and holding out both arms as Sharon and Stephen rushed up, she clasped them to her, one head against each cheek.

The older lad stood back indecisively as his brother and sister hung in their mother's arms, wanting to join them but deeming it juvenile, somehow soft. The tumult of feeling included envy, a thing that had they known, would greatly have surprised the younger pair.

Jan rose, somehow understanding, to rest an arm on Christopher's shoulder. For a moment she looked down at the boy meeting his gaze, but as seconds passed the warm glow in the lad's eyes turned to embarrassment and flickered uncertainly towards the younger pair.

"I've some bread." Producing a paper bag, she broke the developing discomfiture, sensing the need, smoothing those ripples of daily life as always, a natural unconscious talent that drew the family to her. Swinging to the downstream parapet she tore the slice in three, then watched trout rise as the children, competitive again, strove to be first with their crumbs on the water.

"Come, while it's still light. I've something to show you." Ignoring questions, Jan started off at a run, leaving them to chase after, still demanding information, until the rapidly moving procession rounded a group of willows, coming abruptly to a halt before the massive lunchtime rock fall.

"Gigantic!" Christopher's comment came in a hushed voice as other eyes wandered silently over tumbled stone stretching to the skyline. "Can we climb it?"

"Ask your father," Jan indicated the far side of the heap where Gordon collected large stones. They raced off.

Seeing the children approach, he straightened, turning to meet them. Sharon rushed to be lifted in his arms but with not quite the spontaneity she had approached Mum, hanging back a moment, checking how dirty his working clothes were and the likely effect on her own blouse and skirt. The boys, eager with more questions, were close behind but stopped short. Close personal contact with Dad was more rare, restricted to the odd family tussle on the caravan floor rather than open emotional displays. Dad was a more ambiguous figure, supportive always but sometimes severe, demanding obedience, especially when tired; lacking then, the ever understanding patience of their mother. Fun often, good when they had a problem but also the one who handed out extra work at unpredictable intervals.

"Yes it's quite safe now, for a time at least, until it gets steep again. Climb all you want. I've been up already, the top ten foot is steep but safe."

The light faded as they climbed, Christopher naturally leading; Sharon, worried about her shoes, in last place.

Over tea in the caravan shortly after, with the gas light gently hissing and darkness descended outside, they listened as the details unfolded. Their mother, pausing between mouthfuls while the family ate, related the story of lunch interrupted by the landslide, the sudden noise and the great cloud of dust that had at first obscured the event. A stern warning, stressing increased danger whenever the face became more sheer, drew nodded responses from the older two but Stephen's expression clearly indicated that to him, the spoil heaps had only become more interesting.

* * *

"I've found another one!"

Christopher bent over, tugging at something among the jumbled stone, extricating a slim brown object less than a foot long, pieces of rock adhering along the sides. On hearing no reply he looked round to find his father struggling with a massive stone. The boulder, streaked with white quartz, was lifted, carried in a series of single steps, each one a separate physical effort, until with a jolt that seemed to vibrate the intervening ground, it smashed down into the excavator's bucket. As Gordon straightened his back, flexing stretched fingers, Christopher hoisted the object up over his head, signalling his find before bending again to strike it against a large slaty rock, dislodging more of the adhering surface debris.

It was Saturday, no school; they were working together, picking large stones from the previous day's huge fall. The stone stockpile was growing again. Christopher necessarily chose those of a smaller size but was diverted periodically by finding another chisel.

Old miners' chisels (the chisels were old not the miners,

there were no old miners, they just didn't live very long) had begun to turn up among the stone. They were something over an inch in diameter and seldom much more than fifteen inches in length. These were the discarded ends of long iron chisels once used underground for drilling blasting holes. The texture of the iron was interesting, a stranded appearance like a bundle of fine iron wires stuck together, attesting to its age. In olden times this stranding was caused by a process known as puddling, stirring and stretching the pig iron to expel carbon, producing a less brittle wrought iron.

Usually Gordon worked alone when loading, for the big machine could be dangerous. Only after a recent fall when the larger stones were being picked out by hand did Christopher come to help. Sharon seldom offered as it tended to spoil her skirts and Stephen was still too small to lift anything of a useful size.

"Bring it over here," Gordon called, when another chisel was unearthed, and led the way to a section farther along the valley where the waste had not yet been disturbed. Producing a length of string, tying the chisel to one end, he passed it to Christopher.

"Take the string and hang the chisel over this sloping part, here where that growth of heather indicates it hasn't been disturbed for years."

When the lad complied, his father produced a tape and measured the height of the string, then the distance from his son's hand horizontally across to the sloping heap.

"Why?" asked Christopher with curiosity as they walked back to the section being worked.

"Stability. Now I can calculate the angle. If we build our stone walls at a slope fairly similar to the natural angle at which this waste has stood for years, then those walls should never fall down."

"How high will you go?" The lad looked up at the tall face outlined against blue sky above.

Gordon followed his gaze. "Not right up there, caravanners would get vertigo. We'll have terraces, giant

130

steps up the hill; some with stone walls to the top, others only part way. We'll make four or maybe five such terraces, special pitches with views across the valley, and plant shrubs along the top edges for shelter."

Moving waste seemed never ending, the children had rather lost interest except to check on progress each evening, generally offering the criticism that not much had been done. With the latest fall, the first to reveal discarded chisels, Christopher decided to help. Even when they changed to loading the trailer, having tired of lifting the larger stones, the lad remained on watch, signalling for attention when a chisel appeared, sensibly not running in to retrieve it until a hand waved in acknowledgement from the digger's cab. He also rode on the trailer; chisels often appeared when the stone was tipped.

It was time for a coffee break. Quite a section had been levelled, loading quicker with loose material from the recent fall. Christopher had discarded his new jumper, for the day was mild, very mild for early December; now he couldn't find it anywhere.

"I don't think Mum is going to be very happy, she only bought it for you last week. We'd better find it!" his father warned.

They searched together but without result. Saying Jan would 'not be too happy' was bound to have been an under-estimate - particularly after the recently lost shoe! Buying a replacement must surely eat into the weekly budget to which she rationed herself! They searched on.

Christopher suddenly remembered taking the jumper off while riding the trailer, and leaving it lying inside. The garment might be buried under tons of stone - perhaps not too deep; might even be visible poking through the surface. Racing down to hurriedly search the latest tippings revealed nothing. Even fetching shovels and digging around failed to locate the slightest sign. After almost an hour they gave up.

The prediction had been right. Jan was not pleased! She was annoyed that coffee, made for the normal time, had been wasted, and on hearing the reason for their lateness, turned with a few choice words of disapproval, directing them not at her son, but at his father.

"I didn't lose the jumper," he protested, "why should I be in the doghouse?"

"Should have watched what Christopher did with it. You're big enough and ugly enough to know better!" The words were spoken quietly but with every appearance of great feeling.

Ouch! That was the second time she had used the expression. Silently he wondered, "I'm certainly not very big, but...?" He shrugged, about to turn away, then from the corner of one eye, saw Jan wink at the disconsolate Christopher, who brightened immediately.

"I saw that! You're not really angry at all!" Gordon accused in surprise. "You were winding me up!"

"Why shouldn't I? Serves you right! You and the boys do it to Sharon all the time! The jumper isn't that serious. I put a little housekeeping away every week for the children's clothes; Christopher will just have to wear the old one until his turn comes round again."

Despite the assurance given by last season's takings, money continued to be a problem in that it permitted groundwork only, funds would not yet stretch to further building. Not that landscaping was unimportant, but some variety of work would have been welcome. The one small essential plumbing task had been completed soon after the site closed. Several times during the season, shower taps had been found sloping downward, only a few degrees to be sure, but always in the Gents. Obviously, some boys had been swinging on them, and equally clearly it was bound to happen again next season and eventually the pipework must fracture.

Quarter-inch-thick mild steel plates had been cut, thirteen of them, all twelve inches wide, six inches deep. Into each plate, two holes almost an inch diameter were drilled to take the threaded ends of the Finch shower tap sets, which would be held solidly in place by brass nuts behind. More holes were drilled round the edges for large stainless steel screws to fix each plate to the wall. As an additional precaution, a half-inch mild steel bar was welded on, projecting some two inches at right angles, positioned exactly to support the bottom of each shower set.

"Another sledgehammer to crack a nut!" Jan suggested in frustration. "That's in case a team of twenty-stone acrobats decide to use them for press ups, I suppose? They look ugly!"

"They're not finished yet. Anyway, it should stop the pipes bending, because they're fairly strong!"

"Strong! Are you sure? If someone fixes a dirty great crane to one, and pulls hard, it won't break before the building moves, will it? Anyway, they'll go rusty."

"No they won't, I'm having them galvanised."

"Oh yes, how many meals must we miss to cover that cost? And why thirteen, we've only got eight showers?"

"For when the next building is complete, that will have four showers too."

"In ten years time! That's still only twelve. Don't tell me, the last one's a spare in case one of them breaks. Breaks! Like when someone leaves an atom bomb in a shower compartment!"

Jan had been scathing but Gordon would not be deterred. The plates returned from galvanizing some weeks later. Having finished the job, reinstalled the shower equipment and painted over the plate, he led her into the building. Entering a shower and gripping the taps, which were nearly shoulder height so no one would hurt themselves if they slipped, he hoisted himself clear of the ground, demonstrating the strength.

"There. Do it properly and it should last indefinitely. Now nothing should go wrong in the season."

"Hm. Of course. Don't want it crumbling like the Sphinx after twenty thousand years! What about earthquakes!" She stomped off.

That had been a month before, now there were no such diversions. Clearing ground and shifting mine waste had fallen easily back into place as a way of life, just as it had in the period after their first arrival when still awaiting planning permission for the toilets. Like then, there was now no building work to offer a change, no alternative jobs other than digging out gorse roots, to give a little variety.

The amount of material already moved was enormous. He spoke of it to Jan one lunchtime after another hard morning's work that seemed to add only fractionally to the area available for use.

"Do you remember when my hands were all cracked and sore from building last year, how keen I was to return to loading for the odd day?" Seeing her nod of agreement he continued, "Must have been mad! I could really enjoy some plumbing or block-laying, or anything for a change, any little diversion." He sighed, then struck by an idea while cutting the last sausage on his plate, asked, "Wouldn't like a dog kennel, would you?"

"We don't have a dog."

With a gesture of the hands, he said "Ah well," and continued eating.

"It's lonely this year without Stephen," Jan spoke quietly, wistfully perhaps, wishing the young boy was still at home. "That's why I walk up to see Jim and Audrey and I go out shopping, but you never stop. How do you manage? I'd go mad if I didn't get away sometimes. Don't you feel it? How many acres are left to clear?"

"About a dozen more, at a guess; years of work. And yes it is lonely, certainly compared to our old lives, but in a way I begin to like it - well, get used to it. I talk..." He paused, "I find... substitutes."

"Substitutes? Plural, more than one; not just that Robin? Yes, I've heard you. Try not to crack up completely!" Her broad grin brought an answering smile. She turned to pick up a letter, some sort of circular, and passed it across the table. "By the way, we had this in the mail. What should I do about it?"

He glanced at the paper, saw some closely-packed printing and pushed it back.

"Tell me, I'm not reading all that."

"They want a donation for children in Africa, some sort of crisis. We need money ourselves but - they're only children, we ought to do something, shouldn't we?"

A small gift was agreed, not much but as Jan said, 'something'. The suggestion that 'perhaps they could do more later', was a sop to the conscience rather than a real promise.

Back at work shortly after the meal, Gordon continued loading for an hour before deciding to clear a further patch of gorse. The physical effort of forcing out roots with his pick made a welcome change, at least for a while. He was surprised when only the Blackbird appeared. What had happened to Robin?

"Hope he's OK. If not I suppose another will take his place. Will I know the difference? Maybe, but mostly from its actions, not much variation in plumage unless it's a young bird. Where do all the young birds go anyway? Fly off to claim a new territory perhaps, but what new territory? Blackbirds for instance, with all those born every year, why are any territories left, why aren't they thick on the ground, what happens to them all?"

The words were silent, just ideas flitting by, filling an empty mind as muscles flexed constantly, pick swinging, heaving heavily forwards to lever up another root, then swinging again. Laying the tool aside, he reached for the shovel. It had taken time to become accustomed to a Cornish shovel with its pointed blade and extra long, straight handle. The unkind said these tools were not made for work but for resting on more easily.

"It's true, they are good for leaning on." As if in response to the passing idea, he dug the blade in and lent against the shaft, taking a breather, watching his companion scratch over the ground a few feet away.

"Where do young blackbirds go?"

The bird stopped at the voice, head tilted sideways, one bright eye regarding the man.

"You wouldn't understand."

135

The words came unbidden, prompted possibly by the dismissive way the bird looked quickly down again to continue scratching in search of a meal, ignoring him, completely confident and at ease. The mind didn't really care what thoughts came, just so long as something filled the solitary hours. He addressed the bird again.

"Try me. Humans are supposed to have powerful minds." The feathered head cocked up at the sound.

"Really! Is that why you pull the bushes but I get the worms? Two centuries ago, in Roman England, preparing my food would have made you my slave.

"Where do young birds go? Starve mostly. Only the fittest survive, that is what perpetuates the superb quality of Blackbirds, the rest die - sometimes disease, maybe a predator, but mostly starvation in winter."

"The children in Africa starve sometimes. We should do more for them really." Gordon said the words pensively, with a prick of conscience, bending over to pick up a small worm near his foot and flicking it forward. The yellow beak caught and swallowed it in one, then stood watching the man carefully.

"Help, yes. Stopping wars would be a start, and equipment to provide good drinking water. But food, that's more difficult. Suppose you send enough food to keep a young couple from starving for the next twenty years. You could manage that if you did without some things yourself. It would make you feel good!

"Let us analyse what would happen. You would make two people very happy, there is no doubt about that. They would grow up strong and useful. How many children would they have in their lifetime? A well-fed family in Africa will almost certainly achieve double figures. Now instead of two people, can you afford to support twelve? Will your own children after another generation be able to support five times this number, say more than fifty - and will your grandchildren support two hundred and fifty. Even the most dense person must know that this is an impossible situation. In saving the original two people, did you just condemn

136

ten or more others to starve eventually? Did you multiply suffering instead of relieving it?

"I am not saying do nothing. It is important to help all you can, particularly through a bad patch, a drought for instance, or in the case of Blackbirds, a hard winter. But you cannot sustain indefinitely an ever-growing population, much as you might wish to. At some point the food supply must break down. Some other kind of help is also needed. Why will no one discuss it?"

Gordon roused with a jerk, muttered to himself and quickly attacked the next root.

* * *

The Cornwall River Board working their way upstream clearing the river, had reached a point some hundred yards below the caravan. They cleaned every year; some houses in Relubbus once used to flood and were in danger doing so again unless the river continued to flow freely. As well as several men working in the water and on the banks, a very old dragline excavator was in use, the type with its bucket suspended on wires. The operator would cast out like a fly fisherman, dragging back towards his cab, filling the bucket on the way, then throw it complete with contents to some desired emptying point.

That morning, since Jan required shopping in Penzance, the children would accompany her as far as the school, leaving just before nine instead of their normal time half an hour earlier. The River Board usually commenced at eight thirty, so this was the children's first chance to watch. The boys, hearing the machine start up, raced along the riverbank. Sharon, less interested but not prepared to be left out, walked along more sedately some distance behind. Stopping once, she brushed at the short plaid skirt with one hand, reaching to tuck in her blouse more tightly. At eight years old, appearance had become increasingly important. Shaking long dark hair back over one shoulder, she straightened up to follow her brothers again. Gordon, clearing gorse not far away, strode over to say goodbye, knowing they would leave for school shortly.

The dragline operator, having warmed up the engine, threw out the bucket. It dropped in midstream with a huge splash and at the pull of a lever, came back empty. They all saw, but only Christopher was sharp enough to really notice.

"Why throw the bucket in and collect nothing?" he looked up at the foreman standing next to him on the bank.

"Ah! Does that every morning. Stops him catching fish."

Christopher, believing the man to be poking fun, turned uncertainly towards his father for reassurance.

Gordon glanced over his son's head with a questioning smile.

"No, straight up," the foreman laughed. "That's why he does it, to frighten the trout. Otherwise we sometimes catch one in the first bucket. Once we get started most will swim away and there's less problem."

Wonderful control of distance was a talent of this particular driver who could throw the bucket to an exact spot, whether full or empty. They watched him perform for a few minutes. The vehicle's tracks were flat, without projections, all the corners had worn to a smooth rounded finish over the years. It swivelled slightly and travelled a few metres along the bank with hardly a mark. The foreman said spares were getting difficult, in a few years it would likely be abandoned as obsolete. This year would probably be the old machine's last on the river Hayle. Mostly they cleaned by hand, using the machine only every fifth or sixth year since it tended to lower the bed, making the banks steeper.

"That's the one thing draglines are not so good at. It's more difficult to take just the weed at the edge without taking some of the bed from the centre," he confided.

Waving to the men, Jan hustled the children off to school, and drove on to Penzance, returning via Hayle to collect timber for shelving over the workbench, arriving back in good time for coffee break. As she returned to the site, the river near the caravan had become a scene of some activity, with men in the water clearing reeds from a section immediately below the bridge. This short length had always been worked by hand, to avoid undermining the bridge's foundations. Jan put the kettle on, lit the gas and walked out to join Gordon. Having returned for coffee, he stood on the bank, pleased enough to watch instead of working for a while.

The foreman, swinging a scythe, water well up his waders, half turned to speak, got a foot wedged between two stones in the riverbed and tried desperately to regain balance. Dropping his cutting tool, arms waving wildly in the air, he uttered an involuntary shout. Jan saw every head turn as he hit the water with a great splash. Liquid droplets sprayed in all directions, glistening brightly in the sun as the body disappeared momentarily, quite a feat in little more than two feet of depth.

He resurfaced spluttering, to a resounding cheer from the other men.

"Thought he needed a bath on the way to work in the Landrover this morning!" one shouted.

"Hardly fair on the fishes. It's pollution, that's what it is. Should have his time stopped if he's going in for these recreational breaks," another called.

The foreman, having recovered his breath at any rate, if not his dignity, waved an irate finger in a futile attempt at authority. With water still pouring off him everywhere, running down his face from his mess of sodden hair, and from all his clothes, he didn't seem one bit to be master of the situation. The rest of the men just doubled up laughing. With one further attempt to look savage, again raising his finger to point a warning, he gave up, dissolving into unrestrained laughter himself.

Jan, fearing it impolite to join the hilarity but having the greatest difficulty in resisting, had hidden behind Gordon. Hearing a whispered suggestion, she slipped off, returning quickly with a big towel and some soap. "Here, give him these."

The very wet foreman climbed the bank towards a special

caravan always brought with them for storing tools and making tea.

"Take these," Gordon offered. "Use our hot showers to get warmed up. Don't know what can be done about your wet things."

"Thanks," he reached for the towel. "We always carry old clothes just in case this happens." And off he went.

"Will you be all right there on your own?" one of the men called after him.

The dripping foreman stopped, lifted a wet clenched fist and shook it in their direction, but he was smiling. Striding back to the bank top, he gazed down.

"You can laugh, but think about this; who's still working in the river, and who's going off for a comfortable hot shower? Make sure you reach that bridge before I get back!"

When just cleaned the river looked a little canal like, but new growth would burst from the edge next spring. Too quickly many would say, left to its own devices for a few years, vegetation would surely meet in the middle. Neglected for sufficient time the bed might even revert to its former choked condition, before the River Board straightened and deepened its course when they first took over many years previously.

CHAPTER 9

Dad's Chips

Night came earlier as Christmas approached, leaving many hours of evening relaxation to fill. The valley's remoteness and an absence of television discouraged visits by the children's school friends. The radio, their only outside contact, provided news bulletins and certain other programs, but its use was limited to save batteries. Thus, of necessity, the family entertained themselves. That was not new, a similar winter had already passed, but it revealed an unexpected shortcoming of the new accommodation - a shortage of space.

Though twice the overall size, the separate bedrooms and kitchen of their present home actually left less playing space in the lounge compared to their previous single room caravan. The freestanding table and chairs too, while more comfortable in use, caused further obstruction, restricting many former activities. Previously the floor had always been an evening play area, three young bodies spending much time horizontal on threadbare carpet, at cards, draughts or some other pursuit. Spontaneously, one, or all, would jump up or roll over, or jostle and wrestle together, suddenly to resume the game again, refreshed by the bout of more physical activity.

Now, in the new home, they sat most often at the table; more civilised but lacking such scope for an impulsive scuffle. Homework, the serious part of each evening, came first but seldom took long; a quiet time that sometimes involved help from the parents - not giving answers but showing how a similar problem might be tackled. Later, shortcomings of space ignored, the caravan would echo with shouts and laughter, as Ludo, snakes and ladders, cards, draughts and other games were played by the family, together or in various combinations. When the children played between themselves, arguments tended to be frequent.

At some time during the evening, Jan might be persuaded to read; she read well, with a soft friendly voice, usually a tale concerning animals of some description, to which they listened in silence, Dad included. On one occasion she ended a story about a bear in Canada, catching salmon from a cold river; "...and he was the greatest hunter in all the country!" The children sat for a moment, smiling at their mother, content with the ending, satisfyingly complete as the conclusion of most children's stories were. Moments later, the three were rolling together, tussling on the confined floor space, nudging chairs aside, growling, making claw motions with bent fingers. Even Christopher, though he would never have done so had his school friends been present, joined the charade; faced with the choice of playing with his younger siblings or not playing at all, he wisely chose the former. Minutes later they were back again at the table, pencils busy, drawing bears, rivers, and fish.

Dad's contributions tended to aim at making the children do the work and the thinking, hearing them read aloud and posing questions that taxed their intelligence, like making paper beams to span between two books on the table, seeing which folded shape would carry the most weight.

Often the parents would sit reading or just chat together in low tones ignoring these noisy outbursts. Occasional passing remarks, usually by Sharon, indicated that such quiet conversation did not entirely escape the youngster's attention.

One long winter night was notable for another reason too. Something had again grubbed up patches of turf - and not rabbits! Rabbits dug in banks; when they did attempt a hole in flat ground, the disturbed earth showed as a pile of fine particles, scratched out by small claws. In this latest nocturnal damage, turf lay in large chunks, ragged golfer's divots, each torn with a single stroke of some powerful paw. But how large? Vague rumours did circulate of strange sightings within the county, rumours the family had always considered on a par with the Loch Ness monster. Fanciful as this gossip might seem, there was no denying that some creature had played havoc with the grass and it must presumably live in the valley!

The night had been chilly, the merest touch of frost. It was cold nights that saw similar damage last winter. Fortunately, frost in West Cornwall was rare, so the damage might not occur often. Even so, Gordon wanted to locate the cause, preferable from a safe distance, at least until the nature of the perpetrator became clear. He spoke of it to Jan and the children.

"Frost only occurs on clear still nights with no insulating layer of cloud and no wind off the sea to keep air temperatures up. On such nights something is out there! Next time conditions are right, I intend to stalk this creature if it means staying up half the night. I'll take a pitchfork. Anyone want to come?"

No one offered.

* * *

The following day, the Sunday before a very special Christmas, the first since the site had successfully opened, the two parents planned that the family attend an evening carol service down river at St Erth. Though not devout churchgoers, they nevertheless did not want their children growing up strangers to the church and its teachings. Jan informed the children late that afternoon, seated in the lounge, the gas light already burning.

All three looked up with concern, protesting mildly, unsure what was entailed. Sharon and Christopher had been before, and Stephen too, but not since arriving in Cornwall. Seeing apprehension in their faces, their mother felt a certain regret. She shouldn't really have let work prevent the children visiting church more often, but work had been survival in this case, at least survival of their hopes for the new life. Perhaps she should have taken them on her own, but felt that would somehow imply Dad didn't believe.

"It's good for you," Jan smiled at them reassuringly, but seeing expressions of resignation rather than agreement, wondered, "How many times do adults say that to children without any explanation." Gathering her thoughts, she tried again.

"Knowing what goes on may be useful later in life. You shouldn't be embarrassed to attend a church sometimes. Suppose you had a special friend who wanted to go, what would they think if you didn't know about services?"

She saw Christopher's expression change and momentarily suspected that he might be thinking of a girl, then believing him too young, doubted that he had. Turning particularly to Stephen she spoke softly.

"When they sing, don't worry if you don't know the words, it's not necessary; some adults only pretend to sing if they're not very good at it. Just follow what other people do, when they stand, when they sit or kneel. Dad and I will be there each side of you."

"Take a prayer book when you're offered one," Jan whispered, ushering them in as they entered the church porch. She knew Stephen could not yet read but it would give something to hold, be reassuring, more like other people. When the books were accepted, she took the little lad's other hand and led him down the aisle, choosing a row of pews three back from the front.

Looking up and around, the pleasant old church had a high barrel roof supported on shaped stone pillars, not all of which may have been from the same age. It felt ancient rather than rich, a place of character.

As they sat, parents each side, Stephen next to his mother, Sharon next to Dad, Christopher in the middle, Jan leaned quietly towards the children. "It's usual to say a small prayer when you first reach your seat, most people do. Think of something nice you'd like to happen, not just

144

for yourself, something that's good for other people too. No need to speak aloud, just think the words silently; your secret." She spoke to all three, and particularly to Stephen, knowing he would have no memory of a previous church visit, casting a quick glance towards Sharon at the mention of a secret.

Satisfied, Jan leant forward onto the back of the pew in front, resting head on clasped hands and with the family very much in mind, made her prayer. Dad quickly adopted the same position, having his own thanks to give and not wanting the boys to think praying was only for women.

Sitting back again in the outer pew, Gordon looked down on the children between them.

"She's right, they should be comfortable in church, but I wouldn't want them to get the impression that goodness is just church, it's how you behave towards others, animals as well as people. If I'm honest, I probably consider that kindness to animals is more important."

He had a very personal feeling that now was the time to give thanks for their new life, for his own luck in having a family with courage enough to take on such an uncertain enterprise and the fortitude to be happy under somewhat difficult living conditions. This happiness had to be more than just chance; they should repay it somehow. Perhaps they could, by giving people not only happy holidays but an environment where an interest in nature, in wild creatures and wild flowers, might flourish or at least be encouraged.

He remembered with slight embarrassment a conversation back in the autumn, when he had perhaps been a little presumptuous, quite unintentionally. The vicar had come to see them, leaving a list of service times for themselves and would they mind displaying it for future visitors?

"Of course, after all we are in similar lines of business." Gordon had replied, and sensing a certain censure in the vicar's stance, had explained "If we do our jobs right, you send them back to work spiritually refreshed and at peace, I send them back physically replenished and happy."

Looking round the church and waiting for the service to begin, feeling the quiet reverence, the holiness of that place, he did hope it would be possible to do his job right.

* * *

They were sitting in armchairs, gazing idly through closed French windows, south along the river, the boiler creating a pleasant warmth compared to a bright but cold day outside. Coffee steamed nearby.

"Look at this," Jan proffered *The Cornishman*.

"What about it?" Gordon waved the paper away, checking the time. Ten minutes before returning to work, minutes intended for relaxing, not reading.

"News on the front page. It's never had that before; first page has always been adverts. Civilisation has arrived?"

"'Bout time. Anything interesting?"

"The road through Marazion will close for a week in mid-March; won't matter much, too early for visitors. Oh yes, there's an article about a woman swallowing a stolen watch. Guess the headline?"

"Not a clue, what?"

"One way of passing the time!" Jan quoted with relish, knowing he would groan, and seeing the grimace, continued, "You realise it's my birthday tomorrow?"

It was early January, just after lunch. Dirty dishes remained stacked in the little adjoining kitchen awaiting her attention, but for a short time they would sit, enjoying the companionable comfort, lazily swapping idle conversation, happy in each other's closeness.

"I hope you've got me a present?"

She felt sure he hadn't, he had hardly left the site all winter but that was no reason to overlook the omission or the chance it offered for a little gentle ribbing.

"Let's see, 1971, that makes you, er..."

"Never mind what that makes me, you forgot last year as well."

"No I didn't, I gave you a card." He smiled, more an

146

admission of guilt, knowing she was right.

"Yes, a card you made that very morning after the children reminded you. You forgot!"

She didn't care but it was fun to remind him, good to get him on the defensive for once.

"Well it's difficult for me."

"Why?"

"When I look at you, you never seem a day older, just like when we were married. How do you expect me to remember another year has passed if you always look so young and lovely."

He beamed at her, pleased with himself. It was such an infectious smile, she couldn't resist smiling back, and she knew there was a certain amount of truth in it. He did still love her, just as he had at first, maybe more.

Reaching out to smack his hand gently, she whispered softly, "You're wicked."

"Go on then, be angry with me."

They leaned together and kissed, not with passion and lust, just a deep gladness at being together.

"Christmas went rather well," Jan sighed, easing back in the chair. "I think Audrey wanted a celebration, their first winter in the bungalow. Will we ever have a house?"

"Yes. Well probably." He thought for a while, weighing likely profit from next season against the cost of building materials, but there were too many imponderables. Who could guess what this year would bring, wealth or disaster? He sighed, "You know I'll build you one eventually. I must - to keep you in the luxury to which you've become accustomed!"

She took a swipe at him but it was never meant to make contact, just part of the camaraderie between two people with no other company. She loved the new life and the valley, and particularly the closeness it had brought between them, but every now and then the isolation became overpowering. Stephen's absence in the daytime had affected her more than she believed possible, more than when either Christopher or Sharon had first attended school. But there had always been more people around then she recalled, and always a younger child to care for. Now, in the daytime there was no one. Occasionally somebody walked along the riverbank, often days apart. Once or twice, on seeing such a stranger approach, she had gone outside on a make believe task deliberately to fall into conversation.

Jan, gazing through the window lost in thought, looked up as Gordon rose to leave. She wished he wouldn't, longed to detain him, make him stay, but he wanted to get on, always wanted to get on. She rose too, crossing to the sink, then he was through the doorway and gone. She sat again to watch through the window as he strode quickly round the bushes and out of sight, her eyes staying long on the empty spot, remembering.

He had finally learned the reason for that pile of old newspapers on the corner cupboard. She kept her secret to the last; he might never have found out except for Stephen's remark at breakfast one morning, a typically short comment, but it gave the game away. The children had been surprised at the laughter that broke out between their parents; Sharon was quite upset when her mother refused to explain. These newspapers were being placed, a few at a time, under the children's mattresses in an attempt to soak up condensation that as predicted, did form when temperatures dropped, even though it had seldom been very cold. The mattresses were still aired each day, but with the newspapers they seemed to dry quicker.

Sighing, Jan rose again to commence the washing up.

Since the new year, only the slightest of frosts had so far occurred, sufficient to paint a faint white hoar on grass tops one or two mornings, but on those particular days something was again digging up patches of turf. Try as they might, they could not discover the cause. Gordon had stayed out until well after midnight one moonlit night, skulking in the deep shadows, creeping from one area to another, but something with keener sight or perhaps a sharper sense of smell may have watched him and waited.

Morning revealed slightly blackened footprints on much of the nocturnal route, betraying where his boots had bruised the frozen grass, but also more diggings on those same areas, diggings that had not been there when he passed!

So far, the hot showers remained working, Jan's strategy had been successful, neither was now prepared to give them up unless it became unavoidable. The prospects for keeping them going looked good, less than eight weeks remained until opening day of the second season! It seemed to spur on the work, though progress came slower than Gordon would have liked. An inborn trait of super optimism ensured he always expected to manage unbelievable amounts each day and by evening was, more often than not, disappointed. With only occasional wall building and topsoil spreading to make a change, the relentless clearing seemed to crawl along as days passed. Progress however, was not really slow. Nearly thirty thousand tons of stone had been shifted since their arrival; he added each day's number of loads to the diary, keeping a tally. Obviously the heaps contained much more than originally estimated. It just didn't seem to cover the ground very quickly.

One thing at least was satisfactory. By working round existing trees, using differing ground levels separated by stone walls of varying heights, making some areas large, others small, the natural setting was very much being preserved.

Jan had started repainting inside the toilet buildings, dashing back to the caravan occasionally when the telephone rang with an early booking. She welcomed the diversion, someone else to chat to, still unable to completely accept the loneliness of working totally on her own. On impulse, she walked round to see Gordon, watching him placing the final layer of stones on a new length of dry wall. He strode over to join her, standing back, admiring and commenting on his own handiwork.

"There are no straight lines in nature, so never have a straight line when you can have a curve instead, that's my landscaping motto."

Looking round at the newly levelled areas she could

only half visualise the final effect, but knew it would be good. Before them lay a kidney shaped patch of bare new soil all fully prepared for seeding, though the ground was not warm enough yet - sufficient space perhaps for an extra six caravans. It was backed by an almost completed stone wall showing lots of white quartz, varying in height from three to four feet and topped by several trees that would be added to as suitable saplings were found. Beyond lay another stretch not yet entirely levelled, and behind that, a copse of taller trees waving bare branches in the light breeze.

He watched her taking in the scene. "Did you marry a genius deliberately, or was it just my animal attraction?"

Opening her mouth, Jan stopped speechless; frantically searching for something suitably crushing.

"Must be insanity in my family!" She swept an arm to the curving wall, "That's not genius. Just like the electric sockets in our old house, you never could get anything straight!"

Much newly-levelled ground remained as hardstanding without grass, finding sufficient topsoil proving difficult. West Cornwall lacked any great abundance of good earth, that is, unless one wanted to pay for it! Generally they waited for some local work to start where the contractor would need to remove the top layer before erecting his building. Gordon would then call in and offer a place to tip, guaranteeing the lorry would never get stuck.

Cornwall was known as the granite peninsula, so a shortage of soil should have come as no surprise. They did succeed in getting over a hundred tons, but unfortunately while each fully loaded lorry looked like a lot of earth, it covered a pitifully small area of ground when spread.

Coming to announce tea was ready one evening, Jan stood, the three children with her, examining an almost complete section for which topsoil seemed unlikely to be found, at least not for some time.

"These new stony areas are fine for bad weather, especially for big motorcaravans, but they look so poor. Can't you make them smoother?"

Gordon scanned the surface, shaking his head. "Difficult to get a better finish, stones roll under the digger bucket. Push one down and another comes up; but it's level. The children could pick off the loose ones if you like."

"There's thousands!" Christopher gasped with alarm, seeing dozens of stones lying scattered across the surface. "One of the boys at school has a steamroller... or his father does."

There the matter rested, the group walking back together. At Lunch on Thursday however, Jan outlined in biro an item in the *Western Morning News,* passing it across the table with the comment, "Christopher may have been right."

A heavy roller was advertised for hire.

For the next three days, Gordon carefully filled all the potholes along the road. They were minor compared to its original state but thin layers were harder to join in smoothly. When Jan told the children at tea that the roller would be coming, the younger two turned to Christopher, who visibly grew in size, shoulders just that bit more upright, head back, an expression of pride on his face at having made the suggestion.

"Hm," Sharon cast her eyes to the ceiling. "We'll never hear the end of that!"

"You won't be here to see, it's expensive, hired for half a day only. But remember who to thank for saving you all that work!" Jan nodded in her son's direction.

Christopher's chest expanded as he cast a superior smirk down at his shorter sister.

"What did I tell you?" Sharon sighed, trying to conceal her own smile, turning again to her mother with a whisper that all were intended to hear. "Think I'd rather collect the stones."

The following day the roller arrived, under its own steam so to speak, that is to say, not on the back of a lorry. However, though similar in appearance to a real steamroller, one large front wheel, two behind and a canopy above, it actually ran on diesel.

The driver was quickly shown various areas requiring

attention and warned to leave enough time to roll the road on the way out, making it clear that the half-day booked was all that could be afforded.

After three hours, with the site areas complete and all loose stones squashed satisfactorily into the surface, the roller trundled off across the bridge to start on the entrance road. Within five minutes the machine lay tilted at a crazy angle, a rear wheel having overhung the road edge and found a soft spot. Max could never pull this one out, it was on the point of going over, any attempt to move it would topple the machine.

With the aid of a short thick plank and a ten-ton jack of ancient design, the driver hoisted the sunken rear wheel a few inches clear of the ground. Gordon rushed off to load the excavator's front bucket with stone, returning to tip it nearby. He and the driver worked together for the next half-hour throwing shovelfuls under and around the wheel, periodically adjusting the jack while Jan trundled off driving Max, returning shortly with further stone. Eventually the roller regained the hard road, finished the job and left.

Later, darkness long since fallen and homework finished, the family relaxed together drinking a late coffee. Sharon, remembering the smoother surface seen when walking home from school along the road, asked about the roller, anxious to confirm that all loose stones had disappeared from other areas too.

"You needn't worry, they're all gone, you won't have to pick them up!"

Reassured, the children drifted off to play, managing to make room on the floor, their parents still resting at table.

"It will certainly be kinder on tyres and visitors' feet," Jan mused quietly, "but the appearance, do you think it's really an improvement, looks more car-parky than ever to me. What will we do with those area eventually?"

"They are a bit grim. Rain may help; wash the white quartz stones, make them show. Could look better then. Another thing, now it's rolled I can mow the weeds, cut them low rather than pull them out; little green patches

152

may develop, soften the appearance, moss too perhaps."

"Wouldn't they be better with grass?"

"Sure. That's the intention with most areas if we ever get enough topsoil, but some needs to stay stony for those big motorcaravans that occasionally arrive. I don't want to be for ever repairing the ruts they leave when the ground is soft."

The site and everything about it was discussed continually, the main topic, often the only topic of their frequent conversation. This venture was more than just a living; their thoughts, their entire lives had become completely wrapped up in the creation. No detail was too small to consider, a rare plant to nurture, the compromise between trees and shadows for one could not exist without the other, how to prevent trout disappearing under the onslaught of many young fishermen, everything came under discussion. This was going to be the best site ever.

Already aware of the intention to keep some hardstanding places, Jan nodded and switched to another topic. "We're open in a few days, how will we do this season? How many more years must we live in a caravan? The condensation was quite bad once or twice even though it's been mild. Could be worse in a severe winter."

Both were speaking quietly, content, but unsure what the future held, casting an eye from time to time at the youngsters, squeezed between chairs and cupboards, still playing on the floor.

The first visitor arrived on 27 March. Jan, alone in the caravan preparing a meal, watched it turn across the bridge with quiet satisfaction, not the panic that had struck when their first customer arrived the previous year. She led the caravan off to a pitch then chatted with the couple for some time before running back to restart the meal, having turned off the gas for safety.

Over lunch, discussions turned naturally to the new arrival. How pleasing to have someone in March; those advertisements taken in various magazines would perhaps, produce results.

"Just two people for three days but the woman says they may want to stay on, she's not sure yet." Jan answered the question, rattling some coins in a tin. "Don't like this new money; fifty pence pieces seem much less value than ten shilling notes."

Easter came, Good Friday, and with it a little flurry of caravans, five to be exact but after the long winter it seemed like a crowd. The first open Easter; at this time last year the plumbing had still not been finished! As a sprinkling of extra people arrived over the next three days, they abandoned work, strutting round chatting to visitors, absorbing praise for the winter's progress by some who had returned from the previous summer.

One unforeseen problem was the arrival of a gaudily coloured, hand-painted motorcaravan with an oddly dressed couple. Gordon had shown them to a pitch with an uneasy, but not quite definable feeling. Returning to the caravan, he stood by the French windows looking pensively out across the balcony and field, and was still there when Jan entered, having walked up the riverbank with Sharon and Stephen.

"What's wrong?" She sensed his unease immediately.

"Nothing really. I had a motorcaravan in, strange couple, well enough spoken but... I'm not sure quite how to describe them, unkempt I suppose. The people I intended putting them next to looked upset so I moved on a bit. They're over in the far corner now."

Sharon walked to the window and stood on her tiptoes trying to see, but only part of the roof was visible.

Over the following days, washing lines sprouted, clothes and bedclothes were laid over nearby bushes, bits of plastic bag and several old newspapers littered the ground. The whole area around the garish vehicle began to take on a slum appearance. The nearest caravan left one morning in spite of having paid for two more days, its occupants complaining of music and noise in the night.

Gordon started towards the offending vehicle intending to have a few words but halfway across the grassy area, noticed the people were making ready to leave. He walked on, slightly altering his direction to disappear round a group of bushes, pleased enough that the problem looked like solving itself.

The children, finding new friends again, were off like wild things, leading a mixed band of boys and girls, low site numbers forcing different ages to combine. This happy boisterous group disappeared for varying periods, off on safari again to the wilder, yet unreachable parts of the valley – unreachable that is, so far as adults were concerned. They re-appeared at intervals for food; scratched, clothes awry, hair blown and tangled, only Sharon usually returning with some sort of neatness though she clambered and climbed with the rest.

By midday most caravanners were out, often taking Christopher and Sharon with them and this year Jan had decided even Stephen would be allowed to accept invitations, but with all three she insisted on knowing who was taking them, roughly where, and when they would return.

Easter passed and May was fast approaching. Numbers fell short of those hoped for but a fundamental problem that required a decision had begun to unfold. Dotted over the course of the early season, a few caravans had arrived made enquiries and left again, complaining that the site had insufficient facilities and there was nothing to do. It was beginning to emerge that holidaymakers divided broadly into two types. Firstly there were those requiring everything; clubs, pubs, bingo halls, takeaways, amusements, entertainments and so on. Such people tended to find the site unsatisfactory.

Secondly there were caravanners or campers who wanted only a quiet clean place, a peaceful base from which to venture forth and return, finding whatever else they fancied in the surrounding locality rather than on their own doorstep. Relubbus was exactly suited to this later group;

the peaceful surroundings, nicely remote from roads or habitation, well sheltered and certainly visually attractive. Persuading these more conservative tourists to come and look however, had proved difficult. Building up trade based solely on this type of visitor could take longer, both realised that and had discussed it before.

"More visitors and the extra money would certainly be nice. I could do with some new dresses for a start, but what choice do we have? Can't afford pools and entertainments anyway, not that I want them."

Gordon nodded, "Even if we had money, going for lots of activity would be a mistake and I'll tell you why. Most people who demand those things have also expected a beach on their doorstep, at least the ones I've spoken to do. They would leave anyway when they saw how far inland we are. You notice it's mainly coastal sites that advertise these so-called attractions. If we installed them, our lack of a beach might still keep those visitors away. In addition, we couldn't expect the site to remain quiet and that would scare off people looking for a peaceful, restful holiday, which is everyone we get now. We could fall between two stools as they say. I think even a clubhouse could be dangerous for us. Another thing; every extra facility means more overheads. Running as we are now, the site can be open and profitable with only a few paying guests. Stay as we are, all of us like it that way." He paused, seeing her both nod in agreement and sigh sadly at the same time. "Cheer up, things will improve - you might be surprised, could happen quicker than we expect. Even some who usually opt for more activity might get to like the valley. By the way, did you know we had another of those doubtful ones last night? I had three complaints this morning."

"That very old motorcaravan with all the children?" Jan asked. "I said they might be trouble. It seems madness to turn trade away, but should we have pretended the site was full?"

Neither was sure, this problem had not occurred the previous year, or had gone unnoticed in the ferment of that first season when so many new things had demanded attention. In any case, the idea ran contrary to their thinking; it was drawing people in not keeping them away that had most exercised their minds.

An unusually windy day persuaded two tourers, friends travelling together, to forsake their coastal site and seek shelter in the valley. Several other couples came to look round but had already paid elsewhere. Never mind, they seemed impressed and might return next season. The extra activity suggested that leafleting might now be worthwhile but a quick run to Bodmin ruled it out. On the sixty mile round trip only two caravans were encountered, a total waste of time and petrol; premature by several weeks.

"Probably means we'll get a few extras whenever there's a big storm," Gordon suggested on the homeward journey. "If your caravan rocks at night, it's natural to search for somewhere more sheltered, we should mention that in our adverts. A site with sea views is nice, but looking out over the Atlantic when a storm is brewing it's a good idea to remember there are no windbreaks within 3000 miles."

Fortunately, this dearth of visitors left Jan cooking all the meals; at lunchtime for two and again in late afternoon for the whole family.

"Mum. Why don't we ever have chips?" Christopher asked at tea one evening.

Stephen and Sharon were quick to offer support.

"All right, I'll do them tomorrow."

Accordingly, next day Audrey's deep-frying saucepan with its wire holder were borrowed. Tea would be egg and chips. Gordon was not really involved, just sitting at the table having come in fifteen minutes early. He had brought Max over to top up with Diesel then decided the fuel filters were overdue for changing and returned to the caravan to study the parts book and maintenance manual. Jan was muttering to herself in exasperated frustration.

"What have I done this time?" he wondered.

Apparently however, her annoyance concerned only the

chips, which remained stubbornly white and raw-looking in spite of the improved cooking facilities.

"Ah well," she said, lifting one on a fork, waving it in his direction, "it's done right through, just refuses to brown. Perhaps they won't notice?"

Putting a shallow metal tray on the other gas ring, she added a dash of oil, and when hot, moved it aside to make room for the frying pan with the first two eggs. These would be cooked and kept warm in the tray. Shortly after, seeing three small figures appear far up the track, she popped eggs for the children in the now empty pan. In those few minutes it took the youngsters to reach the caravan, wash their hands in a cursory fashion and get seated, plates of fried egg and very white chips appeared on the table. Christopher and Sharon looked at each other, then back at the chips. Both prodded a few with their forks.

"They're supposed to be cooked Mum." Sharon's frown showed disapproval.

Stephen nodded agreement, wrinkling his nose.

"They're meant to be sort of brown." Christopher ventured doubtfully.

"I know, but our gas rings are poor. The fat won't get hot enough. They *are* cooked, try them." She turned to Gordon for support, "They're quite nice, aren't they Dad?"

"Er? Oh! Yes! Wonderful dear." Caught off guard, he popped one in his mouth and chewed with intended relish. A spasm of distaste twisted his facial muscles and changed the attempted smile of pleasure to a grimace.

"Dad doesn't like them either!" Stephen piped up in triumph, pleased for once to prove Mum wrong, any sense of tact totally lacking.

Bringing her own plate to the table, Jan was becoming annoyed. She had spent a considerable time trying to make satisfactory chips. Obviously her efforts were not being appreciated.

"Well Dad doesn't need to eat them. He can go without!" The reply, ostensibly to Stephen, hit out at the lack of support. Turning suddenly to glare at Gordon, she caught the glimmer of a smile that disappeared a fraction too late.

"Think you can do better? OK. You make tea tomorrow, I refuse to have anything to with it!"

Jan was super when angry; eyes shining, chin up, little nostrils flared out and breathing heavily. It took ages to get her going; normally imperturbable, taking everything in her stride. Here was success without effort. He must take advantage!

"Of course I'll do tea tomorrow. Chips again kids? And you'd like them brown! OK. No problem. I'll see to it. Piece of cake!"

He had often seen pictures of St George rescuing a fair maiden from a flame-throwing dragon, but looking at Jan he suddenly imagined the dragon cringing, flames coming instead from the nostrils of the young damsel!

Her foot was tapping on the floor.

"Right!" she drew in a deep breath, lips compressed. "Right..." Clenched hands tapped on the table top, seconds passing before the words erupted, spat out through features set tight with rage. "You needn't think you're going to wriggle out of this. Either it's chips tomorrow or you'll never get another meal cooked by me!"

He shouldn't have said it, he realised that; the last straw – but he just couldn't stop himself.

"Promises, Promises."

FLOP! A plate of fried egg and very white chips hit him bang in the face.

He flinched momentarily, but finding the heat bearable, remained still. Three small bodies drew back startled and a little fearful, this sudden unexpected action altogether beyond their normal experience. The plate dropped away, to bounce off the table's edge and clatter unbroken on a thinly covered wooden floor. Most of the chips followed, just two adhering as Dad sat unmoving, egg sliding down over the deadpan expression and dripping off his chin.

The children held their breath; to grin at each other in relief as a slow smile wiped the tension from their mother's face.

"I *always* wanted to do that. I never remember anything *so satisfying*!" Her last words were drawn out, slowly and with feeling!

During the next day Gordon mulled the problem over, thinking as he worked.

"Men are superior. No doubt about that! It just needs a little logical thought. Man is good at logical thought. In fact, only man is capable of proper logic. If it can be done, a man can do it!" He nodded to himself with certainty. "Making chips go brown might be difficult for a woman, but... Hm, no problem!"

"What was it Jan had said? 'The fat would not get hot enough'. OK, so all I need is hotter fat! How about using half the amount of cooking oil? No, must have enough to immerse the all chips. Would the pan cover two rings? No, never be wide enough."

At mid-morning coffee break, Jan popped up to see her mother for a few minutes at the bungalow. She had awaited Gordon's arrival, preferring never to leave the caravan unattended in case of incoming telephone bookings. Using this opportunity to check the stove, he lit the gas, noted the flame's appearance and quickly turned it off, not wanting the metalwork to get hot. Taking out the gas jet and cleaning it then re-lighting the flame, produced no change. It looked exactly the same. No good! The second ring showed a similar result. Other ideas came and went during the afternoon's work, but inspiration that felt almost within grasp, eluded him.

Surely he would not have to admit defeat and let Jan triumph? Little jibes and reminders would continue for months! Much as he loved her, this challenge had developed into a trial of wills. Enjoying herself at breakfast, obviously convinced he would fail, she had already reminded the children that Dad was cooking tea, hinting he was not up to it. These hints, without the children realising, questioned not only the ability to make chips but his very manhood!

It was not until these wandering thoughts caused the

shovel handle to break while trying to lever out too big a root, that a possible solution occurred. The shaft snapped near the bottom, about nine inches broke off with the blade. He took it to the workbench in the second toilet building, the service passage having been made five feet wide for that very purpose. Putting the blade in the bench vice, the broken shaft end flew out with a swift blow from a big hammer. A spokeshave, a two-handed plane such as used by the old wheelwrights and barrel makers, quickly reshaped the remaining shaft. Reaching to replace the plane in its proper place, a blowlamp on the shelf nearby caught his attention. The tool was old, not a modern gas blowlamp, economy had precluded that. This was an ancient brass version, operated on pressurised paraffin and started with methylated spirit, probably a relic from the days when plumbers used its fierce flame to wipe joints in lead pipes.

Jan vanished to Jim's bungalow at mid-afternoon. "To meet the children," she said, but Gordon suspected a deliberate disappearance during tea preparations, almost certainly in the hope and expectation of being able to say, "There. Told you Dad couldn't do it."

Well, not if he could help it!

When teatime approached he carried the blowlamp into the caravan and having prepared the chips, struck a match, igniting the gas ring as normal, setting the deep pan of fat on top to heat. Lighting the old plumber's lamp was difficult; allowing methylated spirit to burn down, preheating the metalwork took time. Pumping steadily produced an intense flame, which roared noisily from the nozzle, to be played directly on the pan's side. A well-worn heavy wet towel lay nearby in case the whole thing caught alight.

Fire was a real possibility. The very old piece of equipment should, and indeed would, have been replaced long ago but for the cost. It had a tendency sometimes to stop vaporising properly. When that happened, it suddenly became not a blowlamp but a flame-thrower. A jet of burning liquid paraffin could arc halfway across a room. This, with the already highly flammable pan contents, more than

161

justified extra precautions.

Pumping again intensified the heat; fat bubbled more fiercely, bluish smoke filled the caravan and one outer side of Audrey's shiny chip pan darkened gradually to a black sooty texture. Never mind! The chips were changing colour, definitely browning.

Gordon knelt, rummaging in the cupboard, his left hand still directing the flaming nozzle now held above head level. Extracting a big frying pan for the eggs, he rose carefully, placing it on the other ring, turning on the gas and igniting it with a quick blast from the blowlamp. Pointing the flame back toward the chips while simultaneously pouring oil into the pan, a moments inattention caused the nozzle to swivel, almost singing the curtain.

When Jan and the three children appeared walking down the road, he extinguished the blowlamp, hid it under the caravan, turned the chip pan round so the blackened side was concealed, and left the caravan door wide open to disperse the smoke. Four eggs were cracked, slightly overlapping, into the pan and basted as the children preferred, rather than flipped over the easy way. A quick glance through the window found the family had paused on the bridge, watching the trout. Just time! Gordon served up the eggs, cracking another into the pan for himself, then quickly drained the nicely browned chips, tipping some on each plate. Putting these on the table already laid with cutlery, he quickly flipped the egg still cooking in the pan and turned to the door to greet them.

"Ah. There you are. Good day at school? Sit down quickly while it's hot."

They squeezed round the table and started eating.

"This is great," Christopher expressed surprise and pleasure as Dad brought his own plate, squeezing into the corner to join them. The others agreed nodding, their mouths too full at first to offer verbal comment.

"How did you get them so delicious?" Sharon spoke the words quickly, lifting another fully loaded fork.

"Oh, it was nothing." He waved away the compliment

as if making chips brown was the easiest thing in the world, and from the corner of one eye saw the line of Jan's lips compress.

"You should cook for us a lot." Stephen suggested, still eating, tactless as ever.

"I can't do it often, there's such a lot of site work." Gordon turned to Jan, a little smile of condescension touching the corners of his mouth, "Anyway, Mum's not that bad a cook really." Swinging back to the children, he smiled. They all smiled back.

It was just too much. She dropped her knife and fork and lunged for him, trapped as he was in the confined space of the caravan. Leaving her seat, she pummelled, punched, grabbed his hair and bounced his head off the side of the caravan, increasingly annoyed because he was almost helpless with laughter.

"You bighead! I've a good mind to make you take over all of the cooking."

Fending off the attack, he grabbed her wrists. She struggled, eyes flashing, little fists clenching and unclenching as she saw him wink at the children. Breaking free, she grabbed again for his hair, but he pulled her close, kissing an ear, the cheek, then lips - and suddenly her hands were off his hair and round the back of his neck, responding strongly. He paused momentarily, glancing at the children who were eating hungrily. All pointedly looked down at their plates immediately they saw his gaze swing in their direction. Turning back again he blew a stray wisp of hair tenderly away from her ear.

"I do love you," he whispered softly so only she could hear, and kissed her again, then recovering a hold on her wrists, said in a louder voice, "Eat while it's hot, you don't get food of this quality round here often!"

As she attempted to free her hands again, he held on tightly. They struggled for a few moments, both laughing, before he let go. She punched him gently on the shoulder, returning to her chair and the meal.

"You will see to the washing up?" he enquired.

Chapter 10

Meditation

Anything that affected trade interested the family; a sailing competition in Mount's Bay, the annual music festival at Prussia Cove, and those various traditional celebrations in local towns, all tended to draw extra visitors. Cornwall, where history and myth were often indistinguishable, was blessed not only with an abundance of saints, but a liberal scattering of these local festivals

Flora day at Helston was one such; first and perhaps most famous in the far southwest, rooted in ancient Celtic culture, its true origins lost in the mists of time. Even this early in the year a handful of caravans arrived expressly to attend the event. Anticipating visitors' questions and anxious to grasp any opportunity that might boost River Valley's own standing, Jan had obtained such information as was available, including some gleaned chatting in the village shop. Academics might argue on Flora Day's origins, but one point was generally agreed; it had always been a spring festival welcoming in new life, giving thanks for the end of winter. Streets, buildings, shops; all would be decorated with bluebells and gorse to honour the year's early growth. Starting at seven o'clock in the morning, processions of dancers would follow various routes through streets steeped in history.

Almost a millennium ago the Manor of Helston was held by Harold, Earl of Cornwall, brother-in-law to Edward the Confessor, the reigning monarch. On Edward's death in 1066, Harold succeeded to the English throne, only to be killed later that year by an arrow at the battle of Hastings during his defeat by William the Conqueror. Harold's fate is well known, but few are aware of his Cornish role. In the more recent past, tin mining became a major industry. Helston was one of only five coinage towns in Cornwall. Tin from surrounding areas was brought to the coinage hall for stamping. Coinagehall Street is still the only really wide carriageway among a host of narrower roads.

The town had its legends too. One told of a terrible duel that started in France. St Michael, being beaten by the Devil, escaped with his life to St Michael's Mount, over the channel which Satan could not cross. In his anger the Devil wrenched the lid off Hell and hurled it at St Michael. It missed, but fell in the west wall of the Angel Hotel in Main Street, Helston, where it remained ever since.

A nice tale, good for the hotel concerned, no doubt - and believable enough. Surely the devil did remain in France, blocking roads and burning sheep; but had he, in those intervening centuries, found a way across the water, tucked perhaps, in some politician's diplomatic bag? Let's hope St. Michael will always keep him from Relubbus!

One caravan arriving for these festivities provided Sharon with some new friends, two sisters, Mary aged eight like herself, and Bess two years older. With longer evenings, and no other girls on site, these three spent much time together and having explored the valley for a while, would usually find some hidden corner to sit talking, exchanging confidences and information in a quieter, less physical relationship than that found between groups of boys. When talk turned to cooking, Sharon found herself by far the more experienced, but was surprised at the home environment that her friends enjoyed and which they considered normal. She listened enthralled and a little envious as Mary described her bedroom with its own wardrobe, dressing table, chests of drawers and bedside cabinet, sighing deeply as the girl recalled a long list of the clothes they contained.

Later Sharon returned to her own caravan and sat quietly in a chair, still picturing her friend's room, longing not so much for the space and the dresses though she would have loved both, but for the privacy that Mary had taken for granted and hardly appreciated. Jan, sensing her daughter's sadness, drew the other small armchair close.

"What's wrong?" The question was asked with a quiet gentleness, reaching out to hold the small hand.

Sharon gazed back at her mother, then towards the floor, not sure how to explain. "Nothing's wrong exactly, it's just Mary; she has so much - things to wear, games, furniture, lots." She paused, sighing again and looking up. Seeing her mother's head nod slowly in understanding, the girl continued, her face sad, a wistful voice revealing the thing that touched her most deeply. "And a bedroom all to herself. Her family even knock on the door, waiting for an answer before they enter."

Jan patted her daughter's hand, wishing she could promise, but there was no way; no way to be sure.

"I know you want a room for yourself; Dad too, wants you to have one. He works so hard to make life better for us all, but buildings costs money, lots of money. We both want to start but I can't promise. You know it depends on the visitors, how many, how long they stay. I can't see what more either of us can do. Don't be unhappy, surely we must have something they admire?"

"They like the river. Oh yes, the rabbits we had in the caravan and the buzzard, they wished they'd had those. And I'm better at cooking; their Mum and Dad are going out tomorrow, they've agreed we can cook in their caravan; something for tea when I come home from school,"

Seeing her daughter look happier, Jan smiled, "What do you intend to prepare?"

"Mary says they've eggs, salad stuff, potatoes and peas. I can cook some sort of omelette, lots of trimmings to make it more attractive but what I'd really like is for Christopher to catch me a trout. I know they're small but it's different, really special, a fish straight from our own stream, something they could never do at home. I wouldn't mind them being a bit envious too."

166

"You think he'll do it for you?"

"Not for me, never! But I'll tell him Bess doesn't think he can. He likes Bess, looks at her sort of funny. Don't you say anything or he won't catch one for us!"

Surprised and pleased at her daughter's developing subtlety, Jan broke into a huge grin of delight. Both girls were laughing together as Christopher came through the doorway to stop in surprise. From the guilty expressions and quickly turned away faces, he guessed their merriment concerned him.

"What's so funny?" he stood, features rigid, regarding the two with disfavour and a touch of uncertainty, though he looked mainly at Sharon, not wanting to include Mum in his resentment. Jan, always trying to be even handed with the family, was about to explain, but Sharon, aware her secret might be revealed, spoke first.

"Sorry. I wanted you to catch me a trout for tomorrow night. I'm cooking for Mary and Bess then, but Bess said you wouldn't be able to. I was just telling Mum."

The following evening, less that fifteen minutes after returning from school, Sharon ran round to her friends' caravan, proudly displaying the trout.

"Now, we'll do the omelette last, a big one cut in three; they sink if you don't eat them straight away. Your mother does have a whisk? Good. Potatoes first, boil for fifteen minutes then cut in slices and fry them with the trout, it's small, but enough to give us all a taste, I think Christopher caught it specially for you, Bess."

Bess turned away, pretending to peer through the window but the two younger girls could tell she was pleased. The meal went well. Sharon arranged a small lettuce leaf and several segments of tomato on each plate, fried the trout surrounded by sliced part-boiled potatoes, crisping them in the hot pan, then placed both in another saucepan with a touch of oil showing Mary how to finish them off. While waiting, Sharon cracked and separated the whites and yolks of three eggs, seasoned and whisked both separately then

167

folded delicately together and slid the mixture into the now vacant well-greased pan. The soufflé omelette drew admiring comments as it rose. Sharon shook the pan gently backwards and forward to prevent sticking, then flipped the mixture over with a single quick wrist action. After cooking slightly longer, the finished soufflé was scored across the middle, folded over, cut to serve as three separate portions and added with trout and potatoes to the plates. Her friends were impressed.

"Your mother lets you cook often?" Bess asked. "You do it so quickly and it looks great!"

"I cook most meals in the school holidays. Mum's away giving out leaflets and Dad's always busy. They don't *let* me, it's one of my jobs. I have to, don't have any choice - but thanks for the compliment, my brothers would never admit it's good."

Mary was indignant. "That's not fair, don't cook for them, let them go hungry!"

"I don't mind, they're not bad and I like cooking. I can handle them - usually. How do you think we got the trout?"

As days passed the girls became very close, but all too soon the new friends departed, their car disappearing up the road in a constant turnover that saw May numbers varying wildly. On some nights, caravans and the occasional tent reached double figures, on others the site was almost empty. As always the clear water flowing under the bridge drew people like a magnet, particularly in the evenings. Gordon or Jan, sometimes together, would wander over to chat, Sharon or the boys coming too if other children were present. Of all the questions posed by visitors, the river intrigued them most. For a start it flowed the wrong way. Knowing Relubbus lay near the south coast, many were surprised to find the stream flowing almost north, not realising the coastal town of Hayle and the Atlantic ocean lay only four miles in that direction.

The water's extreme clearness made every single item beneath the surface stand out with sharp clarity, the individual strands of an underwater weed, a tiny pebble on the bed, the row of waiting trout, every detail, every mark somehow enhanced, magnified. The line of fish, ever patient, sifting food brought down by the current, chose their position in expectation of bread cast on the surface, a practice that early visitors found irresistible, as had many in the previous season. Tufts of weed growing from the gravely bed also provided shelter for the occasional eel.

Two types of reed dominated the Hayle River. Bulbous Reed grew completely underwater, grass-like tops streaming red in the current. Underneath, its foliage was bright green, something discovered after the first river cleaning.

"Why?" Jan had asked in surprise when the tops soon turned red again.

"Sunburn?" Gordon suggested, jumping quickly out of range.

The Common Reed's stronger, upright growth, was kept in check only by the River Authority's annual cleaning. It colonised the banks then over a remarkably short time encroached on the river, working towards midstream, closely-grouped stems checking the water's flow. This reed rapidly became detrimental to the site's attractiveness, particularly to newly arriving caravans, for by mid-season, its broad foliage hid the river from view in many places, seed heads rippling as ripe corn in the wind.

Beside the stream damselflies were prolific, several species fluttering innocuously, butterfly-like along the margins, metallic hues glinting in the sun, the delicate creatures coming to rest with wings above their heads. Dragonfly wings on the other hand were spread horizontally when settling. They were more rare, hawking up and down in search of a meal. These larger, stronger fliers, moving fast in direct lines made some visitors uneasy, especially the younger ones. Strangely, their own children also distrusted them, practically the only river feature with which they were not entirely comfortable. In spite of their father's assurance that dragonflies were harmless, all three youngsters retained a deep suspicion of the creatures.

This fear was reinforced by an incident back in the first

year, about six weeks after their arrival on site. One evening towards the end of June the family had been taking their regular bath in the river. The longest day approached, the sun still shining strongly when Stephen stepped naked into the water with his mother. The two older children, protected only by towels wrapped round the waist, waited their turn on the bank. Dragonflies normally disappeared towards evening but one had suddenly arrived. It moved in strong fast flight, flying as if to investigate the pair waiting on the bank, then passed several times under the arch near Stephen and his mother. The children had all been afraid. Though Christopher tried not to show it, he had quickly backed away several paces. Jan too had been disturbed, only Dad sitting on the bank above, keeping watch for approaching strangers had not been bothered. "Ignore it, they're harmless," he had called down, but none of the family had been ready to accepted this advice. The fear lingered still, even after two years living beside the stream they remained suspicious. Dad's repeated instance that dragonflies were not dangerous, met with little success.

Stephen, his attempts to catch trout causing him to sit often alone on the bank, had stopped running away from the creatures. Instead he carried with him a stick, standing his ground and striking out, in spite of being told several times that they were not to be harmed. The warning did have an effect; at least it had to an extent. Instead of lashing out immediately, Stephen now turned round first to check that neither his father nor mother were nearby. Having ascertained that he was not watched, the lad then struck out, knowing it to be wrong but happy in the belief that his actions would go undetected. Fortunately, the occurrences were rare and so far he had been unsuccessful.

One afternoon on the run up to May Bank Holiday, a yell of horror rose from the riverbank. Jan, rushing through the doorway and down the steps, almost collided with Sharon, who ran headlong towards the caravan, looking over one shoulder in fright. Gordon sitting at the table, hurriedly squeezed from the confined space, missing most of Sharon's panted explanation, but hearing her mother's attempt at reassurance.

"I don't think it really chased you."

"It did! I ran up the bank but it followed me. Christopher says they sting like two hundred bees!"

"He exaggerates, you know that."

Hearing her mother's even unworried voice and seeing Dad approaching, Sharon felt calmer. She must be safe now?

"Yes, I know he does but if it only stings like twenty bees, it's not stinging me! I don't want to be stung even by one and it must be worse than that."

Gordon laid a hand on his daughter's shoulder and squatted down by her side. With his legs bent double they were not far from the same height.

"You really don't need to worry. That dragonfly is never going to sting a young girl like you." He wore a serious expression, trying not to smile at her concern.

"Why?"

"It can't. It doesn't have a sting."

At tea that evening Jan challenged Christopher.

"What's this about dragonflies stinging like two hundred bees?"

Christopher assumed an expression of innocence, as if having no idea what his mother referred to, but under the concentrated gaze of everyone round the table, his eyes wavered.

"Well... it's what one of the boys at school said."

Shaking his head, Dad assured them, "That's wrong. Dragonflies have no sting. They're quite harmless."

The children resisted, suspicion written clearly in their faces. Sharon wanted it to be true, but partly due to Christopher's exaggeration and to other tales heard at school, fear of the large insects had penetrated deeply. She just could not bring herself to believe.

As luck would have it, a couple of days later, on Saturday, a newly emerged dragonfly was seen, its wings not yet fully inflated. The find was more than pure chance, Gordon had deliberately cast an eye along the river margins in passing for several days, knowing it to be the season. This young larva had climbed a reed stem, emerging from an underwater life to split its old outer casing at the neck and burst forth as an adult, resting before pumping up its wings.

Lifting the creature carefully onto his palm, steadying it with a finger crooked over, he walked back, calling to the children. Jan leaned out from the doorway, then strode over to join them. The five gathered on the riverbank, parents sitting close together on the hard scorched ground, children hanging back still doubtful. All watched in fascination as the wings slowly expanded and the tail lengthened.

"This is the Golden Ringed dragonfly, probably the same type Sharon saw the other day?" their father explained, looking towards his daughter, seeing her nod of confirmation before continuing. "The pointed end is for planting eggs. When those eggs hatch, only a matter of weeks, the young are just like the adult except no wings or strong colours. They don't undergo a total change as with caterpillars and butterflies. Did you know this one will get more colourful when it's eaten and flown about a bit?"

The listening children had crept steadily closer. Sharon, well in the rear, poked her head out from behind Christopher.

"I still don't like that pointed tip to the tail!" she said with obvious distrust.

"It really is only for egg laying, definitely no sting. You sometimes see dragonflies hovering above shallow patches of water, tail vertically downward, dipping below the surface quite fast, spreading the eggs or burying them in the mud, I'm not sure which. The larvae when they hatch are carnivorous, eat other bugs not plants, and shed their outer coats five times before emerging like this one has."

Suddenly the dragonfly moved!

All eyes stared spellbound. After an upward jerk, the tail slowly curved, bending back over the head, scorpion like, the pointed end approaching the palm against which it was pinned by the bent finger above.

"It's going to sting you Dad!" Stephen yelled.

"It is! Drop it quick!" Sharon made several rapid backward paces.

The arching tail did indeed look most sinister; alarm and conviction rang in the children's voices.

Dad waited, arm still outstretched. Could they be right after all? The doubt was instinctive, against logic, an inner urge telling him, 'Dump it fast! '

The arched end curved downward, then with another jerk, stabbed against the hand...

"Agh!" With a strangled gasp, his eyes flew wide, regarding the hand in horror as the children shot farther backwards. Mum, sitting next to him and unable to rise quickly, leaned sharply away as his shoulders sagged, head drooping downwards.

Squinting up obliquely under lowered lashes, Gordon watched. Seeing their eyes riveted on the dragonfly and outstretched hand, he waited a few more seconds before straightening, breaking into a broad smile. The pointed end was quite blunt and harmless. The creature had used this extra leverage to try to push itself free.

Christopher recovered, leading the children slowly forward again, Sharon lagging in the rear, still apprehensive. Carefully they inspected, not so much the insect as the hand below, their young minds still doubtful. Jan regarded this suspicion as a good sign, pleased none were too easily convinced, though she was peeved at having been taken in by the alarming performance and reached over to prod Gordon's ribs. He swung the still outstretched arm towards her with a warning.

"I'll set Lancelot on you!"

Though now convinced of its harmlessness, Jan swayed backwards, staying just beyond reach and no one else wanted to hold the large insect. Strolling over towards the river, they walked together down the sloping bank, watching the creature gently placed in a clump of reeds spreading out from the water's edge.

May Bank Holiday approached and Jan went leafleting again for the greater part of each day, leaving Gordon in charge of cleaning, seeing new arrivals, attending the needs of existing customers, and except when Sharon was home at weekends, the midday cooking too! Moreover another trouble arose. Simultaneously with Jan's success in waylaying extra visitors, a putrid smell began to permeate in and around both toilet buildings, particularly when a north wind blew. Caravanners noticed, and were starting to comment.

"Has something died?" one man asked, wrinkling his nose in distaste.

The children, returning home after school, were equally unhelpful.

"Puts you off your food," Sharon claimed, but she still ate everything within reach.

"It isn't Dad, is it?" Christopher asked.

Jan, back from leafleting, sniffed in Dad's direction.

"Probably. Pretend not to notice."

Sitting with them at table, Gordon smiled back, making no denial. He had cleaned, scrubbed, swept and washed, everything in sight, then checked among neighbouring trees and other vegetation, hunting for a dead animal carcass but with no result - the smell persisted.

The situation was serious! How long would visitors stay? At what point would they no longer tolerate the terrible pong that grew ever more potent?

The following day, having looked everywhere else, he clambered onto the roof. A rotten smell wafted from ventilation pipes sticking through the tiles, its strength drove him quickly down again. Having found the cause, what to do? These pipes could not be sealed, that would be asking for an explosion. This was gas, mainly methane, produced by decomposition of rotting scum on the septic tank surface. The gas had to disperse, foul as it smelled.

Grasping for any solution, the outlet pipes were extended four feet higher into the air, allowing wind across the roof to carry any gas away rather than swirling it down towards ground level. Surprisingly, these higher outlets proved effective, if silly in appearance - somewhat reminiscent of those tall funnels on early steam-powered river boats, giving a fleeting impression that the buildings would sail away.

In the hope of finding an alternative solution Gordon discussed the situation with the Council's Building Bylaws Chief, Neville Hodgson. A curious fact emerged. Had the smell been tolerable for another week the problem would gradually have cured itself. The trouble had not after all been caused by excessive activeness of bacteria in the tank as he had assumed, but rather by the very lack of such activity. With only the family's waste products entering the drainage system during the winter, most of these microbes had died. When the tank's floating scum increased with rising numbers of people on site, there was more than could be eaten away by existing bacteria. The rest rotted in the tank, adding a noxious smell to the normally odourless methane. Now the tanks were more used, these bacteria would soon increase, the scum decompose quickly and no smell would then be generated. The family were not to know how useful this knowledge would later become!

* * *

"When are we going to build a house?"

The scrape of cutlery on plates subsided abruptly, normal chatter around the breakfast table dying at Sharon's question. Gordon turned towards her but said nothing, looking at her earnest face, wondering how best to reply.

Last autumn this caravan, inherited from Jim, had appeared the last word in affluence. So it was, compared to the previous single room caravan with central boiler. However, winter had found the bedrooms very chilly, the whole family catching a series of energy sapping colds. Such fun as the children first derived from the shallow three tier bunks had rapidly worn off. The ultra thin mattresses became increasingly uncomfortable with use, even with Jan's newspapers underneath. But the bunks were not Sharon's main concern. She wanted her own room! It was two years since first arriving on site, she was growing up. A girl of eight should have her own room. Gordon had thought about this before, been aware of the need but powerless to provide for it. The caravan bedroom had nowhere to store clothes, school books, or indeed any of the things a young girl likes to have around her. More than that, it lacked privacy. Her hair had grown long and dark but even a little thing like combing it, playing with various styles before a mirror, could not be done without being overlooked and ridiculed by her brothers.

Christopher was also keen for extra space. With more advanced school work his need may even have been greater. Though quietly making the best of their present situation, his interest in building was no less. He was growing too, now ten he would be changing to the senior school at Penzance in eighteen months time.

Sharon's question directed towards her father, carried a certain impatience, almost yearning, mingled with a touch of hopelessness. She expected an unfavourable answer.

The silence lengthened, all faces including Jan's had turned towards him, waiting. No one prompted, they knew he would reply, could see him thinking, and they waited. This was no idle comment, Sharon had voiced a longing felt by all, even to some extent Stephen, in spite of having no memory of a room to himself.

Gordon looked at each one in turn; what could he say? They wanted a promise he was unable to give.

"I don't know." He saw disappointment tinged with annoyance in Sharon's face, and continued. "It's not that I'm trying to put it off, we just don't have enough money to build yet. You know the revised plans were passed in March. With a good season we might even start this autumn, when visitor numbers fall."

Not only Sharon, but the boys too brightened up.

"How long will it take?" Christopher asked.

"How hard can you work? There will only be the five of us. We must do everything ourselves. Remember, you all eat, you..."

"...all have to work!" The children's voices in ragged

176

unison, interrupted before he could finish.

"Yes!" he paused, watching the grinning faces. "Well, when we do get started I'll remind you. We're unlikely to have enough money to finish, you realise that?"

They nodded solemnly, Jan too; she had sat with him often during late winter, reviewing the drawings, making little changes and improvements, considering things not given much attention in a normal house.

Above all she had insisted the kitchen, dining room and lounge windows should all face at least partly towards the bridge to ensure arriving visitors could be seen, or so she had told Gordon - a half-truth, just that touch of deception? Somewhere deep inside she knew her desire stemmed more from wishing always to see the river, to gaze at odd moments over its surface, sometimes rippled, at others with a smoothness marred only by the expanding rings where a trout had jumped. She wrestled with her conscience for a while, wondering whether to explain, but decided against.

Electricity was a problem, or rather the lack of it - the cost of a supply, totally out of reach! No electricity meant no central heating pump. A gravity system seemed unlikely to be terribly efficient, at least if the one in the caravan was anything to go by. The solution Gordon suggested was not to rely too heavily on heating but increase the insulation. He had drawn three leaf walls giving two cavities and plenty of space for rock wool to reduce heat loss. It would be more work but blocks were cheap; with smaller radiators and boiler they might actually save money - and it had to be done at the outset, no way to do it later. Such walls would give wide window sills, reminiscent of older granite built houses.

Because of the need for an office, only one bedroom could be included on the ground floor. Two more would be constructed under a steep 45-degree roof pitch, utilising otherwise wasted roof space.

One wall remained blank without windows but with a doorway, making it easy to extend the house later. Land size was no problem, ample space existed to build a palace;

they could double or treble the size should it ever be needed, provided the finances would stretch that far.

These and other slight amendments had been approved. All plans were now ready, rolled up in a cupboard, hidden but not forgotten, in the hope of taking sufficient cash at least to make a start - sometime. Would it be this autumn, that was the question.

* * *

Gordon was in the council offices at Penzance, talking to Mr Smith. The council seemed full of Mr Smiths, the planning department, the health department, but this was Mr Smith of the trees. Land along the east side of the entrance road from the village part way to the site was to be planted, the intention being to make the approach more attractive.

"The ground is very wet sometimes. It's not far from the river, the water table is only a few feet down. What can I set? The plot is several hundred metres long, what trees will grow well?"

"Big trees, or low bushy ones?"

"Tall. An effect like the French avenues, a sense of being farther south, emphasise the warmer climate, make our entrance more grand. A little variety perhaps, not all the same? If possible, a cash value when they mature - something for our grandchildren one day maybe?"

"Shallow root systems is what you need," the Council officer advised, "but for a big tree, those roots, not being deeply anchored, will compensate by spreading widely. Does that matter?"

"Not really, the stony road surface runs along one side; the stone is deep, but not down to the water table, the roots can anchor themselves underneath."

The tree man sat for a while doodling on a sheet of paper. "Certain poplars are used by the match trade, you could plant those mainly. Perhaps a group of cricket bat willow somewhere, they should be saleable, and maybe a couple of alder though that doesn't have much timber value. All those are good above a high water table."

The proper names were written down with brief instructions on spacing and growth habit.

"There you are," Jan commented on his return as they discussed the planting over coffee. "Councils do serve some useful purpose and the advice was free! Where can we get the trees?"

"Duchy nursery, apparently they stock them in a variety of sizes, over towards Lostwithiel. Wonder if the Monastery is still there?"

"Monastery?"

"Lot of nuns lived there, way back, before we were born; at least, before I was." He dodged back grinning as she struck out.

"Don't be rude. You're older than me; most of the year anyway. And Nuns live in a Convent, not a Monastery, ignoramus."

"Can't stand intelligent women... but you're nice really," the last words were added hurriedly as she lifted the cup, bending her wrist suggestively.

They watched each other, a hint of humour on both faces, waiting, thinking, searching for an opening.

"You look delicious," he broke the silence with a compliment.

She relaxed, smiling openly, her head giving a little nod of acknowledgement and thanks.

"That's the Cornish delicious," he spoke again.

She regarded him quizzically, not comprehending for a second; then, expression changing, grabbed a cushion and slung it directly at him.

"What did I do?" he protested laughing.

"Don't think you can put one over on me, I know what you meant. Cornish delicious - like clotted cream I suppose, *'Thick and delicious'*, that's what you were trying to say!"

"It's a compliment! Good-looking birds are not meant to be intelligent."

They regarded each other, both smiling broadly, pleased

179

with the little verbal skirmish.

"I know about convents, went to school in one for a while, remember? What about this one at Lostwithiel?"

"I slept there one night."

"They don't have men in convents!" Jan, uttering the words automatically, immediately saw the opportunity offered and rushed on. "Perhaps in your case it..."

"You want proof?" he cut in, forestalling the coming jibe.

"Mm, perhaps - but not right now. Tell me about this night with the Nuns?"

"They had left long since, as I told you, before our time probably. It's a youth hostel now or used to be when I was twelve. Stayed there with a cousin and her friend. We slept in separate dormitories, one for boys one for girls. A certain amount of midnight rovings were met with stern rebukes from a fierce matron as I remember. Every room had a name over the door. The toilet was labelled Meditation."

* * *

"You must leaflet," Jan insisted, early one June morning. "I'll be indisposed for a few days."

Gordon muttered agreement and continued writing on a pad. The boys were absent, both outside down by the river doing something. Sharon, washing up at the sink, peered shyly round at her mother, more in curiosity than concern but not liking to comment, certainly not with her father present.

Jan smiled at her young daughter, nodding confirmation to the silent question.

Later, as he sat by the roadside, Gordon thought about the look that had passed between the two women of his household and which neither realised he had noticed. Sharon was growing up. She'd be nine in two months; in a few years now, she too would... Anyway, she must have that room of her own soon. He had worried about it several times recently; better be sure to start the house this autumn and hope to finish the following year.

Traffic was light at first, flowing freely but expected to increase as morning wore on. A lengthening queue made leafleting less boring and in a way, easier. People were more apt to take a brochure when stationary or slow moving for some time. For the moment there was little to do except wait, watch, and let the mind wander.

Over the past weeks some changes in outlook had taken place. Certain happenings this season had spoiled the park's atmosphere, not in general but on one or two particular areas when a caravan appeared whose occupants showed little understanding of acceptable behaviour. He and Jan had talked much together over coffees and lunch while the children were at school, and decided to be more selective. If the site was to get a high reputation and be enjoyed by most people, then accepting unsuitable caravans would have to stop. Although numbers concerned would be tiny, the loss of cash was regrettable; but for the sake of ordinary visitors, for the village and for themselves, they were determined to run a quiet park.

"What are we going to class as unsuitable?" Jan had asked. "Obviously those atrociously tatty and uncared-for ones; experience has shown other visitors dislike being near them. Do you think that's why they look so bad, don't care about anything, including other people's feelings?" She had paused before continuing, waiting for a response but not really expecting one. "We do get other complaints though, not many, but virtually all are about other people rather than the site. Strange. We always anticipated it would be the facilities that caused problems."

The discussions had extended over several days; there was no easy solution. If anyone was refused a place it should only be those likely to cause major discomfort to other visitors. The eventual conclusion had been a somewhat experimental approach, a promise to notice what sort of unit caused problems and to adjust their policy accordingly. Parties of young people whose boundless energy needed an outlet would be warned of the lack of activities; perhaps people with a great number of children should be too, for it might not be a good holiday for the mother with little to amuse a large brood.

"Dogs." Jan had said, "We get most complaints about dogs, those that keep barking and those off a lead. The majority are good, it's only a few cause the trouble. If they bark continually when the caravan draws up, should we be full?"

These thoughts were interrupted as a single caravan appeared to join the still short queue. He hurried to offer it a leaflet before returning again to sit and muse.

"Strange," Jan had said, "not anticipated." She was right. He *had* expected to be a builder, gardener, plumber and gas-fitter, but the need now was for some super-tactful policeman. That had definitely not been foreseen! Nor did he much care for the task or feel competent to do it. Clearing a smelly blocked drain was far preferable!

Approaching mid-morning the queue extended, allowing little time to ponder further. He ran down the line, then back to the mini-van for more leaflets before haring off again. Unfortunately, returning on one occasion he mistook his place and offered the same caravan another leaflet. They treated the error with amusement, probably glad of a diversion and a chance to laugh in the sluggish traffic flow, but it was slightly embarrassing. Shortly after, he approached another, leaflet held out ready to hand over. Only at the last moment did he see the total mess inside the estate car, and knew positively that this was one of those units they had agreed to discourage. He made to step away, but the window wound down and a rough hand appeared, reaching out. Momentarily tongue-tied, Gordon hunted frantically for an escape route, somehow managing to blurt out, "Are you on the rally?"

When the head shook, he moved quickly down the line.

CHAPTER 11

Don't Answer

As befits any ex-policeman's wife, Audrey was in most situations, scrupulously straightforward and honest. True she had condoned certain minor fiddles to do with rationing that Jim had indulged in way back during the war, but what now passed through her mind was different; against her nature, contrary to her whole upbringing. Something had come up, making her fret, wrestle with her conscience.

Rising from the chair once more, she paced under the archway and into the kitchen, fiddling, wiping the sink over, checking the food cupboard, opening the fridge to look yet again at the cold lunch they would eat shortly.

The post had arrived two hours ago and with it the bill. Audrey wanted to talk to her daughter but with leafleting continuing, the talk would have to wait. Just as well perhaps, for she had still not definitely decided what to do. With June numbers steady rather than spectacular, Jan usually returned early enough to call in briefly, before rushing off to prepare tea for the children, but Audrey needed to catch her alone.

She was alone now but that was no help either. Jim would be back soon. He had driven down to the site as on most weekdays during the season, minding office and phone for an hour before lunch, or sometimes just after, ensuring no missed phone-calls while the toilets were cleaned. In spite of her best attempts, he still drove the Hillman; it should have been sold, his worsening leg made braking difficult. Audrey closed the fridge door, returning to gaze from the window. She loved the garden. While mowing, trimming and weeding, local people walking their dogs would stop to chat. Visitors from the site too, often strolled up to explore Relubbus. Some, the regulars, came in occasionally for coffee.

The area within her bungalow that she most loved, was referred to as the sun room. Large windows on two walls facing roughly south and west, allowed the sun in all day, apart from a few hours each morning. Here, she and Jim sat when not working in the garden. As the stony track to the caravan site ran in front of these windows, she had deliberately kept the intervening stretch of garden free from trees, so not to obstruct the clear view. The elderly couple sitting in a pair of old, somewhat upright but comfortable Parker Knoll chairs, waved to everyone who passed. Back in April after the first few visitors arrived, Audrey became so inspired at seeing these occasional caravans turn in from the main road that, unable to contain herself, she had risen, hurrying to the phone and ringing the site.

"Another one coming!" The excited exclamation ignored entirely the cost of that unnecessary call.

This practice had continued, even as caravans became more numerous. Audrey knew the two minute warning of visitor arrivals had proved very helpful, particularly when things were slack; offering whoever took the call sufficient time to slip out of working clothes and avoid being over shabby to greet new guests.

As weeks went by, numbers and of course costs, escalated! Audrey looked down at the telephone bill in her hand - she was shocked. Jim was a considerate man but blunt, saying what he felt regardless, expecting others to do the same. When he returned and they ate together, he failed to notice her anxiety, or perhaps it was well concealed. Whatever the cause, it went undetected and nothing was said. When Jan called in around teatime on her way back from leafleting, Audrey still avoided the subject, having wrestled with her conscience throughout the afternoon without any definite result. Not until early evening did she finally make a decision and set off downstream towards the site. Having greeted the children when they ran to meet her, Audrey led them on to the caravan, and stayed chatting.

Jan was surprised. Visits late in the day were unusual, occurring only when some juicy piece of news or gossip had come to hand; something so important or so scandalous, it couldn't be contained until they met the following day. As a rule, late calls were not only rare, but short. Having relieved a desire to pass on information, Audrey would quickly become restless, anxious to return to Jim and her bungalow - but not today. Why?

Finding awkward gaps in the conversation and sensing a certain uneasiness in her mother's behaviour, Jan wondered if the children's presence was in some way causing the hesitation. It never had before.

"Didn't you want one of those orchids that grow on our riverbank to try in your wall?"

Audrey failed to understand, but seeing a nod from Jan in the youngster's direction, enlightenment dawned. "Ah." Turning to her grandchildren, she asked, "You know the plants we mean? The flowers are over now, I don't suppose you could still find one?"

Had she asked outright they might have been less keen, but at this suggestion that they might be incapable, both Christopher and Sharon were on their feet and heading for the door. Stephen however, stayed firmly in his chair, watching the two older women.

"Don't you want to help?" Audrey asked.

"No." The little lad continued to sit, offering no further comment but watching carefully.

Jan wondered if he sensed their wish that he leave; it would be typical of his character to do exactly the opposite. Not wanting to order him out, making him feel rejected, she wondered what persuasion would work.

"Feeling poorly are you? Ah! Never mind you stay with us." She rose, took the single step to where her young son sat, picked him up and sank back into the armchair, cuddling the little lad in her lap.

"Get orf." He struggled to rise, broke free and fled for the door.

Left alone, the two women smiled at each other; both in their own way only too familiar with the manipulation of males.

"Orchids are difficult to transplant." Jan warned. "It may not grow but we've so many, it's worth a try. Christopher's good at things like that, he won't damage nearby plants." She paused before asking, "You've something else to tell me?"

Audrey looked through the window, across the balcony, watching Stephen run to catch his older brother and sister. After a while she turned back, pausing again before offering a tentative suggestion.

"When the phone goes, don't pick it up until the third ring."

"Why?" Jan was puzzled, not only by the request but by her mother's somewhat hesitant, almost guilty delivery.

"If it only rings twice, that will mean a caravan coming. It's silly to pay for every call."

* * *

Earlier in the year, an electricity official had arrived to broach the subject of a pylon line crossing the site. This well-dressed gentleman carrying a folded map marked with lines and crosses, had led the way some two thirds distance down the site, before stopping. Looking at his chart, around at the various landscape features, then back at the chart, he moved a little farther downstream before speaking.

"About here, that's where it will cross."

The prospect, though less alarming than that raised by the Water Board a year earlier, was serious enough. Absolutely no one would want to camp under these enormously high voltage lines, or near an unsightly great pylon! Moreover, escape from the scheme seemed unlikely, for this was no feasibility study, but a definite plan.

What to say? Officials were seldom known for being amenable to persuasion, not normally swayed by other people's problems! The man would expect outright opposition, was probably paid to ignore it. No good appealing to his better nature, working for the Electricity Board he was after all, almost a civil servant!

Gordon tried to appear pleased, enthusiastic.

"There will be compensation, won't there?"

"Compensation?" The neatly-dressed man took on a defensive air. "It's just waste ground." He frowned, shaking his head doubtfully, damping down expectations.

Indeed, it did look like waste ground. Apart from the narrow riverbank on which they stood, the area before them gave no sign of ever being touched by the hand of man. Any such indications lay buried under layers of vegetation. Willow bushes, many horizontal with age but still sprouting branches, intermingled with old leggy gorse, brambles in abundance, patches of bracken and the occasional taller tree. Among this jumble bloomed copious wild flowers, singly and in colourful clusters, predominantly bright pink and yellow. Butterflies flitted to and fro, mixing with damselflies near the river, and small birds flew from bush to bush. Lying far beyond the areas so far levelled and unlikely to be ready for many years yet, this land had that important extra - prospects!

"Waste ground? Certainly not! This is perhaps the most valuable land for miles around. Permission for caravans all over it. A wide swathe under your new power cables will be sterilised so far as development is concerned." Gordon paused, keeping a straight face but pleased to see the look of alarm on his companion. "Could affect between ten and twenty units directly. Is compensation also payable for reduction in value of neighbouring pitches?"

"I wouldn't think so." The man hesitated, unsure, shaking one hand from the wrist.

"What about kites? Many families want their children to fly kites. Can you guarantee their safety?"

That had been months ago. Today, Tuesday 22 June, the enquiry was in progress in Penzance. The projected power lines however, had already been reconsidered and were now planned to cross the river farther downstream, just beyond the end of the site. No compensation but no lines overhead; a success! Jan had stayed home for the day, so Gordon could attend the hearing. The Electricity Board man was speaking. At the back of the hall his voice was indistinct but the name sounded like Roy Shaw. Apparently the population of the area had actually decreased by 3000, but more electricity was needed since demand per person had increased three-fold. Again the words were difficult to hear, over what time span this had occurred, was not clear.

"Sure, and it's increased 10,000 times in the past century, since nobody had electric before then," Gordon thought, searching for reasons to disagree, but had to admit demand would go on rising, bound to. He listened as protesters tried to prove the new line unnecessary, and wondered how many would be prepared to cut their own consumption of power. "We are the only ones who can object with a clear conscience on that score, we don't use any, can't use any; we've no supply."

Eventually, with the actual hearing over, the inspector commenced his calls at places along the line, listening as people made individual points. He visited River Valley since a pylon would now lie only just beyond the boundary, clearly visible from the site. In a discussion of the effect on tourists, the Boards representatives suggested they might plant tall trees round the pylon to make it less obvious - "less visually intrusive" were the words their man used. How fine that sounded, but was it actually a promise? The inspector nodded approval and the entourage walked upstream towards the fleet of waiting cars, stopping halfway to watch a baby all-black rabbit, unconcerned by the spectators, sunning itself on a sandy bank by the entrance to a burrow.

The little cavalcade drove off, heading for St Michael's Mount. Having crossed to the island and climbed the steep slope to the castle, the small party was ushered to a high flat area surrounded by battlements. From here the pylons would be seen marching across the distant skyline, three miles or more away. His Lordship appeared, greeted the people in general and talked directly to one or two. The Inspector spoke, pointing to a map, then to the horizon.

"I suppose you'd like that section underground?"

His Lordship nodded thoughtfully, "Well, I would really."

That was it. No arguments, no objection and counter objection as there had been in the hall and elsewhere. So civilised. What must it be like to have that sort of power?

But The Mount *is* perhaps Cornwall's greatest historic building; it did deserve protection, there was little need to elaborate. Gordon nodded to himself, "Perhaps that's one of my many shortcoming, I don't know when to say little!"

* * *

During some evenings, the children took charge for a short while, minding the office, answering the phone and welcoming any late visitors. This help, not always entirely voluntary, gave their parents chance to change clothes, put on a tie which had tended to get discarded as the summer progressed, and stroll round the site. It had become almost a ritual, helping to keep in touch, making them aware of their guests' preferences and any shortcomings or new ideas.

While walking, they paused here and there to chat, invited often to take coffee or a sherry with various caravanners or the occasional camper, for tents were still a rarity. Late in the day and with school holidays not yet started, trade was sufficiently slack not to hurry. Stephen, being a few years younger, usually escaped to play, but both the older children were very capable. If someone arrived they could manage, and not only in the evenings. Either Christopher or Sharon, they took turns, stayed in the office for much of Saturday. It was always the busiest day when even before peak season, quite a number of new tourists would arrive.

Looking in the small mirror stuck to the narrow wardrobe door in her parents' bedroom, Sharon reached round to brush the back of her long dark hair. She liked the way it shone in the light, and swung her head again making the strands fan out, then shifted each side back behind her shoulders with a flick of the hand.

She was boss! Christopher and Stephen were out somewhere with friends; Dad had led a caravan off to choose a pitch. Until he returned, she was completely in charge. Still gazing in the mirror, she twisted her head to show one profile then the other, before returning to the lounge and gazing out through the window to check if any caravan approached down the track. None.

The young girl scanned the room. Everything rested in its proper place, she had prepared morning coffee for herself and her father not long since but the cups were already washed and away. Lunch would be next - only a snack. Something quick to prepare and to eat; being Saturday there might be little time for either. Omelette would be easy but would spoil if a queue of caravans delayed the meal.

"Beans on toast, I can keep them hot, even re-heat them; a tablespoon of water stirred in will cure any drying out, though they do tend to mush a bit if you're not careful."

Having made the decision, she was moving to sit at the table when a man with a gas bottle appeared striding towards the caravan. Sharon opened the door, meeting him halfway across the yard.

"Bring it this way please." She led towards the service passage where bottles were stored, turned a key in the lock, entered and reached for a blue ten-pound butane gas cylinder.

"Can you manage?" the man called from the doorway.

Hoisting the bottle, she swung it across, bumping the weight down heavily on the raised threshold before him and took the empty in return.

"Fifty-six pence please." Sharon, having no trouble with the new decimalization, held out a hand, accepting a pound. "I'll get your change from the office." Locking the door, she ran off, returning with two twenty-pence pieces and some copper while he still walked towards the caravan. He thanked her and disappeared.

Her father returned, giving a nod on hearing of the sale but not looking up, intent on writing in the daybook, noting how long the last customer had paid for and where they had pitched. No sooner had he started to write than another caravan drew across the bridge.

"Can you finish entering the last one, Sharon. Six days, I've done the first." Then he was gone.

Knowing the system, she picked up the book. Each day had its own page. Her father had already entered the price paid and full details on today's sheet, it only needed the customer's name and three letters of the car number on each of the next five pages. Inclusion of car letters ensured easy identification of various Smiths and Jones. These entries were quickly started, block capitals as always for clarity. Hearing an engine, she peered out to see yet another caravan crossing the bridge, and hurried to complete the last record. Standing and glancing down at her short summer skirt, she tucked in the blouse more tightly, brushed with fingers round the collar and shoulders to ensure no stray hairs and quickly left the caravan, descending the steps to greet them.

Only the man got out, his wife stared through the window but made no acknowledgement when Sharon smiled at her.

"Good morning," she addressed the man, who showed slight surprise, not expecting to be greeted by an eight-year-old. "My father will be back shortly, he's pitching a caravan and won't be long. Would you like to see the facilities?" She waved a hand towards the nearest toilet building.

"I'd rather go and pitch. Been travelling for most of the night." He stopped, looking round as if intending to go back to the car.

"You'll need to wait for my father, he'll tell you which pitches are best." Sharon feared he was going to be difficult, they sometimes were after a long journey. She half wished Christopher was around but pushed the involuntary thought quickly away; she would never admit even to herself that her brother's help was needed. Lifting her chin a little higher, she waited.

"OK. I'll take a decko at the river." A faint easing of tension at the man's mouth edges could have been a smile.

* * *

Trade varied, good days, poor days, usually only weekends at all busy. The intermittent slackness continued with little peaks and troughs until the last week in July when their own children also started school holidays. That Saturday a surge of tourists suddenly engulfed the site. Mass arrivals continued for the next few days, to treble site numbers.

Returning from pitching a caravan at teatime one evening, Gordon remarked to the three children, "That's another 50 building blocks."

Christopher looked up quickly, one could almost see his mind counting back through other tourists arriving that day, mentally adding, "A kitchen window!" or was it "Tiles for the roof!"

The two older children became much more interested in all new arrivals from that moment on, only Stephen remaining relatively impervious to the realisation that each visitor equated to a bit more house!

Mowing became difficult with so many units, almost everyone choosing grass. It made little difference. Not much growth took place in the dry weather, apart from under caravans where shadow prevented scorching and pulled the grass upward. The light green of these patches, visible when a caravan left, contrasted strongly with the faded, somewhat browning colour of surrounding exposed turf. This contrast was highlighted in many cases by an even more vivid green, where water had overflowed from a waste bucket that someone had accidentally, or in some cases deliberately, forgotten to empty. Was this good or bad for the ground? Nobody knew, so nothing was ever said. All the new grass areas made during the previous winter were in use, spare pitches disappearing then re-appearing as visitors arrived and left. More would obviously be needed for next year. Hardstandings were available in abundance, used by a few but seldom preferred when the sun shone!

Life had become hectic again, hectic but good. During the day, Jan walked down an endless line of vehicles at that Scorrier junction. She hurried to reach far enough down the queue so no one would escape without a brochure when, at the warden's signal, the traffic periodically flowed through. As the cars moved, she ran back, following towards the junction, attempting to maintain eye contact with the last one approached, to avoid looking silly by proffering another leaflet.

Gordon, left behind on the site, was learning to handle people's needs faster without appearing abrupt, and in the process gaining to some degree that knack of persuading visitors to obey the rules without giving offence. A small, rough-looking, dog wandered off a lead but showed little sign of causing any severe problems to the neighbouring caravans. It was tempting to ignore the matter and he did on the first occasion, suspecting it may have broken free without the owner's knowledge. However, there were fourteen other dogs on the site, most much bigger. Once one ran loose, others were bound to follow, the previous year had shown that. Seeing the same dog still free later, Gordon approached the couple concerned.

"Your dog really must be on a lead."

"He's well behaved. Not causing trouble is he?" There was a touch of antagonism in the voice.

"No. Wonderful dog, wish they were all like that. What worries me is that other owners will copy, let their dogs run free too - that big alsatian for instance. Do me a favour, keep it on a lead."

It was partly true, not much wonderful about the mangy specimen, but it had been quiet and listless, both excellent qualities in a roaming dog! More to the point, its owner's co-operation had been gained without ill feeling. Happiness in the close proximity of a caravan park was infectious, affecting to some extent the enjoyment of neighbouring visitors, a thing to be nurtured. Anyway, leaving someone happy made Gordon feel good.

Not all confrontations were solved so amicably and they were unending! Someone wanted to park by trees but never wanted to be in shadow; how many pitches did they have with trees only to the northeast? Another was too near the toilets, and yet others too far away. One wanted a tap near the caravan, then complained that everybody came past to fetch water. Gordon, supported by either Christopher or Sharon alternately minding the office, sorted these problems, fixing them all with varying degrees of success. It was stress, living on nerves, but exciting! Never a moment to be bored, seldom a time when the next happening was predictable, when the next meal could be anticipated with any certainty. Not even Jan's arrival home could be forecast; it depended entirely on traffic. Heady days, a test of stamina, of endurance, of the marriage itself; but that thrived - they drew strength from each other. Tired as they were, rising at six, retiring at eleven or later, the nights were not entirely given over to sleep.

Sitting in the lounge together, the parents chatted; children already asleep down the corridor. Darkness was falling, demands of visitors over for the day, barring some sudden emergency or someone running out of gas.

"I'm exhausted, but I love it! Everyone relies on us, even when I get back in the evening it's still busy. Only now, as day ends, can we relax." Jan sighed, stretching with a yawn. "So many visitors. They like it you know, the site; wonder if any have the slightest notion how much work it's been."

"Not many. Did we ever consider that when we went camping? We thought the owners lucky, that's all, never questioned how. We *are* lucky though - at least I am, to have you and the children," Gordon stretched out a hand. "Sometimes, when I get half a second to think, I wonder..."

"Wonder what?"

"If I treat them right, show enough appreciation for what they do; work them too hard? Being constantly pleasant and understanding with customers, well with most of them, do I forget with my own family?"

"You do, quite often. Not to worry, we understand, realise the pressures, most of the time anyway. But don't always take them for granted, they're only children; sometimes you expect too much. And try listening to them more, to their suggestions, don't just reject them out of hand, particularly Christopher. He's sensible, some of his ideas are good, like that roller."

"It's not just their ideas that get rejected, nine out of ten of my own are too, after I've mulled them over. But you're right, they are entitled to more consideration. When we don't use some suggestion, I'll try to explain why, show them how to think it through - but it's not easy always to remember when you're tired and pressed for time."

Everyone on site did indeed seem happy, pleased with the facilities, pleased with the quietness and beauty of the valley, and extra pleased with the weather to enjoy it. Things couldn't be sweeter - apart from the dustbins!

Lines of twelve bins were arranged alongside each toilet building, full ones being regularly removed to a collection area then replaced with empties. Some trouble had been experienced with foxes that knocked the bins over, dragging bags of rubbish considerable distances. Squirrels had also become very cheeky, eating holes right through the black bin lids, sitting upright, bushy tails crooked behind or coiled tidily round their feet, eyeing any passing visitors casually, without concern. At intervals they would bend over to take another mouthful, not particularly for access to the dustbin contents, but just seeming to enjoy the taste of plastic.

"Something to do with the moulding oil," one caravanner suggested.

These bins were suddenly inundated under a tidal wave of rubbish from the mass of newly arrived visitors, rubbish that appeared in totally uncatered for quantities. Gordon hurriedly phoned various local bargain stores and located one that had recently received a large consignment of bins; on sale at £1. He raced off as soon as Jan returned from the days leafleting, to strike a bargain for fifty at seventy-five pence each; grabbing the chance, sure the price was unrepeat-able. Although these bins stacked inside each other, fitting the whole consignment into the little green mini-van had been difficult. Most of the lids ended in an untidy pile on the passenger seat, collapsing to cover the gear lever on every sharp left-hand bend.

Arriving home, Gordon insisted against Jan's wishes that the bins were unloaded before tea.

"You haven't actually started cooking yet; this is more important. Come and see!"

Without waiting he leapt through the doorway, heading off at a run. Surprised at this unexpected exuberance the children looked to their mother, who masking amusement with a shrug of the shoulders, signalled them to follow. Once down the steps the youngsters quickly dashed ahead, taking the lead.

Their father waited by the van, impatient for the family to catch up, then stood to one side swinging the doors wide, proudly displaying the purchases with a sweep of one arm like a magician producing a rabbit.

"Bit bright aren't they?" Jan eyed dubiously the mixture of orange bins on one side and light pastel blue on the other.

Gordon glanced at them again, frowning slightly. Praise had been expected, not criticism. Perhaps they were a bit garish but nothing should detract from the achievement of buying so cheaply. He squared his shoulders, took a deep breath and ignoring Jan's comment, addressed the children gathered beside her.

"Make them easy to spot. Stop people dropping rubbish elsewhere. Don't you think they were cheap!" He spoke as if the colour had been deliberate, nodding his head while speaking, correctly guessing the children would nod back, indicating agreement.

"Hm! Probably no one else would buy them!"

Again ignoring Jan's remark, squatting down to put one arm around Sharon, he rested the other on Stephen's shoulder with a finger pointing at the closely-packed bins.

"This makes us a one-hundred dustbin site!" It was said impressively, as if some landmark had been reached, looking upwards for Jan's approval.

She gazed back down at him, half suppressing a smile and spoke quietly between pursed lips.

"Just as well, there's a lot of rubbish around here."

These new bins did solve the crisis, though the location where full ones were stored needed hasty expansion by trimming back the enclosing bushes. Gas bottles of all sizes rapidly sold out and new stocks were quickly ordered, together with more large propane cylinders for the site showers and extra boxes of toilet paper, rolls seeming to disappear almost as fast as they could be put in the cubicles. Fortunately however, worries that this new influx of people would presage the onset of more smell from the septic tanks, proved groundless. Sampson, on his morning rounds, ran out of both milk and newspapers during the first few days, but soon adjusted to the new level of trade. Problems in every direction were being overcome.

* * *

"Look!" Jan urged in a soft voice, peering out through the window.

Gordon moved to her side, peering across the site, but saw nothing to warrant attention. The field was nicely full with caravans, people chatting, walking to and from toilet buildings, ten-year-old Christopher standing amid a group of friends all approximately the same age; nothing seemed unusual, a normal evening scene. He turned to see Jan nod with a knowing smile, gave her a baffled frown and searched again across the valley. Still nothing caught his attention.

"I give up?"

"It's Christopher," she smiled, a conspiratorial smile that said, 'I told you it would happen'. He shook his head, completely uncomprehending.

"Men are so slow," she sighed, "Look! Look at his

197

friends, the one nearest him. It's a girl. Our son is growing up!"

Christopher and Sharon, now on holiday for the rest of the summer, were frequently out, taken off in cars with one or other of many friends acquired in a seemingly never ending stream as new families constantly arrived. Jan still insisted that before leaving with anyone they should tell her who, where, and when they expected to return. Stephen, now also taking occasional trips with friends, stayed more often to play on site. All three were having another great summer.

Any time they wanted to avoid a particular person or just to be by themselves, an easy excuse was that Dad needed their help. Often enough it was more than excuse; they had to help, like it or not. On Saturdays in particular, with its spate of arrivals, Mum's absence at her roadside vigil made their help indispensable. At weekends, life was one hectic rush.

Jan left at 7.30, climbing into the slightly rusty mini-van, sandwiches and flasks already aboard. She had woken the children an hour ago, after cleaning the toilet buildings. In spite of the six o'clock start, one shower had already been in use.

"Is the water temperature OK?" she had asked over the compartment wall, pleased to hear "It's great" called back. Several questions, mainly relating to beaches had passed back and forth in disjointed conversation while cleaning basins, mirrors, taps, toilet pans, seats and the other shower compartment. The family had breakfasted together before her departure, leaving Sharon with the washing up and Gordon checking dustbins. Driving was relaxing after the invariable early bustle; she rested back, even the hard little driving seat felt comfortable now the pressure of morning tasks lay behind her.

Gordon watched her go, moved the final four bins and returned to the caravan, checking the daybook. Fourteen to leave, five due to arrive. Good, with a bit of luck, Jan would find more than enough to make up the difference. He knew she would use in excess of fifty brochures, maybe a hundred or more if the day was good, but many would already be booked elsewhere.

Christopher was helping this morning. Sharon, having finished the washing up and put everything away, checked herself over in the mirror before leaving to look for friends. Stephen, not troubled about appearance, had already gone, last seen with a young playmate towards the top of the waste heaps.

Things were quiet for a time, the site coming slowly to life. One man arrived for gas, it was often first business of the day, bottles running out overnight. Most caravans carried two, but a few still relied on one, needing a new supply immediately. Sometimes such people came round very late, asking for a bottle, so those who waited until morning were viewed with favour. Christopher led him away, dealing with the sale. Sampson, from the village shop, arrived in his car shortly before 8.30, driving out onto Area 1 in front of the office as he had every morning since mid-May. Opening the back of his vehicle, bottles of milk and other breakfast requirements were dispensed. He moved on at intervals, gradually making his way round the site. Those still asleep when he passed could find him on some other area later.

Two caravans travelling together, drew into the yard, were welcomed and led to a pitch. On returning to the office, a woman was waiting. "This is my father," Christopher made an unconscious gesture with one hand.

"Something is wrong with our light," the woman explained. "We're new to touring, our little caravan only has the one gas lamp. When we lit it last night, the light was so poor we couldn't see to read; it's never been like that before. Can you help us?"

"Have you checked the mantle?"

"Mantle?" The woman looked confused and was about to say more, when a caravan appeared round the toilet building on its way out. The occupants, waving, leaned from the window and spoke, but their words were lost.

"Pardon me a minute," Gordon excused himself from

the woman and ran quickly across to the leaving caravan. They offered thanks for a good stay, wanting to know if booking was necessary for next year? He rushed back, jumped to the balcony and through the French windows - to reappear, booking form in hand. As he reached the waiting caravan and stood passing a few last words with the smiling faces, another man walked purposely towards him.

Waving goodbye, Gordon turned back to the woman but was stopped as the man intercepted him. "My car battery is flat, can you charge it for me?"

"Just a minute and I'll be with you, the lady is waiting." He returned, forgetting for a minute where they had got to.

"It's all right," the woman said. "Your son has explained about mantles and found one for me. He's offered to fix it; can I borrow him for a while?"

"Sure." Gordon turned back to the man as Christopher and the woman departed. "Now, a flat battery; no I can't charge it, we don't have electric ourselves. I've a pair of jump leads you could borrow, perhaps one of the other campers...?" The man nodded, and followed to the service passage where most of the tools now hung from nails driven into walls.

As the morning progressed, more caravans arrived, customers came to book on, others left, a constant stream of people; and suddenly the showers went cold in one toilet building. Christopher, on his own at that moment, raced across to check the changeover valve. The tag showed red. Bottle empty! He swung the pointer to the other bottle, knowing the changeover should have happened automatically. It too was red. These big cylinders contained 104 pounds of gas, far too heavy for him to lift but he could tell by tilting them a few degrees sideways that one was empty, for it moved easily. The other resisted, he felt for the valve and turned; the red tag slid to one side, indicating resumed gas pressure. Had Dad forgotten to turn it on when changing the last cylinder, or did some child deliberately turn the valve as a prank? Entering the passageway, he peered up through the pipework to the bottom of the heater. No flame, the pilot needed re-lighting. Dashing back again, he found another caravan waiting in the yard, stopped to explain that his father, already pitching the previous arrival, would be back soon, and invited them to look round the facilities. This gesture was not merely thoughtfulness on the lad's part, but agreed family policy. Few people left after viewing the facilities and many booked more days as a result, no longer apprehensive about standards.

Leaving them to make their own inspection, Christopher found matches and returned to light the pilot jet on the water heater, then entered the toilets, holding down a tap until the water ran hot. Leaving the building he heard the phone bell and sprinted on, but Sharon was taking the call, making notes on a pad, three girl friends standing on the balcony waiting for her. Dad appeared round the corner, hurrying towards the two caravans now waiting; another approached along the road.

The day, like any other in the school holidays, would likely remain busy, hopefully with a small lull, time enough to grab a snack somewhere towards midday. Fortunately, most people were very tolerant, happy with the valley and understanding of delays; at least, they were so long as the sun shone!

Chapter 12

Cormorant and Bottoms

Stephen crept towards the river, crouching, body hunched over, arms hanging, knuckles brushing the grass. For all his stealth, the small lad moved quickly. A dozen paces and he dropped behind a gorse bush, lying there, flat on the ground, crawling to peer cautiously round one side and down the sloping bank. Behind him in a broad arc the site remained thickly dotted with caravans but the hour was early; though some visitors may already have been awake, no movement yet showed. Sharon had tip-toed in bare feet across the yard to the toilet building only a few minutes before; Stephen had been about to follow but glancing towards the river, something caught his attention.

A faint dew coated the grass, its wetness seeping through, penetrating the thin pyjamas; he paid no heed, craning to see beyond the dense prickly gorse, now devoid of all but the odd dimple of yellow. Below him, right on the water's edge stood his quarry, a cormorant, its head drooping dejectedly, feathers dull and untended. Drawing back, the young lad rose, brushing wet hands unconsciously across his pyjama bottoms, gathering himself like an athlete on the starting blocks. Flexing forward and back twice as if winding some internal spring, he thrust ahead on the third movement, striving for grip, dodging round the bush and on, launching down the bank. Another boy might have used stealth, creeping up on the cormorant, but that was seldom Stephen's way. Probably the more wily approach would also have failed, for the bird had only to fall in the river to escape, having sensibly perched itself on a stone at the very edge.

Had Stephen managed to lay a hand on his quarry, even so much as a single feather, he would certainly have ended in the water, for he gave no thought to slowing. As it was, the bird moved while its would-be captor was still several paces away, allowing Stephen time to swerve to a new course, a dozen steps parallel to the river, teetering on the brink, arms flying to maintain balance on the wet slippery surface before managing to stop.

Later, more children appeared and the hunt continued. Although the cormorant again succeeded in raising sufficient energy to evade capture, it was weak, unable to fly more than a few wing flaps and obviously needed help. Not that the band of little lads had thought much on that score; they might well help look after it later, but that was not their motivation. Young boys were not renowned for noble thoughts or good intentions! Catching a bird, any bird, was difficult; the chance that with this one they just might succeed, that was what drove them on. However, all attempts failed, but not by sufficient margin to discourage the little pursuers.

The chase was abandoned as most families rode off for the day; not until evening did Stephen and his friends finally take their prisoner. They marched triumphantly to the office carrying the bedraggled specimen on someone's jacket supported by many hands, a jumper draped over its head as protection from that long, hooked beak.

Surrounded by children, Gordon inspected the cormorant carefully. It lay, finally exhausted on his lap, resistance negligible, only the lightest of restraining hands needed. Nothing was broken, no obvious injuries but its condition was pitifully low. Stephen, standing close, pointed to a flat fly. There were several, one stepped onto the small outstretched finger. Springing backwards he brushed it off, stamping down in an instant, grinding it in the dust with a twist of the foot. Turning to his friends, chest expanding, one small clenched fist punched the air in success.

With all attention now focused to these little vermin, Gordon noticed more crawling between dishevelled feathers.

One had migrated to his own trousers! Looking more carefully, others had also forsaken the bird. He twisted inside his shirt, muscles crawling; a spontaneous itchy feeling generated by the crab-like sideways movements. Luckily, he knew most parasites were specific to the birds they infested and would not live on people for any length of time. Insects could be very particular. Not only might their physical build restrict them to one type of creature, but often to one part only. Lice that clung to a bird's head feathers, for instance, might not thrive on a wing or a tail.

Someone produced a mackerel, Stephen passed it to his father who broke off small pieces, pushing them into the large hooked beak. He sat outside the caravan, cormorant still on his lap, Stephen's friends gathering closer. After a while, when the bird would eat no more, it was carried carefully to the river's edge and lowered onto the water, still watched by the band of little followers. Unable or unwilling to swim, it struggled feebly to climb the bank, offering no resistance when lifted again and carried to the nearby toilet building's service passage, a place of safety suitable to its present vulnerable condition.

"Now, what about those unwanted visitors, the flat flies?" Gordon asked himself, turning his attention to them. Brushing with a hand proved ineffective, most clung on, quickly disappearing in the nearest fold or opening. Jan, watching from within, saw him head towards the caravan - she reached across turning the key, absolutely refusing entry.

"But they can't live on humans!" he protested, shouting through the locked door.

A window opened farther down the caravan.

"You're boasting again," she called, smiling sweetly; then withdrew, closing it firmly behind her.

The parasites did disappear within half an hour, but for a long time Jan refused to accept they were not just hiding.

"Gone to ground in your underwear probably, or clinging to your body burrowing away at the skin!" She wrinkled her nose in distaste, "You're definitely not coming in here; go and shower!"

Over the next days, many visitors brought food for the cormorant, without doubt at their children's insistence. Kindness perhaps, or more likely the urge for a further accomplishment; the bird's recovery. Boys can be so competitive! Who brought the biggest fish? Whose fish did the bird take first? Which one was consumed most quickly? These arguments continued even as it ate. Certainly they had all grown to like the new arrival, every child had stroked its feathers carefully at some time or another; there was the makings of real affection, more openly demonstrated by several young girls who had now joined in.

Recovery did occur, and with startlingly rapidity, fish soon swallowed whole, taken sideways in the beak, tossed around until the head faced inwards, then consumed, a gulp and some neck stretching marking its passing. At night the cormorant slept in the service passage, but spent evenings in the caravan. The buzzard they had looked after over a year previously, had taken time overcoming its anxiety; not so the cormorant, which was quite fearless almost from the start.

It sat happily on Gordon's shoulder, occasionally reaching for an ear, allowing itself to be stroked, picked up and moved around just like a domestic cat. A natural curiosity caused the beady eyes to follow any new movement, the extensible neck stretching out, allowing the big hooked beak to investigate all objects within reach.

After a late tea on the second evening, Gordon posed the family at one end of the small lounge ready for a picture, but Jan snatched the camera before he could pick it up, making him join the group, the cormorant on one arm.

"Smile please!"

The bird, either startled by the voice or mistaking the sudden flash of many teeth as an intention to eat it, chose that moment to take flight within the close confines of the caravan. Flinching from suddenly flapping wings, all eyes closed at the exact second the camera clicked. With nowhere to go and a wing span not much less than a third of the narrow room's width, the cormorant somehow managed to land on the back of an armchair. Since this chair nestled tightly against a wall, it was unable to achieve a balance and hung on, wings flapping wildly. As Jan, still holding the camera, stepped back in surprise, Gordon leapt across pushing one arm under the webbed feet.

Trying again for a decent picture, the bird was posed on Christopher's arm, the photo quickly taken. Originally, there had been no intention that Stephen should hold it; he was smaller, less capable and the bird had now regained much of its strength. However, the lad was not pleased to be left out.

"I found it." Stephen spoke quietly, no loud protest, almost under his breath; just that suggestion of disagreement, of it not being fair.

Gordon relented and in spite of his son's small size, lifted the big bird onto a large, doubled-over white towel that Mum had draped across the lad's lap. As Stephen placed both hands on the cormorant's shoulders, preventing it standing or opening its wings, Dad stepped back a pace and took another picture.

Suddenly, the long neck extended, snaking out, rotating back on itself until it faced directly towards Stephen from a distance of perhaps six inches. Two beady eyes looked inquisitively into the little lad's face. Stephen stared back.

Both pairs of pupils locked, without waver or blink, like two gunmen in a western waiting to draw, concentration absolute! Gradually, almost imperceptibly, the big black beak moved forward, slightly agape, eyes watching. A mere few seconds had passed, the rest of the family somehow unable to act; concerned, but still accessing the situation, grasping for a decision, a course of action. The beak hesitated, stayed unmoving for a further second, then opened slowly, inquisitively reaching forwards. Those watching held their breath, the slow motion scene and Stephen's intense expression somehow holding them immobile.

With a quick jerk of motion, the hooked bill clamped a firm hold on the little lad's nose. Shaking fiercely from side to side, it pulled hard, attempting to remove the fleshy morsel!

Two lines of blood streamed down the young face, dripping off the upper lip on both sides; a crimson Chinese moustache.

Gordon grabbed at the bird. As his fist closed round the neck, the beak opened in an attempted squawk, relinquishing its prize. He slid an arm under the chest, pulling it away and standing aside, watching with concern as Jan moved quickly forwards.

Stephen made no cry nor any attempt to wipe away the blood. After the first surprise he sat expressionless, looking straight ahead, withdrawn into himself; his usual way of dealing with pain or injury. Dousing the nose thoroughly in Dettol still produced no sound but the bleeding eased. Having tended the wound as best might be, Jan turned to the bird.

"There's gratitude for you! Take it outside, it can go to bed early in disgrace!"

Their feathered lodger was quickly removed to the service passage's safety, an hour earlier than it would normally have gone. Stephen carried on for the rest of the evening as if nothing had happened, though perhaps a little quieter than even his own usually taciturn nature.

Next morning after feeding, condition now fully restored apart from a certain dullness of plumage, the bird regained its freedom. Lowered into the river near the bridge, it dived below the surface; no hesitation, all sign of former weakness now disappeared. An immediate underwater chase after a trout, which it caught, showed suppleness, speed and grace, all plainly visible in the clear water to a group of children gathered, sitting and kneeling on the low bridge parapet to witness the release. Gordon, still standing close to the river, watched with reservations. Though observing the remarkable transformation with undeniable feelings of pride, he now doubted the wisdom of their achievement. If the cormorant stayed, a quick depletion of trout must follow!

Half an hour later the very wet creature stood on the balcony steps, wings held sideways to dry in characteristic fashion, cormorants being one of the few sea birds with insufficient oil to prevent water wetting their feathers. It moved aside reluctantly when visitors entered or left the caravan office, resentful but unabashed.

After three days and several further attempts to oust their new lodger, more drastic action unavoidably beckoned. Cormorants get too tame, too quickly! In the Orient they live like domestic animals, the owners use them for fishing, restricting their neck to prevent the fish being swallowed.

'Cormy' as the bird became universally known among the children, qualified more as pest than pet with its appetite for trout, and especially with that liking for noses. Stopping it dying had been the objective, not providing a pension for life!

Riding on Jan's knee in the mini-van shortly after breakfast, Cormy gazed happily through the window at the passing landscape, for all the world as if vehicular travel formed a normal feature of any cormorant's day. Remembering its strange tastes and unpredictable temperament, she lightly held the bird's neck until arriving on Marazion beach.

A placid sea rolled gentle wavelets towards where they stood, on dry sand above the rising tide, not far from the water's edge.

"Shoo!"

Cormy remained inactive, standing between the two people like a contented child. "Go on, stupid bird." Jan bent over addressing the reluctant protégé, trying to encourage an unwilling swim. "Cormorants are supposed to like salt water!"

She looked round but there was no one to hear; the beach stretching for miles, lay completely deserted.

"Do you always talk to bird's?" Gordon asked tongue in cheek. "You know it's a sign of madness... something I've always suspected."

Jan lunged, managing to knock him over, falling on top in the effort.

"Don't think I don't know you talk to that robin when you're alone." She spoke in gasps as they struggled, trying to rub his head in the sand, rolling over, catching Cormy's tail feathers. The bird emitted a short guttural squawk, hopping forwards, heading off into the waves.

"Look!" her outstretched arm pointed.

The bird swam out a short way, gathered itself up in that way cormorants have, and dived below the surface. Seeing the rear feathers disappear, they scrambled to their feet, rushed to the vehicle, Le Mans fashion, and drove off at high speed.

* * *

"Bums," Jan said.

The children's heads shot up, rigidly attentive, eyes wide with surprise. Had they heard right?

Mum nodded confirmation.

"Lots of them, in a ring outside the office when I came back from leafleting!" She stopped to resume eating a large slice of brown bread thickly spread with butter and apricot jam, apparently unaware that the children expected more.

Gordon, tackling a lettuce and cheese sandwich, observed silently, controlling a smile. He knew the whole story but the children didn't; they continued to look at Jan, waiting. He watched them; Christopher might control his interest, and Stephen certainly, but Sharon could never restrain her curiosity. Jan must be well aware of that. She's clever Gordon thought, glancing through the French windows and out over the site to hide his amusement.

"Mum!" The single word was drawn out in protest.

"Yes?" Jan regarded her daughter in apparent surprise, head questioningly tilted.

"Mum, you can't just say..." She hesitated, "You can't start telling something then stop."

"Why not?"

Knife clenched upright in her hand, bread on the plate still partly spread but forgotten, Sharon was bursting with impatience.

"Because..." She struggled for a reason. "Because I want

209

to know!"

"Ah! I better tell you then, hadn't I." Jan smiled as Sharon's expression lost its frustration, her head nodding eagerly in anticipation.

"I arrived back from leafleting and drove across the bridge. There they were, right in front of me. A whole ring of men's bottoms!"

"Bums," interrupted Stephen quietly with a wicked little smile, a small lock of sun-bleached light brown hair across his tanned forehead.

Jan paused looking at her five-year-old son. Two blue eyes stared back unrepentant.

"There was this ring of gents' bottoms," she repeated, pausing, waiting for a further correction. None came, just an impish expression; rebellious disagreement but no words.

"All sticking in the air. Perhaps as many as eight grown men, some kneeling, some bending over, eyes fixed on the ground, noses almost down in the dust, and all in a big circle surrounding *something*!" She stressed the word, a touch of the sinister, spreading hands defensively in mock alarm; pausing again before saying with a flourish, "Dad was the one with the camera."

She stopped, to stare accusingly at Gordon. The children turned, following her gaze, waiting.

He saw the mischief in Jan's eyes, her satisfaction at drawing him in, putting him on the spot. Picking up the half-eaten slice, she took a big deliberate bite, indicating unmistakably her intention to say no more.

He sighed, knowing the circle of young faces expected an explanation; who wouldn't, the way the subject had been introduced. Did they pay this much attention at school?

"We were watching an *Ammophila Sabulosa*." He paused watching Sharon, waiting for her to demand more, but Jan's hard fingers prodded him under the table and he continued.

"It's a wasp with a long slender abdomen, mainly red but terminating in a black bulb. Must be all of an inch, er, two-and-a-half centimetres long. This insect was dragging a large green caterpillar, about its own length but probably three times the body weight. It struggled forward, stopping at a tiny flat stone, perhaps half the size of a drawing pin head. It lifted and moved the stone aside revealing a hole, a sort of insect 'Open sesame'. How did it remember this one from all the other small flat stones in the dusty yard surface?"

He paused again, but they sensed an answer was not expected, and in any case had no explanation to offer.

"Our wasp dragged the caterpillar down into her tunnel, reappearing head first a little later. Goodness knows how it turned round. She covered the hole again with the same flat stone, scraping some dust over as camouflage, then left."

The children, obviously less interested in caterpillars than in bottoms, turned back to eating, thinking the tale was ended, but Dad continued.

"We opened the tunnel again, and prized the caterpillar out. Why do you think the wasp put it there?"

"Food store?" Christopher volunteered.

"In a way, yes, but not for itself. The caterpillar was still alive, it moved if touched but was somehow paralysed. It couldn't crawl away. Stuck to the end was a large egg, almost pure white. The wasp had provided a meal for its baby. This egg and the grub that forms from it, will gradually eat the caterpillar away while it's still alive. Better than our milk cooler for keeping your food fresh, don't you think?"

Gordon rose and reached for a jam jar with some soil in the bottom. Resting on the soil was a large green caterpillar with a small white cylinder stuck to one end. The children peered in. Jan reached over and nudged the green captive with the wrong end of her teaspoon. It wriggled.

"Ugh." Sharon put her bread down in disgust, pulling a face.

After the meal, the children raced off to discover which of their friends had returned from the beach, leaving their parents still sitting at table.

"Bums?" Gordon asked. "That's the cockney coming out I suppose?"

"It fixed their attention. Did you notice?"

"I noticed Sharon's reaction when you stopped suddenly.

Don't go all innocent, pretending it wasn't deliberate." He paused, smiling. "And *you* tell Christopher, Stephen and me off when we bait her!"

Jan tilted her head back and laughed lightly.

Over the following weeks, the caterpillar remained in the jar. Its size reduced progressively, shrivelling almost to a shell but remained alive as the egg grew and grew, changing gradually into a fat white grub. When the caterpillar eventually died the grub became a chrysalis, but was never to emerge as an adult wasp. Possibly the soil's moisture content was wrong.

The photos were not brilliant, clip-on close-up lenses required an exact distance to within a few millimetres, an accuracy difficult to obtain using a steel tape held against the side of the camera with a moving subject only four inches away.

"Pretty poor," Gordon was disappointed. "One day *when*... no, that's tempting fate, let's say *if* we get rich; a through-the-lens viewing and focusing camera, preferably with a telephoto lens, is going to be something I need. Then we can show our caravanners the birds and other interesting creatures on site."

* * *

Activity increased even more strongly in the first week of August, caravans and motorcaravans and even a few extra tents rolled relentlessly in, dotting every pitch on the areas so far grassed. Others used those stony sections still awaiting their ration of topsoil, some from choice, but most with the promise of a grass pitch when one became available. Jan came home in the evenings, tired but pleased.

"No chance of boredom or the temptation to nibble today. Must have lost pounds dashing up and down that traffic." She pirouetted, demonstrating, full skirt brushing the furniture in the confined space. "Need to take more leaflets, almost ran out today!"

Building a house in late autumn began to look a realistic

possibility. How very quickly circumstances could change! Gordon needed the help offered by Jim, as well as that given by either Christopher or Sharon. Days passed in a whirl of arriving guests, previously sited caravanners adding to the frantic activity, popping in for extra nights or advice, or directions or whatever. People, people and yet more people, a blur of faces to greet, listen to, and show to a satisfactory pitch. The first Saturday in August, Gordon found himself so busy pitching caravans and the odd tent, that mid-afternoon, five hours since his last coffee, he was still attempting vainly to clear the queue. Sticking a CLOSED sign on the balcony railing, he held a hand up to the next couple who were already walking towards the caravan.

"Open again in twenty minutes," he shouted. "Haven't had lunch yet. Must eat or I'll collapse!"

The waiting visitors good-heartedly waved their consent.

Jan returned late from leafleting. Seeing the increased numbers and pleased at her success, she studied critically their own caravan.

"You know, ours is just about the tattiest unit on site. Caravanners are..." she searched for suitable words, "I was going to say snobbish, but that's not exactly what I mean. They're concerned about quality, nervous of anything a little, how shall I say; down market. If we *can* build a house this autumn it will improve our image. We should sell the mini sometime and get a car. Over at Scorrier, early and late in the day when caravans are few, I wait well clear of the van, so they don't connect it with me. I get a better reception."

A few visitors continued to arrive, even after Jan's return. Early evening approached and Gordon's stamina flagged again.

"Another lorry-load of building blocks," she whispered to him, as he had once done to the children.

Finding new energy he dashed off leading the next caravan.

During this peak time the children helped alternately, not just at weekends; swapping days when invited out by a

213

special friend. Considering her young age, Sharon did particularly well, preparing the midday meal or leaving sandwiches for her father and Christopher on her days off. When on duty, she assisted customers and sold Calor gas, efficiently striking a happy relationship with all those who called at the caravan. Her already likeable personality blossomed. Though the boys and to a certain extent Dad, still baited her about cooking whenever given the chance, arousing her became less easy as self-assurance grew. She knew the food tasted good and whatever they might say, everything would be eaten with relish. Only occasionally were the male members of the family subtle enough to get past her new defences.

Many of the first year's customers had come back, the Richardson family, the Lovesays, the Farmers and several others, as well as a host of new faces. Space was again becoming a problem.

Behind the caravan that served as office, reception, and home, was a small wood. This copse, mainly willow growing on sunken ground, separated the dwelling from a newly formed area immediately downstream. This new section had been christened Area Three, simply because it was the third grassy area to be worked on, completed and brought into use. Area Three was intended eventually to take one line of caravans with a broad expanse of grass in front. However, when the school holidays first started this had increased to two lines. Now, in the second week of August, there were three rows, caravans dotting the entire grassy surface; closer than ideal, but no one seemed to object. Visitors also covered areas four and five, both small new areas, now grassed, but capable of taking only four caravans each. Several more lay unfinished, just stone, level but without topsoil, and being incomplete these had not yet been given a number. In dry weather the option of a much larger space on hard-standing was still invariably refused if a grass pitch had become available.

At tea that evening, when Jan commented on the greatly

214

increased numbers, wondering why the site should suddenly be so busy, Christopher offered a solution.

"Many of my friends arrived last Saturday when school holidays first started, but more arrived this Saturday. Since most have come for two weeks, we've two lots now, an overlap - all coming, no one leaving. That's why we're so busy."

Jan looked at her son, nodding thoughtfully, turning to the family with raised eyebrows. Gordon signalled his agreement with a smile of surprise.

"Clever Clogs," Sharon muttered.

During the day, most caravans were empty but towards teatime, cars and their occupants flowed back into the site. Gordon had worried at first that queues would form for a toilet, or more likely at the showers. He checked, poking his head round the Gent's door at intervals, but no such queues developed. More surprisingly, people left all the facilities clean and tidy after use. Jan suggested that because they were usually spotless, caravanners were embarrassed to leave them dirty. Whether due to this care by visitors, or the quality of workmanship, or those hours spent at the drawing-board designing the layout, the buildings had been remarkably easy to keep clean. Not even a sink plug had gone missing, nor had a single item of graffiti appeared, though the slightly roughened texture of the white painted wall surfaces would in any case have made that less easy.

One point raised by a visitor concerned the showers. The taps had been placed towards one corner and high enough so people would not catch their body too heavily if they slipped. This however meant that young children found difficulty in reaching. The matter had not been overlooked, but the assumption made that very young children of four or under, would be safer not taking a shower alone. Putting the taps high would prevent such small children showering without their parents' knowledge as well as making the compartments more convenient for adults. One lady however, had a problem; she travelled without a husband.

"My son is short for his age and doesn't like coming in the Ladies with me." She turned to leave, understanding but not exactly happy.

It was Stephen waiting nearby who solved the problem, whispering to his mother, "Tell him to use a footstool from under the basins."

After the first season some discussion and a certain amount of indecision had taken place over toilet rolls. Should they be soft? Up to this point, Izal sulphite rolls had been used, but sulphite paper was thin and hard, the type that ten years before had been the traditional loo roll in most homes. Gordon wondered if a soft roll, Andrex or similar would give that extra touch of class. Jan argued against.

"You know what others in the trade say of toilet rolls; they keep disappearing, people take them. We get through enough already without making it worse. I use tissues for make-up but soft rolls are just as good; they'll get used as kitchen towels, handkerchiefs, all sorts of things. No one will take sulphite rolls, stick to them, at least until you build our house!"

"OK, if you think so. But they're pretty rough, bad for our image, people look down on them." A ghost of a smile replaced his serious expression as another thought occurred, "Don't think we're scraping the bottom, do you?"

He grunted as an elbow prodded his midriff.

Barbecues were much in evidence in the evenings, adjacent caravans often combining to eat together, sometimes in quite large groups. Frequently adults stayed chatting in portable chairs round still warm coals while children dashed off to play. Many made for the waste heaps, scaling the face then finding a place to slide down on their trouser seats. Fortunately, clearing had stopped after a big fall, so little danger existed of further collapse. Other youngsters made for the river.

Whatever their destination, the children tended to split into groups by age and sex as friendships quickly formed.

216

Groups might temporarily combine for some particular activity, but broke apart again to go off with their own set, seeking some new pursuit at intervals, their span of attention to any one occupation short-lived.

Stephen, with a band of similarly-aged children, were racing reeds in the river, tossing them into the water somewhere upstream, then rushing back to the bridge to see which arrived first. Shortly after, they acquired a large soft ball and were throwing it from one bank to the other, great noise and merriment generated when it fell in the water to drift down on the current. Several small lads moved ahead to lie at the water's edge, friends holding their ankles, trying to reach as the ball floated by beyond their fingertips. When it slid under the bridge and sailed on, then with a burst of speed bobbed down the weir, a cheer went up. Stephen, dashing to overtake it, found a shallow spot and slipping and sliding down the bank, whipped off his scandals to wade in and catch the ball at midstream.

Jan, watching from the caravan window, wondered why it was that so many of the other young children, some of them girls, found the need to go in as well, since the ball was already rescued. Nevertheless, a pile of shoes, plimsolls and socks accumulated on the bank along with the now forgotten ball, that section of river becoming obscured by young bodies. Five minutes later, every single one had gone, the group running off again in the direction of the waste heaps.

Later that evening, Gordon and Jan walking round together, were called over and offered coffee by a group sitting outside one caravan with a large awning. They knew several people from the previous year, the others only vaguely remembered from the blur of faces arriving over the last week. All were adults.

"Where are the children?" Jan asked of one family, knowing they had two sons and a daughter.

"No idea," the wife replied. "That's one reason we come; everywhere's safe. The river's shallow and those big heaps are fine, though my boys are going to need new trousers

217

from sliding down."

"Ours will too," another woman agreed, "Much of the time they're off with your son, playing down the valley, they won't show us where. Must be good for them - more than that, we get some peace! Nowhere else they stay happy without spending money."

Money! Magic word! Not for its own sake but for materials the house would need. Money, a topic the whole family discussed. Christopher, perhaps more than anyone, calculated its value not by the price of ice creams or chocolate bars but by how many building blocks it would buy.

"Each extra day a caravan stays, adds about eight blocks, more if it's a big family," he suggested at tea one evening.

"Eight? That probably means two," Sharon countered.

"No," Dad paused, calculating. "Eight is about right, and bigger families do pay more."

House building was definitely on for late autumn if these numbers kept up; everyone knew it, all waiting impatiently to become involved. The boys in particularly spoke eagerly of helping with the work. During the summer they had built a secret tree camp, hidden deep in some lost corner, helped by a string of friends among the visitors. One of their rules insisted no adults should be shown its location. Probably they now fancied a move to greater things. A whole house built completely by their own labour should satisfy them - or put them off building for life!

The level of trade held up exceptionally well, numbers starting to drop only after mid-August, the decline still gradual. Hours were long, a constant bustle, never being sure just when an overdue meal would be possible, what mini-crisis would happen next - they lived at full stretch! One evening after several attempts to find time for tea, Gordon spotted two cars, one towing the other, speeding round the camping area, using the grass like a miniature Silverstone. Sprinting over, seeing the towed car rip up a length of turf as its wheels locked attempting to start, he ran in front, waving the leading car down.

"Not on my grass, please!" It was said between gritted teeth, hardly a request, more a polite command and even that measure of civility had taken great effort.

"We must, he can't start."

"Then tow him on the road; or off the site!" The veiled threat of those last few words was hardly to be missed. The lead car drove onto the hard surface, little dust clouds rising along the road each time the towed vehicle's clutch was engaged. Gordon strode over to replace and tread down the disrupted turf but the damage remained obvious. He would ask Christopher to water it later, to prevent drying out and encourage re-rooting.

Seldom were there more than a few moments to relax, and not that much time for sleep. Mostly, exhilaration compensated for falling energy levels. Like the winning boat race crew, tiredness was masked by elation; weariness hidden from customers by that potent drug - success! Only in the occasional clumsy handling of a dispute did the fatigue show, and even then few visitors recognised it for what it was. Those who the decision pleased, felt it only their due; the losers left mumbling "Pig-headed idiot!"

Late in August, numbers had declined to a level that allowed at least some time to themselves, a few minutes to sit and read, or wander across to the bridge and talk with visitors, such conversations usually interrupted quickly as business of some sort called again for their attention.

This was a time of year when visitors seemed to know more than they did themselves about going's-on in the area. One week two people asked after the new gig-racing record just set in the Scilly Isles. A few days later a family were talking about the Marazion carnival. Another week some couples discussed the wartime Beaufighter, salvaged from Mount's Bay after thirty years in the sea. All these were relatively local events, Marazion for instance, only three miles away; it might as well have been the moon for all the chance either Jan or Gordon had of attending during the school holiday period.

Another static caravan arrived on site, making three altogether. These statics, larger than the touring caravans, were left permanently sited, owners using them whenever they wished, except during the closed winter season. For this they paid a set yearly sum. It wasn't necessarily the preferred type of trade but everything helped the family finances along! The latest one measured thirty-foot end to end. Fred, the owner, asked to have the chassis painted.

"It's going rusty. Can it be arranged?"

"Yes, of course. I'll work on it once we get less busy," Gordon had assured him, not knowing that later he would tell himself, "That's the first and last work I ever do on the underside of a caravan!"

He started the following week, on slack days when Jan arrived back early. Being conscientious, all the rust had to come off first, with a paint scraper and wire brush. Minimal underside clearance offered no option but to tackle the job laying flat on his back. The old swimming goggles should have been ideal but kept misting up. They were finally discarded in favour of working at arm's length, first one side then the other to relieve aching muscles. Christopher came round in the evening to announce teatime, and being smaller crawled easily underneath.

"You haven't got very far," he expressed surprise.

His father said nothing but passed over the wire brush and scraper and lay back on the ground, closing his eyes. Christopher scraped and rubbed away vigorously for a few minutes with little success before saying, "It's easy really, but Mum says tea's ready. We'd better go."

The next evening it was Sharon who came to call "Tea!" Christopher carefully avoided putting in another appearance.

"He's more intelligent than he looks," Jan commented, when Gordon mentioned the change as they ate.

Several part days later, first the undercoat then two topcoats were applied. It all took so much time, the bill's size was embarrassing. The customer had not been warned it would be so expensive, no one expected it to take so long.

After some debate, the actual number of hours spent was halved and a bill presented for that, though it still seemed higher than anticipated.

By mid-September a couple of dozen units still remained, entirely couples except for one baby. The splendid weather, even by southwestern standards, probably accounted for at least half of these.

One static caravan was owned by a lady who came mostly at weekends but occasionally for longer spells. Returning to the site one Friday evening, she waved and drove on but returned almost immediately. Running round the toilet building, dashing up the balcony steps to the lounge that doubled as an office, she addressed Jan hurriedly, in an agitated state.

"There's a thing in my caravan, it flew at me!"

"A bird?" Jan asked.

"I don't know. It was nasty. Something from a horror movie." She gave a small shudder.

"This I must see!" Gordon thought, overhearing. Perhaps he could guess the creature concerned, rubber gloves could be handy to prevent it nipping a finger. Stuffing a pair in his pocket he led the way to her caravan, opening the door carefully and stepping inside. The lady wouldn't enter, would not even wait near the door but stood well away on the open grass. A quick glance round located it, hanging from a cupboard near the ceiling. As suspected, a little pipistrelle bat, quite common locally. Pippa Tomlin, from Tregembo House on the eastern edge of Relubbus, had said she was named after it. The creature could fly, but not very actively.

"How long has it been trapped?" he wondered, before managing to grab it softly between cupped hands and carry the little mousy flyer outside. Thinking perhaps the lady would like to see the bat before release, he made a gesture to show her but she stepped back.

"I don't want to see it!"

"It's only a little bat. Poor thing probably got in through

the open roof light and was trapped."

"Take it away!" She held up her hands to protect her face, fingers outstretched, stepping backwards with several quick paces. "Poor thing, Hgh! I'll make sure that roof light is tightly closed in future."

"Don't worry, they'll all be hibernating in a month or so." He took it round the corner, looking for a dark place to leave the small creature, and seeing a tree with lots of ivy, placed it between the leaves against the trunk.

Visitor numbers continued to decline; time to start other jobs, quieter ones not involving Max. A batch of trees ordered for along the east side of the entrance road, arrived from Duchy Nursery, root balls tied in damp sacking. There were thirty-two poplars, one variegated poplar, three cricket bat willows, one weeping willow, three alders, and a single walnut tree. This work took several days, the roots being temporarily buried in soil and kept watered until each tree in turn could be properly planted. At Jan's insistence, thirty rhododendrons were also set along the fence line in the hope of offering a spectacular display to incoming visitors.

CHAPTER 13

The House

"Today, if you like. Provided Mum agrees!"

Hearing the answer, Sharon turned to her brothers. Unrestrained eagerness shone in the faces of all three children; broad smiles and bright eyes looking back at Dad, turning to each other in excitement, then back to their mother for approval.

Jan regarded her family pensively, with a shadow of a frown. She could see their impatience to start - knew Gordon had already decided; nor had she missed that hint of humour in his voice when he apparently passed the decision to her. How could she refuse? Normally the children's support could be relied upon, but in this case, only if she agreed!

Dawn was breaking. Although not yet full light, the French windows stood open during breakfast, the weather still warm, wind hardly detectable. Broken cloud dotted the sky, bright pink to the east, fading in stages to ashy purple overhead. While they ate, soft shapes and hues had languidly changed as the sun, still unseen from the valley, approached the horizon.

"Are you sure?" Jan turned eastwards again, eyeing the spreading red glow dubiously.

The children nodded with vigour, their conviction unshakeable, shepherd's warning or not.

An Indian summer had kept numbers unseasonably high. Six caravans still graced the site; unexpected in early October. Starting the house had been delayed in anticipation that numbers would drop, but this Saturday, with the children at home and impatient to help; surely the time had arrived.

Jan was torn. She had been the one who pushed most for commencement, but now, with the moment at hand, she held back. The present accommodation, far from ideal, would deteriorate even more with the coming of winter, particularly those cold bedrooms. However, before building could start, the caravan must be moved. It currently sat in the ideal position to greet arriving visitors; the exact spot where the house must go! All services must first be disconnected. No more running water, no soakaway for water from the sink; back to fetching fresh water in one bucket, catching waste water in another. Moreover, everything breakable must be safely packed and removed, then later be restored to those same cupboards.

All eyes remained on Jan, keenly awaiting confirmation. She looked at the ring of small faces, knew they were right, she wanted it too, but... With a sigh at the inevitable, her head nodded in agreement.

A babble of voices greeted this decision. "Yes!" The exuberant cry mingled with a barrage of questions, all three children, including Stephen, speaking at once.

"Right!" She cut them off with a sharp word, one palm held up commanding silence. "Christopher, you help Dad under the caravan. Sharon, Stephen, fetch those empty boxes from the service passage then help me pack the breakables and take them outside."

Within the hour, the caravan was uncoupled from all services and lowered onto its wheels again; the last crockery box already carried clear. Making a final check inside, Jan heard the digger reverse into position; the floor tilted underfoot as the caravan front rose, hoisted onto the towing hitch. When Gordon climbed to his high seat, she made for the doorway, saw the steps had already been removed, and jumped to the ground, skirt swaying as she caught her balance and walked quietly forwards to watch.

Using its lowest gear the big excavator moved ahead, inch by inch, preparing to ease the caravan carefully over disconnected water and waste pipes still sticking vertically upwards from below. The three children, quite unable to remain still, dashed around shouting to each other as the wheels started to turn.

Suddenly, Stephen raced forward; urgency, almost panic in his movements. Diving for the moving gap between excavator and caravan, he hit the ground and squirmed forward. All wheels stopped with a jerk as the brake slammed on! Ignoring Jan's calls and surprised exclamations from Christopher and Sharon, the young boy disappeared, crawling rapidly underneath and out of sight.

As Gordon dismounted, Jan took a pace forward, placed one hand on the caravan corner and bent to peer beneath. At the same time, Christopher first knelt then lay on the ground straining for a clearer view, while Sharon, equally intrigued but not prepared to dirty her clothes, squatted daintily, dress hem pulled up avoiding the dusty surface.

Whatever Stephen's purpose, he concealed it with his body. Seen through the supporting metalwork, small shoulders moved forcefully, struggling with something. In less than a minute he emerged, squirming out near the front end clutching a screwed up plastic bag. Four pairs of eyes followed him accusingly but he held his trophy, whatever it might be, close to the chest, turning slightly away and concealing it with both hands.

"What is it?" Sharon demanded, straightening up, stance and voice a miniature copy of Jan at her most disapproving.

Stephen turned his head away, the movement saying, "Shan't tell you," as he sidled towards the toilet building, obviously intent on escape.

Watching him, Gordon took a breath, about to ask a question of his own, but Jan, now standing close, laid a hand on his arm and with a slight movement of the head indicated not to.

Having manoeuvred clear of everyone, Stephen broke into a run, disappearing round the building. Eaten with curiosity Sharon made to give chase, Christopher preparing to follow.

"Wait!"

They turned, looking questioningly at their mother, not

understanding, confused by the series of events.

"Let him go. He'll come back when he's ready. Shift those nearest boxes of crockery back a bit farther."

The two moved off, still puzzled, bending to lift the first container together.

Gordon, standing next to her, tapped a shoulder. "What was that about? Those boxes don't need moving, I've plenty of room. What do you know that the rest of us don't?"

She smiled, "I know what Stephen was carrying, what he would risk diving under a moving caravan for." She paused, not to tease, just the softness of sweet memories in her eyes. "It's his stone. You remember the glittering galena? I knew he would hide it but I never asked where. He's very secretive sometimes; keeps things to himself."

By midday the move was complete! Following a period of high activity for every family member, the caravan rested, supported and levelled in its new position, wheels hanging free of the ground, balcony and French windows now facing northeast directly towards the bridge. The handrail, its securing screws always a little suspect, had loosened further during the move and become unsafe. The entire wrought iron assembly was lifted away and hidden in the bushes, leaving the balcony as an open raised platform.

The caravanners still on site were without exception, retired couples. Most had either wandered over or stopped on their way out, curiosity overcoming a natural reluctance to enquire. Water and sewage were no longer connected, nor would they be until the house was finished, but gas and telephone services had already been restored. That was not all. Jan and Sharon were struggling, with some assistance from Stephen, to re-furnish the caravan with the final crockery and other breakables. Cardboard boxes, mostly empty, lay haphazardly strewn on the ground outside.

Additionally, Gordon aided by Christopher had erected a series of small timber profiles around, but well clear of, the future house. Each profile was no more than a pair of short stakes driven into the ground with a board some four feet in length nailed horizontally above, like a low narrow table with only two legs. On these boards the foundation lines would eventually be drawn.

Driving a nail in the top of a stout wooden post, chatting to Christopher as they worked, Gordon explained.

"This marks the front corner exactly. The other corners will have pegs too. They're only temporary, Max will smash them once we start digging. That's why the profiles are set farther back, we transfer the marks to them before excavation starts. First let's make sure the building is square. We'll use two more temporary pegs to make a triangle."

They measured forty feet along the front wall for the first peg, then thirty feet sideways for the other.

"Next, we measure between those last two pegs. If it isn't fifty feet exactly, then it's not a perfect square."

"Why?"

"This evening in the caravan, you draw a triangle with sides 3,4,and 5 inches long; you'll find the corner will be exactly ninety degrees. You can use inches, feet, metres, whatever, it still works; you can even multiply the length of each side by any number, like ten as we have. You'll learn it at school in a year or two, but they won't say it's for houses; people normally use theodolites these days. He made the gesture of sighting through an instrument to make the meaning clear.

Jan, intent on recovering the final breakables, had stopped to listen.

"Good job Dad's not a complete idiot!" She commented deprecatingly, lifting the last box and disappearing again.

From these pegs, and a few more taped measurements, the other three corners were quickly marked and the diagonals compared to check again for squareness. With the help of much string, those marks were transferred to the profiles.

Excavation now could commence!

Lunch covered the small table and the children ate, not because their thoughts were on food, they ate automatically, cleaning their plates from sheer habit like the first year when food was so short. Their minds were elsewhere, outside, running ahead. Between mouthfuls questions were asked; hasty, impatient questions, hardly giving time for a reply before someone butted in with the next. Some of the answers, notably those given in reply to *how long* type queries, might well prove considerably inaccurate.

"Right," Dad rose. "Let's get started."

They followed him, Pied Piper fashion from the caravan, though it was more to watch than to help at this stage.

The engine roared into life, Max's nobbly tyres rolling backwards into position, and excavation started. Within fifteen minutes, the first problem revealed itself. The top layer in this particular spot was 'made' ground, a loose material deposited there at some past time and covering the original undisturbed ground below. Virgin soil, the only suitable base for foundations, proved to be over four feet down.

"Trust us to choose the most difficult place on site to build," Gordon shook his head. This problem had not occurred with the toilet buildings nor in any of the drain runs. He leaned back in the high seat, hands resting on the bank of levers that worked the rear digging rams, and called to Jan.

"Look! To find good ground the trench depth will exceed four feet, maybe deeper; then say another six inches for topsoil. Since the floor must be nine inches above ground level, we need only dig two feet deeper for a basement."

Jan demurred, still doubtful. "Is it really necessary? Won't it mean more work and take longer."

There hung the real crux, he realised; taking longer. She wanted progress, knew extensive work lay ahead and foresaw only more delay, but that wasn't necessarily true.

"It may actually make construction easier and safer." Seeing her continuing doubtful expression, he tried to explain. "Those trenches will never stand without the sides constantly falling in; the ground is too loose. Using the digger I can excavate the entire centre leaving sloping sides, all in a couple of days. It will make the following work easier. The ground floor slab must be suspended anyway. Basement or not, it would never be permissible and certainly not safe, just to concrete over the loose ground."

Work continued through the afternoon, the hole becoming a large crater, expanding in all directions, growing steadily deeper. While digging, tearing up the ground with the big bucket and swinging it aside almost automatically, he mulled over the basement's advantages, toying with a little mental arithmetic. Purely from an engineering point of view, the weight of soil removed would be more than the weight of the house when finished, so settlement that occurred in all buildings should be virtually nil here. The storage space would be useful and designing a reinforced concrete floor should prove simple, a nostalgic throwback to a former life.

"But," he wondered, "will there be much delay in obtaining Council approval of the floor design?"

That evening the big drawing-board reappeared. Work continued late on calculations and sketches.

Monday morning's visit, delivering these plans to the Council's Building Control section, proved encouraging. They promised approval within a fortnight and arranged also that someone call to inspect the new foundations late that afternoon.

By evening the inspection had taken place. All was ready to concrete the combined foundations and basement floor. An order for twelve cubic yards of ready-mix was phoned in, to arrive next morning in two loads, the first due shortly after nine o'clock.

Sharon woke early but lay half asleep, dozing, vaguely aware of her parents already moving around. The outer door closing brought her fully awake; she listened for a sound from the bunk above and detecting none, leaned over to look below. Stephen too, lay fast asleep. Good. This was *the* morning! Mum had arranged it the night before. Climbing carefully to the floor, she leaned back to the far end of the middle bunk beyond where her feet had rested, lifting the tidy bundle of clothes and taking them out along the narrow corridor. None of the curtains were yet drawn back. With her parents already out cleaning toilets, she washed at the kitchen sink, tipping clean water sparingly from the storage bucket into a bowl, then dressed quickly. She was brushing her hair in the end bedroom mirror when the outer door opening drew her back to the corridor.

"Good, you're up. Are the boys awake?"

"Not yet, Mum."

"Wake them. We'll be in the crater; call us when it's ready."

The door closed and her mother was gone. Sharon smiled, nodding her head in pleasure. Often enough she cooked at mid-day, at teatime too if Mum was late back, but being in charge in the morning was rare. The boys would belittle her cooking, that was normal, but perhaps at this time of day she might find ways of annoying *them* for once? She smiled again, relishing the prospect and turned to the small bedroom. First Stephen then Christopher were shaken to wakefulness. The two, expecting to see their mother, raised themselves onto an elbow; it was impossible to sit upright.

"Wake up. *I'm* cooking this morning."

Both boys looked up with interest, sensing a chance to tease. Christopher poked his head over the edge, "Let's lie in, I've gone off breakfast suddenly." At Stephen's nod of agreement, both laid down pulling heads inside their sleeping bags.

"You've got to get up!"

"Who says so?"

"Dad does and I do!" It was not quite true but Sharon felt on safe ground. Mum had said it, and their parents supported each other; Dad was bound to agree. The boys were less likely to disobey if they believed it was Dad's order. She left them, pleased with herself; they would have to do as she said. Her point!

Breakfast was already cooking when the boys emerged. They made for the sink, hoping she would tell them to wash in the toilet building, so they could refuse.

Sharon almost obliged but something in their faces warned her, and with a struggle she forced herself to turn away without speaking.

The boys, disappointed, sought other ways.

"Smells terrible," Christopher commented, "like old socks."

Stephen nodded, holding his nose before realising his fingers were wet, then flicking them at Sharon.

Turning towards them, drawing in breath, their sister was on the brink of an indignant outburst when an idea struck.

"Smell does it? Probably the drains. Stephen! Empty that waste water bucket!" Her young brother wrinkled his nose at the imperious command but she had already turned away, attention elsewhere. Tipping the remaining fresh water down the sink with a flourish, she turned to Christopher. "There! That should clear it. Now I need more water to make Dad's coffee. Go and get some!"

Since these were their allocated chores, the instructions were unnecessary, but in ordering the tasks she was on safe ground. It reinforced her position of being in charge; made her feel good.

Like a red rag to a bull, the boys resented it. A job that would otherwise have been taken in their stride without a second thought, suddenly became a burden. Reluctance showed in their faces, in their very stance, but no way to refuse; it was their job and Dad would insist. Grudgingly they complied.

Sharon swelled with pride, having somehow scored a point from this simple activity. With no further tasks to impose, or at least none they would obey, she wisely desisted and by suggesting Dad might need help, persuaded them to vacate the caravan during the final breakfast preparations.

The boys left; quickly in a happier frame of mind as they climbed down into the large crater to assist in making ready. A great wooden tamper, its base a long thick baulk of timber with makeshift handles each end, lay to one side, and pegs indicating top of concrete sprouted like a small forest of branchless trees round the entire area. Christopher, followed by Stephen picked their way to where Jan collected stones that had rolled down the sloping bank overnight, and joined her throwing them clear. Shovel in hand Dad worked nearby, making last minute adjustments. Everything must be ready when the concrete arrived.

From the caravan, Sharon could watch their progress by stepping to the French windows, quickly returning to tend the almost prepared breakfast. Walking to the excavation's edge shortly after, the young girl called down.

"It's ready. Don't let it get cold!"

She stood, hands on hips, one leg slightly forward as if addressing naughty children, waiting with an air of impatience while they laid down tools and started to climb out. Turning towards the caravan, she paused, speaking over her shoulder, "And don't forget to wash your hands!"

Jan and Gordon looked at each other with repressed smiles.

When they sat down, the fried breakfast was good and filling, a suitable start to a day when lunch might or might not be more than a cold sandwich. The boys, as expected, did pass derogatory comments on their sister's cooking, but even that was done in a spirit of good humour commensurate with the happiness that working on the new home created. Christopher suggested, "A big pasty would be better. Like that one at the Star Inn in St Erth."

"What do you know about The Star?"

"Nothing," Christopher protested quickly, hearing suspicion in his mother's voice, "only one of the boys at school said they had a pasty six foot long."

"How big? I read about that in the paper. Didn't it say two foot long?"

"Perhaps he made a mistake?" Christopher shrugged, realising all eyes had turned in his direction. Knowing everyone suspected him of exaggerating again, he hunted for another excuse and failing to find one, looked back down at his plate with an attempted frown of displeasure. "Well, however big, I bet it was properly cooked."

"You don't need to eat it!" Sharon was on her feet, the diversionary tactic working.

"Better finish it or Mum will be annoyed," He quickly took another mouthful, speaking again as he ate. "Anyway I'm used to poor cooki..." He stopped as Mum glanced up sharply. "Er, at school I mean."

"I should shut up and eat, quit while you're ahead if I were you." Jan suggested, to happy smiles all round and a grin of relief from Christopher.

The children had reluctantly left for school before the first load rumbled into view. The driver reversed his vehicle, near as he dared to the crater's edge, but even with a fully extended chute, the concrete reached only halfway across the base, forming a sticky grey pile, growing steadily while they watched.

Gordon signed the ticket and climb down as the lorry departed. Jan looked towards the huge grey mound, all of ten tons, to first move, then batter to a smooth finish with the heavy tamping bar. Turning, she smiled weakly in response to his broad grin, then dug in and heaved the first shovelful to the foundation's far extremity, her thin blouse pulling tight where it tucked into small white shorts above large Wellingtons.

"Hardly elegant?" she had commented as they dressed, but he had thought differently.

"You should wear them more often, that knee and length of bare thigh, it does something for me. Those great boots only emphasise how small the shorts are. Pity the concrete's coming."

That had been whispered shortly after the children left, while she was changing clothes, donning her thinnest blouse, anticipating it would be hot work. A rough hand had reached for her bare waist, pulling her towards him while her arms were still trapped behind in the sleeves. Smiling at the memory, she heaved another shovelful into the far corner.

By quarter to ten Gordon had stripped to the waist. Jan looked at her own blouse, wishing she dare discard it; great

233

circles of sweat extended from each armpit and another down the front.

One of the remaining caravanners came over, looked down from the top of the hole and disappeared, returning five minutes later in Wellingtons, to climb down offering help - they quickly gave him a shovel.

Heavy stuff, concrete. Six cubic yards would take some shifting, particularly if it started to set, as it would inevitably in an hour or so. After a while Gordon discarded the shovel and reached for a pick. Wonderful tools, picks. It was not swung, just pulled through the stiffening pile, spreading and mixing simultaneously, flowing the slowly diminishing heap in the required direction, keeping it soft, reducing slightly the amount and distance that needed shovelling. The weak October sunshine highlighted runnels of sweat trickling down his body as Jan watched his muscles flex backwards and forwards in seemingly endless motion. After a time he lay the pick aside in favour of a shovel again.

Their new friend worked steadfastly on, a dentist by trade, and carrying just a 'few' pounds of surplus fat.

"That's what comes from a sedentary life." Gordon reflected, "He's game though. Perhaps it's wrong to call a dentist's job sedentary - my own dentist might come to hear of it."

He turned glancing up to see the man's wife staring anxiously down from the edge of the excavation, and raised an arm to acknowledge her. A patch showed on the shovel shaft where the hand had been, darkened with moisture that accumulated under the grip, having run down from biceps and shoulders above.

Swinging back to resume work he saw the stain but had already dug blade into concrete again before realising the cause. A thought formed idly as the shovel swung to and fro. "We must be keeping this concrete wet with the sweat from our bodies alone." The idea prompted another, "Ah no. Apologies to my wife. Horses sweat, men perspire and ladies gently glow, or so the saying goes. Well according to that, Jan is no lady and I'm definitely a horse!"

As expected, only a quick snack proved possible before the second lorry arrived. Fortunately, this load should be easier. The heavier work, concreting the far side, had wisely been done while they were still fresh. The new driver could reach the nearer areas, placing his load approximately where needed. There remained some shovelling work however, then tamping to give a smooth finished surface and ensure proper compaction. The dentist returned, helping right to the end, inspired perhaps by the sight of Jan up to her welly tops in concrete, bashing one end of the tamper or heaving a heavily loaded shovel. Gordon, stopping for a few seconds to catching his breath, watched her, hair awry, clothes stained with perspiration and liberally coated with patches of cement. As she swung the shovel he noticed a long wet smudge where the light blouse clung between her shoulder blades. Not many women would be prepared to work that way alongside their man. Her eyes flicked upwards as if sensing his gaze. She smiled, pleased to have caught him slacking.

He dug the shovel in, hurriedly resuming work.

Later they struggled, together with their dentist, up the slope.

"Out of the cavity," Gordon thought as they stamped boots to shift the adhering concrete. "Hope he doesn't get too many that size to fill!"

Their helper's wife stood waiting at the top. Jan thanked them both, they were due to leave the following day. The man promised to be back next spring to see how the house progressed. His wife's parting expression however, was quite specific.

"Oh no you won't!" it said.

The concrete would take several days to harden, but in spite of her initial impatience for progress, Jan was past caring. She staggered back into the caravan, quickly drew the little curtains, stripped off blouse and shorts, and sank back into an armchair. Moisture glistened on her skin, now covered only by diminutive underwear. Arms sagging vertically down, she rested, unmoving but for the spasmodic twitch of a single muscle on her left forearm.

Gordon watched from the other chair, running his eyes over her body, momentarily wishing... but the energy just was not there! How few women would have managed it. She *had* done well. He reached out and brought her hand, limply compliant, to his lips. Lowering again, he let it fall the last few inches, to swing loosely, pendulum like, without resistance.

"You were the one who wanted progress," he pointed out.

She smiled feebly. "Did I?" The words were flat, expressionless, only the lips moved. He thought that was all, but after some seconds she sighed, "You once said there must be insanity in my family."

Over the following days, lorries arrived carrying loads of blocks, all the roof timbers and bundles of steel bars for reinforcing the ground floor slab. Directly sufficient hardening made walking on the concrete possible, the positions of all external and internal walls were accurately marked out.

The three children dashed round, demanding again to know how long it would take and a dozen other questions. When Sharon asked where the windows would be, Gordon realised they had not fully understood about basements.

"No windows. Not down here. This is underground, the proper rooms are above. They'll be the same though. When I build these, you can see the various room sizes."

The idea caught their imagination. Great! They liked it. Secret cellars, hidden dungeons, would it have stairs or just a rope ladder? Could they play in it, help to build it?

"Yes, if you want to."

Mum listening, guessed there would be more work than they expected, much more! There would be moans before the end, little doubt about that.

That afternoon, block-laying started, Jan mixing batches of mortar, the children rolling more blocks down the sloping

236

banks in the evening, making them quicker to reach next day. These were six-inch blocks, just for the basement, heavier work than the normal four-inch ones to be used above, and too heavy for the children to actually carry, though Christopher could manage with difficulty.

That evening a motorcaravan arrived. It quickly manoeuvred round in the remaining space and drove off again up the road without a word. The cause was not difficult to fathom! Heaps of sand, granite chippings for making concrete, a pile of empty cement bags held down by a stone and the big excavator with its mixer all stood on one side. Elsewhere lay building blocks by the thousand, Delabole slate for the outer walls, a great pile of treated roof timbers, steel reinforcing bars, and sundry other building materials and tools. Add to this their own somewhat tatty caravan and the little green mini-van, both now with a liberal coating of cement dust; reason enough for the rapid disappearance. It seemed doubtful if anyone would consider staying. They had tended to ignore appearance, wrapped up in progress and the prospects of a new home. Other people obviously saw things differently. It gave warning of problems ahead if work remained unfinished by next season!

The building's corners were kept a day's work ahead, carefully checked with a four-foot level to make sure they grew exactly upright. This allowed the cement to harden sufficiently to stretch a string line from corner to corner, forming a guide for the blockwork between. Jan found each large mortar mix she made, lasted over an hour. Sand and cement measured by the level bucketful to ensure correct proportions, were emptied into the mixer, a drum with no engine, attached to and working directly from the excavator. With Max's engine running, this drum churned the dry mixture inside. Adding water, she watched the consistency carefully, then backed the machine to the excavation edge, emptying the contents into a wheelbarrow. From there it was carted down in buckets, for the excavation sides were too steep to wheel the barrow down. Sometimes, at weekends or evenings, Christopher would carry the buckets for her.

Keeping a regular supply ensured faster progress.

Gordon anticipated the arrival of each new batch with pleasure. One advantage of working on the house was Jan's more frequent presence. The children were keen to be involved each evening after school; not since the first showers were built had they shown such interest. The extra company was welcome, his more regular companions had little time for work that produced no food! Robin did fly in one morning midweek to perch on a corner, the highest point available, and scanned the working area.

From habit or whatever, and not expecting it to stay, Gordon started chatting immediately, asking the bird's opinion of the building. His mind, as it had so often in more solitary periods, ran on, interpreting the bird's response; or was he really hearing those replies?

"No good working here, not a worm in sight, waste of time." Robin looked disappointed, stretched one wing out and appeared to yawn.

Gordon shook his head, speaking the reply aloud. "Most important job yet, this - it's our home.

"You must *have been desperate! Fancy choosing a mate who couldn't build her own nest. You spoil her. Stick your chest out a bit, tell her you're off to dig worms and you want this place ready in a fortnight. Females! Be firm, keep them in their place."*

The robin flew off, as the man leant back against a wall, watching it go, wondering, "How would Jan react? Should I try, or is that bird braver than I am?"

As the walls grew higher, a widening gap appeared outside, where the excavation had been dug with sloping sides to prevent the soil from falling. This gap was gradually being re-filled with the original material that stood in great heaps some distance back from the working area. Filling in layers, a little each day, maintained ground levels at a comfortable height for building the next blockwork courses, and it was quick to do using Max. Inner walls were built using a plank between two stepladders; primitive but cheap!

Once the external walls reached full height, even the

taller stepladder was too short for easy access. Gordon could put both hands on the wall and lower himself onto the top step. Christopher could manage too with a struggle, but not Sharon or Stephen, though Stephen would probably have jumped down had he not been forbidden. Of the children, only Christopher could leave unaided, which he did frequently, showing off his prowess much to the consternation of his sister and younger brother.

Obviously some easier form of access must be erected. A concrete staircase answered the need, not from a lorry but mixed, small amounts at a time, in Max's mixer. A few steps were cast each day, the job sandwiched between finishing internal walls and laying sewer pipes. No matter how badly the children treated these steps, they would survive, probably for a thousand years.

Chapter 14

Lights Out

Still occasional caravans appeared, and by dashing out to intercept them, offering both apology and explanation of the chaotic entrance yard, a few actually stayed. Flattering as it might be to assume these successes were due solely to powers of persuasion, two other factors were more likely responsible. Firstly, blockwork was now visible above ground level, making the disarray more easily understandable. Secondly, the critical point, no other sites in the area remained open in late October. However, few stayed more than three days, and tonight there were none. The season was dying; half term at the coming weekend might see three or four arrive, but in just over a week's time the site would close. Uncle David should come tomorrow, Thursday, for his first visit; only Christopher could remember him. Days were shortening again, it was already dark before seven. When the clocks went back, tea would be delayed until nightfall, making full use of available daylight.

Jan lit the gas lamp; a soft yellow light spread across the lounge as it gently hissed into life. She drew the curtains, pulling the small armchairs to one side, leaving space for the children's homework. They had been allowed to play outside while the light lasted and now settled down quickly, all three at the table. Though Stephen had no work from school, he understood his older brother and sister must not be interrupted, and drew various shapes with a pencil, set square and compass, shapes his father had shown him how to construct. The parents sat reading, occasionally raising their heads to cast a glance at each other but saying nothing least it disturb the children's concentration.

With an empty site for the first time this season, gas lamps in the toilet building remained unlit. In winter last year, when the caravan had been farther away and Sharon a year younger, she had made a point of tripping across before darkness fell, it had become habit. Tonight she failed to notice and part way through her homework, rose, crossing to open the external door - quickly turning back.

"Mum, the lights are out!"

"Yes, take a torch."

Picking it up, she made for the caravan door, descended the steps and ran lightly round the corner towards the Ladies entrance on the far side. The windows appeared strangely different, as did a ragged boarder of bushy trees across the stone track. How dark everything was now no lights glowed brightly from within. Inhaling deeply she pushed the door, pausing as the shadowy cubicles sent a chill crawling up her spine.

With cautious steps, the torch swung to illuminate one recess, then a second, breath held as each jumped into stark relief in the otherwise dim interior. She moved to the next cubicle, not wanting to check but unable to stay unless she was sure - her legs ready for flight but sensing that if anything did suddenly appear, those legs might stand transfixed. Turning to the showers, she scanned the first and looked towards the second, to that small door in the far corner, but her feet refused to approach. There was something unfriendly, more than just darkness about these toilets tonight; the cold, the quietness? Why so quiet? Often before the building had been empty; it hadn't seemed so silent then. The lights? Ah yes, even the hiss of gas was missing. Hurriedly she entered a cubicle, bolting the door with a small shiver.

When leaving the building she felt it again, the hairs on her neck seemed to curl. With the torch pointed ahead, she shot a backward glance while lunging for the handle, and seeing deep gloom behind, snatched opened the door.

Hesitating momentarily, shining the torch to scan shadowy bushes outside, an imaginary hand seemed to reach from behind; the girl felt it, sensed it, a shudder ran between her shoulder blades. Jumping through the doorway, she raced for the corner.

As the warm caravan lights came into view Sharon slowed, feeling silly, almost as if she were six again in that old, part-finished building. Gathering her composure before entering, she checked her clothes, straightening the jumper and brushing her hair with a hand, determined the boys should detect no concern. A nine-year-old girl could not allow a brother to sense her fear; she would never hear the end of it.

An hour later found the children playing together on the floor, cards in hand, the boys sprawled horizontal, elbows down, Sharon sitting side-saddle, skirt neatly spread around. Jan had tried the radio, but nothing appealed.

"Coffee?" she asked, catching her daughter's eye.

Sharon rose, walking into the kitchen next door; the sound of a match striking and of water being dipped from a bucket into the kettle followed. Before it could boil, the lights began to dim.

"Gas running out?" Jan asked

"Probably." Gordon rose, picked up the torch and went outside. In the service passage where the gas was stored, he searched for a full cylinder. With the season virtually over, they had decided not to re-order and had let the stocks run down. There were plenty of bottles, mainly awaiting return. He was hunting for butane, a large blue cylinder, but all were empty; so were the smaller ten-pound size - no gas. He checked again then returned to the caravan.

"Sorry, no gas. Thought we had another bottle. There's plenty of propane but it needs a different regulator. I'll get some tomorrow."

Jan moved round the table in the dim light, went to the kitchen and turned off the gas under the kettle, it was no more than a faint flame anyway. Immediately the gas lights responded, brightening, but nowhere near the proper brilliance. She poked her head round the doorway.

"You mean I'll go, don't you. I can't see you taking time off to fetch a gas bottle. Whatever made you let stocks get this low?"

"Um, er... Sharon's fault, she boils too many kettles."

"Only for your coffee!" Sharon was on her feet. "I can stop. I don't mind if you..." she paused, interrupted by Christopher who had murmured "Rotten coffee anyway."

"OK!" Dad held up a hand forestalling trouble, "It's my fault, I admit it. In the struggle to build a better home, I forgot. Of course in a brighter family, someone might have noticed..."

Howls of protest cut him off, and somehow everyone ended on the floor in the fading light. The evening had promise! Fighting his way gently to the surface, Dad offered another suggestion.

"Perhaps a man with a scientific mind could brighten things up a bit round here. Let me try."

He rose as they released their holds, and made to leave, turning back with a warning, "No one is to open this door until I return."

"Wait!"

The forceful command held him, hand on door, as Jan continued, "Oh no you don't! I know what you intend! You take water from the kettle. Here, I'll get it for you." She reached in the cupboard for a large jug, part filling it, dipping a finger to find the water only moderately warm.

Gordon went outside. Almost immediately an improvement showed, and he returned with the empty jug.

"What did you do?" Sharon asked.

"Tipped it over the gas bottle. Gas is liquid under pressure, it boils off, like steam from a kettle but that cools the cylinder down. The hotter the liquid, the quicker it boils off. That's why pouring warm water over it improved the lights."

Christopher nodded agreement, indicating he knew already, and spoke to his mother. "What was Dad going to do before you stopped him?"

Jan looked across at Gordon. The watching children saw them smile at each other. She turned back to her son.

"I'm sure you don't want to know about that."

Nothing could have more sharpened their curiosity! The trio continued to stare at her and wait, Sharon's annoyance increased further on catching a glimpse of Dad's grin as he turned away. Seeing it too, Jan leaned forward, "Ask your father."

Gordon, adjusting his position more comfortably in the chair, nodded to the watching faces.

"It's what the Eskimos do. In lands that are extremely cold, everyone wears very warm clothes, and particularly on their hands. Gloves are not good enough, the fingers, being very small parts, are vulnerable. They need to keep warm together, and thick material would be difficult to get round individual fingers. Mittens are used, losing one can mean losing a hand, so each mitten is tied to a cord that goes up inside the sleeve, across the shoulders and down to the other mitten. This is good because the mitten can be slipped off and on easily if needed. Now, when the hand is bare, like maybe putting a new cartridge in a hunting rifle, any metal touched at those temperatures will immediately stick to bare skin. If the hand is pulled away, the skin is torn off, still frozen to the metal surface. A wound like that can be fatal in sub-zero regions, so they need to warm the metal first.

"Now this is a problem you must solve for yourselves, because I'm not giving the answer. Out in that frozen tundra, travelling across snowy wastes, where would a man get some warm liquid to unfreeze his hand? When you find the answer, that was what Mum thought I intended with our gas bottle."

The story finished, Gordon eased back in the chair, and immediately it was obvious that Christopher understood. Stephen and Sharon turned to him but when he refused to say; they let it pass, knowing he would tell later when the three were alone in their small bedroom.

The family had settled down again, but the light rapidly diminished. Reading soon became hopeless, the children abandoning their game. Far from being upset, they rather enjoyed the novelty, in that way youngsters have with anything unusual. Stephen picked up the torch but was made to put it down again; it would have lasted half an hour at most. There was little to do other than talk but that represented no hardship, the family were used to entertaining themselves in the evenings.

"It's like wartime and the blackout," Jan commented. She could hardly see their faces. "Did I ever tell you about wartime in London?"

The children drew closer, in a ring on the floor.

"Wait." Christopher stood, making his way out of the room, along the corridor and into the narrow bedroom, shortly stumbling back again. Jan could vaguely see something white under both arms as he approached. Placing his own pillow in the centre, he passed one each to Sharon and Stephen, then settled down to listen.

"Before you start, the light is only a glimmer, I'll turn it out. If that flame dies with the valve open, the caravan will smell of gas." Gordon reached over, turning the knob. Blackness descended, to excited chatter from the children. While standing, Dad drew back the French window curtains, letting in the quarter moon's pale light.

"When I was younger than Stephen we lived in London, not far from Camberwell. Gramp, as you know, was a policeman." Jan used the children's name for Jim, her father. "It was a rough area, not very safe to be out at night. Policeman usually went in pairs, but not Gramp. He would go anywhere; used to be boxing champion in the Guards before joining the police. The villains respected him, he was tough but treated them fair, never booked them for trivial things, never tried to make life difficult, though he nabbed them quick enough when they really did wrong. He'd mixed with rough people in the army, understood them. Inspectors at the station always chose Gramp to accompany them anywhere dangerous. He took me with him sometimes, only in the daytime. One of my first memories is of a little uniform. The police nursing home was at the end of our road, I went there often, it was on Gramp's beat. They made a nurse's outfit specially for me."

Mum paused, gathering thoughts. The ring of children was unusually silent, listening intently. She could just see Sharon's eyes shining in the moonlight at the mention of the costume.

"We had bombs drop all round us. Mum and I used to hide under a little flimsy table when the siren went. Ridiculous really, useless against any bomb, but it made us feel safer. One bomb blew a crater right in the middle of our road about a dozen houses along. The vicar fell in it. He was riding his bicycle; nobody was allowed lights and he just rode straight in. It was deep, Gramp had to rescue him. The raid was over by then, Mum took me outside to watch. She wouldn't stay though. 'I'm not having you listening to language like that, and a vicar too!' That's what she said as she dragged me back inside." Jan paused again.

"What did that vicar say?" Christopher asked quietly.

"I didn't understand; words I'd not heard before but he was shouting. I've never liked bad language much. When the war was almost over we had doodlebugs, flying bombs, little planes full of explosive with no pilot. You could hear them coming for miles but when the engine cut, watch out! They crashed down to earth then, and exploded. We used to listen with the window open sometimes. If the noise stopped we hid under that table, threw blankets over our heads in case of flying glass."

Jan bent over, hiding head under hands, simulating the scene, her actions just visible as their eyes became accustomed to the faint moonlight.

"People sat like we are now, sometimes. No light was allowed to show outside, it made a target for bomber planes. If you couldn't get hold of thick black curtains then you had to sit in the dark. Little men went round all night checking for lights."

"Did any houses get hit near you?" Sharon asked.

"Several, and a factory down the hill towards Peckham. It made toilet rolls. There were rolls in the street by the hundred, and up in the trees, some hanging down like streamers; more across land on the far side of the road - everywhere. Women were out with baskets, picking them up, pushing each other aside, almost fighting for them. Toilet rolls were hard to get. Audrey said if a bomb had to drop, it should have fallen on the other factory, the one that made... Liquafruita I think it was called. Horrible stuff, at least I thought so, some people may have liked it - for constipation; when you don't use the toilet regularly," she elaborated, sensing rather than seeing their confusion over the word. "The place smelt awful where they made it. Funny, those two factories being near each other."

"What happened about food? A boy at school said fishing vessels were used to find mines in the war."

Christopher's question surprised Jan, she had hardly expected that the war would still be talked about, but supposed one of the boys had been boasting of his father's boat.

"Food was scarce for some people. We were lucky. Gramp had an arrangement with a factory where he bought big boxes of sweets. He drove me into the country to some farm, always at night-time. They unloaded the sweets and filled the car with trays of eggs. An exchange you see, couldn't get sweets in the country, couldn't get eggs in the town. If you take something from where it's common to where it's scarce, then it's usually worth more. I sat on the back seat in blankets, eggs each side of me and in the boot, all carefully covered over. If we were stopped I was supposed to say I had chicken pox, to put them off investigating too closely. All very illegal but people did things like that in the war. When you weren't too sure how long you would live, it didn't seem too risky. Gramp sold eggs to pay for the sweets, most people at the police station had some, eggs and sweets; and we ate quite a few. But he never tried to make money for himself, gave the rest away to people in need. Folk helped each other like that in the war. I was very young then, can't remember much more. I never did find out why it was illegal. Nothing was stolen, nothing was wasted, everyone got something they wanted; rules and regulations I suppose."

Jan paused for a while, then added an afterthought. "It was quite terrifying, the bombs, that whistling sound as the near ones fell, not knowing if this one had your name on it - I mean not knowing if it would fall on you; and then the blast... Many people were killed. But in a funny way, it did do us some good. Ours was a three-storey house, we only rented it, police pay wasn't very high. With that close bomb, the one that made the vicar swear, all our ceilings fell down and the landlord had to replace them. It happened twice more at the height of the blitz. In the end Gramp was offered the property really cheap and he bought it - he could never have afforded to at normal prices. That's what people mean when they say every cloud has a silver lining; however bad a thing may be, someone somewhere will probably benefit."

Talk had gone on long into the night, talk and a game of I-spy played in near darkness, objects chosen from memory of the room, apart from once when a cloud made the darkness total and Dad claimed to see something beginning PB. A good deal of merriment accompanied the children's retirement to bed, undressing and finding pyjamas by feel, their voices drifted through to the lounge for some time after, no doubt discussing what Eskimos did, but eventually faded as sleep overcame them. Jan rose making her way through, touching gently, checking they were all properly tucked in, then returning to the lounge.

"Quite a successful evening, after all," she sighed, seeing Gordon rise to meet her in the almost darkness. Anticipating his intention, she lowered her face so that only their noses met, then moved her head a mere inch side to side, and stepped back.

"What's that for... No, don't tell me, I've guessed already! Eskimos again?"

Breakfast was cold, just bread and jam, but stoking up the boiler and placing the kettle on top had produced some lukewarm coffee. Loading four empty gas bottles into the van, Jan set off taking the children; the route to Penzance passed through Marazion, close to their school. She had thought of refusing to do it; running out was after all not her fault - but discarded the idea, realising it would delay work on the house. In any case, making Gordon go might not be so easy. Mostly she had her way; sometimes if she was subtle enough, without his knowing it. Even when he did realise, nine times out of ten he let her win; but on some things, particularly those affecting progress, he could put his foot down and insist. She didn't mind - well, not most times anyway. That was what made the marriage so good, their wish to please each other, fall in with each other's ideas.

The basement walls, including all internal ones, now stood above ground level and were complete. Concreting the ground floor, which also formed a roof over the basement, would be more complicated. Costs for such work were generally calculated as being in three parts. One third for the concrete itself, one third for the labour, and one third for the timber deck to provide support until the floor hardened.

Paying for the concrete was unavoidable but labour would be free and Gordon had devised a method of support using the roof timbers, recovering them later. Almost the entire supply of building blocks so far delivered, had been placed in columns to support these timbers, which were now all firmly in position. It only remained to cover the deck with plastic sheeting, and above this to lay the steel reinforcing bars on little cement spacers with wire ties, ensuring it stayed exactly in position during the work.

After the children returned from school, Christopher helped place the final steel bars. He pointed to the plastic membrane that now covered all the timber on which they trod. "What is this for?"

"It will keep the roof timbers clean," his father replied flippantly, for indeed it would, but he went on more seriously to explain. "It does two things. Firstly it stops the cement grout escaping, which gives a better finish, and secondly it stops the floor drying out. If concrete dries too quickly, the chemical reaction which causes hardening is affected and the floor will never reach full strength."

A caravan had arrived earlier in the afternoon, it was surprising the visitors stayed in view of the mess, but the man pushed apologies aside, saying he was in the building trade himself. Later, he walked over as they worked, looked at all the reinforcement and after a while asked, "What are you putting on that floor, Centurion tanks?"

Concreting the following morning proved more arduous than previously; more complex that is, it could scarcely be more energetic. The profusion of steel bars caused difficulty in placing feet and moving about. Luckily Gordon's Uncle David on holiday for the week in a caravan, agreed to help, and with no school that day, Christopher helped too. The extra assistance was indeed fortuitous. After twenty minutes of strenuous shovelling, Jan caught a Welly boot between two reinforcing bars and in trying to extricate it, her foot came away while the boot remained trapped. She nearly fell and to save herself put a white sock in the wet concrete, where it promptly sank to the ankle.

"Ugh!" She quickly yanked it clear, to overbalance backwards and sit heavily on the wet pile from which they had been shovelling.

Concrete covered the backs of her legs, her little shorts, and up the rear of her blouse. Everyone turned in surprise. Pushing on the shovel, she wobbled unsteadily upright on one foot, relieving worries of possible injury. Christopher's laugh received a withering look that cut him off sharply.

Gordon, not seeing her anger but thankful she remained unharmed, covered his initial concern with a light-hearted comment.

"You're supposed to be shovelling, not playing with it."

"Right!" She swivelled round towards him, balancing on one leg, attempting frantically to dig her shovel into the concrete, without doubt intending to throw some, it was written clear in her expression. She would do it too, but struggled under a handicap, not wanting to put that bootless foot down again in the gooey mess below. Four quick but careful paces closed the gap; he swung her into his arms, resisting at first, and carried her bodily in the direction of the caravan. Some of the wet cement that coated those small shorts, quickly transmitted itself to his own clothes but after a few paces the struggling ceased. Nearing the caravan, two arms wrapped round his neck, ostensible to stop herself falling. Drawing her closer he whispered softly in an ear.

"You get cleaned up and have a sit down, we'll manage for a while. I'll rescue your boot and bring it to you. Join us again when you feel able."

She clung to him slightly longer than strictly necessary, before he set her feet directly onto the caravan's top step. Looking down from this high perch, a soft smile spread on her lips.

"You can be quite nice sometimes."

"Got to protect my investment, after all I paid seven shillings and six pence for you!" He made the amount sound enormous, recalling again the cost of the marriage licence.

Her smile only broadened, not even offering the usual reminder that it was Jim who actually paid. Standing there, covered in cement, she adopted a typical pin-up pose, "Don't you think I'm worth it?"

"Oooh!" He stepped back, stroking his chin doubtfully with one hand, looking her up and down, shaking his head sadly from side to side, "Just have to make the best of a bad job."

Two days passed allowing the concrete to set, then treading carefully in soft slippers, the upper walls were marked out. The floor's true quality however, must lay hidden until it had fully hardened.

Two weeks later the supporting timbers were finally removed. Standing in the basement and shining a torch up at the underside of that concrete, the surface was brilliant. It shone glossy and hard, the plastic had indeed prevented both loss of grout and any premature drying out. Little ridges, the outline of individual roof timbers used as supports, could clearly be seen. Above this floor, the walls, windows and door frames had continued to go up in a flurry of unending work. Whereas building below ground had seemed slow, each day now the children saw significant progress on returning from school. Reaching the roof, Gordon decided the nine-inch by three-inch timber purlins, while adequate, could be improved on. Instead he announced the intention to construct an eighteen-inch-deep reinforced-concrete beam running the full roof length on both sides.

"Is it necessary?" Jan asked.

"The children are home tomorrow, they can help. Want it strong, don't you?"

"Strong? It's got so much concrete, this building may outlast the pyramids!" She walked away throwing her arms in the air in despair.

As with all other lintels and beams, this concrete was made in Max's mixer. Jan again helped, shovelling gamely, muttering every now and then, "Must have it strong. Hm!"

Gordon passed bucket after bucket up to Christopher, who sat astride the ceiling joists emptying them into a timber casing that formed the beam. While waiting for the next bucket, the ten-year-old tamped away with a wooden block and tapped the formwork continually with a hammer, compacting concrete tightly around the steel bars.

Stairs to bedrooms in the roof were also concrete, cheaper than wood and very solid. Stephen again escaped with the lightest jobs, carrying less heavy materials and moving empty cement bags to the bonfire area.

By Christmas Eve the roof timbers, felt and battens had all been erected and more than half the tiles laid, but hurry as he might, Gordon could not work fast enough to complete the roof before darkness fell. Eventually he admitted defeat, climbed down the ladder, wearily up the caravan steps and sagged into an armchair.

Jan brought two coffees and sat in the chair opposite, while from the adjoining kitchen the smell of beans wafted in as Sharon prepared the meal. Half an hour later, the entire family were seated at table, empty plates scattered across its surface.

"Will you finish in the morning?" Sharon asked eagerly.

"No. Not allowed to work on Christmas Day." He watched Jan from the corner of one eye, knowing she wanted the roof completed, but remembering her insistence in previous years that Christmas should be work free.

She looked directly at him, a ghost of a smile in her expression, recognising the challenge; a private duel between parents, done openly in front of the children but totally beyond their understanding. This was an invitation to admit to a change of mind, tantamount to admitting she was wrong.

"How much is there to do?" she asked.

"Two, maybe three, hours."

"Just about the time I would have taken to cook lunch. But as you say, no work on Christmas day!"

Sharon was about to protest that she would also be helping cook, but something in the expressions, the intense look that passed between her parents, made her feel excluded, forgotten. Nor did she understand the little bow of defeat and sweeping gesture with the right arm that her father made in response to the last comment.

The roof was completed that Christmas morning, it took longer than expected but the last tile was fixed in position shortly before lunch.

Jan had watched progress with occasional swift glances through the caravan window, glances taken under the pretext of placing or retrieving something from the table, to conceal them.

"Why are you in such a good mood this morning?" Sharon asked as she helped prepare the meal.

"Good mood? I'm usually in a good mood, aren't I."

"Yes. But you keep humming, and smiling to yourself today. Is something going on?"

Jan was pleased. Pleased with her life, pleased with progress on the house and pleased with the rapport that existed between herself and Gordon. Returning Sharon's questioning gaze she simply said, "I just feel good today."

The two girls laughed together in shared delight, though

253

Sharon was still not quite sure why. Jan, glad her daughter was developing a proper feminine feel for atmosphere, wondered if the boys would have sensed her mood so well. Unlikely, she thought.

The house had taken eleven weeks, without any outside help other than those two days concreting. Even that help, first by the dentist and then by Uncle David, was free! The total floor area, counting the basement, exceeded 2000 square feet, like six big caravans joined together; cause enough to celebrate their achievement!

"Smug!" Jan said to the assembled family in reply to a question asking how she felt. They were sitting back relaxing after the meal. "We couldn't have given ourselves a better Christmas present. I particularly like the Delabole slate on the south and east faces. Pity we couldn't afford some on the north end too. When the other walls are white, it will set off the slate's dark colour perfectly."

She rose, walking to the window, gazing up yet again at the completed roof of the house and attached garage.

CHAPTER 15

Moving

Something was wrong. It penetrated her sleepy haze, she moved restlessly, pulling the bedclothes closer with a small shiver. What was it? The caravan lay in darkness but that meant nothing; could be midnight or almost morning. Carpentry work inside the house needed full daylight, they had risen later recently, only by twenty minutes or so but pleasant, particularly at weekends when the children had no bus to catch. Jan pushed the thought aside, trying to settle again, turning carefully over, feeling a gust of cold air as the covers moved.

Her eyes blinked; the room was full of light. How had that happened? Must have dozed off. Breakfast, usually eaten in the half-light, was late already! Surprisingly Gordon still slept, and no sound from the children either, though that was normal enough, they seldom woke until called. Swinging feet carefully to the floor, she eased down the narrow aisle between bed and wall, a gap no more than fifteen inches wide. There was little space even in the bigger bedroom. That uneasy feeling still lingered - Gosh, the air felt cold this morning.

Softly making her way round the bed and down the corridor, she peeped in at the sleeping children then on to the kitchen, tipping water from the plastic bucket into a bowl to wash. Having dressed, Jan quietly moved to the door and drew back the small window curtain - to pause in amazement. It had never been expected here.

There had been no warning, no forecast; or had there?

The little radio was not used continually, it ran through batteries too fast. The entire landscape lay shrouded in snow, pure white and untouched, rounding contours and softening edges, extending along the level ground and onto more distant slopes. Not a wheel mark or footprint marred its even covering as far as the eye could see. No bird moved, no hidden chimney offered a trail of rising smoke. The scene lay postcard still.

Moving closer to the window, trying to see sideways across the valley, her breath condensed on the glass, frosting it. Like most caravans, this one opened with a stable door. Throwing the top half wide, the expanding view caught her breath; she let go, forgetting to ease the opening section back gently. It flew on to land with a clunk, loud in the silence, clipping itself to the caravan wall. A line of small white curds broke away where they overhung the roof edge, to plop on the surface below.

Leaning on the closed bottom section, she looked out over the site. Snow covered everything, hedges, bushes, even taller trees. Only the toilet building windows remained unobscured; these small black rectangles, more wide than deep, watched sightlessly over a landscape without contrast, consistently white and still. No stirring of wind to move the coating off twigs, no faint creak of branch rubbing against branch, not even a babbling from the river - she glanced across. It flowed as always, a dark patch just visible on one bend, the rest hidden by white banks now that the caravan lay farther away in its new position.

Warm rough hands slipped round her waist as Gordon moved up behind; they stood a while, absorbed by the new scenery. Three years had past since they last saw snow and that was not in Relubbus but three hundred miles farther north. A villager said the last here, fell nine years previously. Jan leant her head back on his chest with a little shiver.

Feeling the tremor he shifted to cover her shoulders, nestling close; a strand of hair touched his lips. Unconsciously his hands moved to protect her. Bosoms, hard in the cold air, warmed and softened under his cupped fingers. Her

256

shape brushed the tops of his thighs, just a suggestion of motion, delicate, sensitive, asking... And still they gazed silently out, both aware, neither prepared to break the moment.

The little white blouse was not intended for outside; goose pimples were beginning to show on her bare arms.

"Come back to bed."

Hearing the whisper as he nuzzled an ear, she twisted to him, breathing deeply in the crisp air, giving a small nod. It was unnecessary, he had seen agreement in her eyes, felt her push harder towards him. She smiled, well able to feel the effect on his body. He moved, adjusting position to find a more satisfying contact. They kissed long and slowly, savouring the closeness, intending to creep back past the small room, returning again to their own bed.

Suddenly, children were everywhere.

"We see you!"

"What are you doing?"

"Where's breakfast?"

Jan stooped to one knee, wondering how long they had watched, slipping an arm round Stephen, shrugging at her husband with resignation and perhaps the unspoken question, 'Should she send them back to bed?'

It was Stephen of course, who had asked about breakfast. Gordon shook his head, hardly a movement, deliberately too small for the youngsters to detect, but she understood. There would be another time.

Sharon noticed the snow through the still open door and shouted. Instantly they wanted to rush outside, it brought their mother back to reality, banishing dreamy thoughts still drifting in her head. She stepped in firmly.

"Breakfast first! Something hot - bacon and egg?"

After dressing and a hearty though gobbled fried breakfast, they dashed outside, well wrapped and bursting with energy.

"Keep to the area in front of the caravan," Gordon instructed. "I'll photograph the rest when the sun's a bit higher. May be years before the next chance."

They raced off. No school today fortunately, for although scarcely two inches had fallen, a local chap who moved to Cornwall from the north of England many years before, had given a warning, "If snow ever does fall down here, stay off the roads. No one has the faintest idea how to drive on it. Crashes everywhere."

True or not, they had no intention of finding out. The boiler, banked and set low the previous night, was topped with logs and turned to maximum setting; a refilled kettle placed over the gas. Camera and film were checked. All was ready - so they waited.

"Stephen probably can't remember the last snow, he'd be too young," Jan looked out through window. "Five more minutes I should think."

That seemed about right, time to relax a while. The children played for another fifteen - hardier than supposed. They burst back in, fingers painfully red from snowballing, having forgotten the after-effects of ice on the hands.

How quickly the young recover! Hot mugs of coffee and biscuits all round, they sat on the floor beside the boiler, faces still glowing. Five minutes later, no longer shivering or rubbing hands in pain, they itched to be off again.

"Take your photos Dad," Sharon urged. "We want to go everywhere!"

"Come with me if you like but don't run ahead. I want it like it is, the unmarked snow, white and pristine - to capture that crispness, that simplicity, the world as it once was, a pure white carpet untrodden by man or beast."

The children listened with mild surprise as their father, after the initial warning, spoke with increasing zeal, bending towards them, hands held out, palms upward, attempting to catch their imagination, trying to emphasise the words and finishing with a flourish as one arm extended in a sweeping gesture to include the whole valley.

The youngsters turned to each other.

"Goofy," Christopher muttered. Sharon, standing to the side, furtively pointed one finger against her temple, rotating the wrist.

The party filed off; Wellingtons, coats, scarves, gloves, Dad leading the way in a woolly hat, camera hanging loose, Mum staying in the caravan. From the first few vantage points he snapped the view while the children behind threw snowballs at the bushes, dislodging minor avalanches of white powder from the branches.

"Look!"

As they stopped again Stephen pointed, not with an outstretched arm, just a gloved finger held slightly above waist level, drawing attention to a set of fresh tracks. An impish grin sat on his face as he looked first at Christopher and Sharon making sure they had seen, then back to Dad, defying him to take this picture without prints. The twisting trail led across open ground to disappear round a group of bushes, the first sign that any living thing had moved in the night. Was snow so rare here that even the animals found it a mystery and stayed home? The tracks were sharply clear, two long prints side by side, two short ones close together in front.

"A rabbit?" Christopher asked as Dad took another photo, trying to show the tracks in the foreground.

He was almost certainly right. Sharon, not wanting to concede, suggested squirrel, but bending close they could detect no little indents that the claws usually made, and anyway squirrels should have been hibernating.

Farther on badger prints appeared, like a big dog but more pitched forward, all the rear toes in an arc, the front prints with one toe out of line, as the thumb on a hand is out of line with the fingers. The trail disappeared into a big burrow in the sand heaps, one entrance to the badger setts.

"What do they tell you?"

"That it snowed in the night," offered Christopher, grinning facetiously at stating the obvious.

"Brilliant!" Dad looked at the other two, rolling his eyes upward in a 'heaven preserve us' expression, a gesture that the whole family seemed to have copied at one time or another from Mum. "Anything else?"

"That we've got badgers, but we knew that," Sharon

frowned.

Her father nodded, they certainly did know that, had finally found it was badgers that tore up the grass in frosty weather! Never mind, it was worth replacing divots just to have them on site. He scanned the young faces but no other offers surfaced.

"It probably stopped snowing before daybreak. Look, no loose snow in the prints. Badgers are nocturnal."

A frown from Stephen prompted the further explanation, "They only come out when it's dark."

The children peered closely at the prints, checking, and saw it was true.

"I did say it snowed in the night!" Christopher claimed, to howls of protest from his brother and sister.

Photo taking finished and the camera packed away, the little party moved off, progressing around a circular route, heading back towards that warm stove. The three youngsters now free to lead, raced ahead and back, and ahead again, a wide swathe of disturbance in their wake. Some bird tracks marked the snow at one point but no one was expert enough to identify them.

Bringing up the rear as they approached the caravan Gordon was hit by a flurry of snowballs. A salvo of four quickly followed by a hail of single shots came at him from a hastily organised ambush, with Jan directing operations!

After more warming coffee, work inside the house continued unaffected, no hold-ups resulting from this unexpected weather. A little snow blown through unglazed windows was quickly removed, and that covering the ground outside disappeared without trace in two days. With the roof complete, glazing and plastering, the only jobs being done by others, had already been arranged and would start shortly. It was not that the family were unable to do these things, but glazing at least was not worthwhile, hardly costing more than the price of glass and putty. Hiring plasterers would speed the work, because at this task Gordon was capable but slow. It should ensure a finish before next season's opening. That was important. Although most building materials had now been used or removed, their own increasingly tatty caravan and a large heap of sand still dominated the entrance; an entrance that the house had been expected to improve! So it should when finished, but much remained to be done. Ceiling boards, door linings, soffits and guttering were the immediate concern, all required before plastering could start.

* * *

"Is Relubbus having street lights?" Christopher asked as the family ate. Automatically Sharon looked through the window towards the village, though no house nor the top of a single roof could be seen, even had it been full daylight. In the descending gloom it was just possible to distinguish a hedge on the farther side of the nearest field. Winter darkness fell shortly after the children arrived home from school, so tea was taken early now. In any case, work on the house could not continue once dusk approached, light failing more quickly inside the building. Tonight Jan had delayed turning on the gas lamp, the family sitting eating in semi-darkness while the valley sides around them gradually disappeared.

"These new lights, will we see them?" Sharon asked.

"I'm not sure," Jan leaned forwards, automatically following her daughter's gaze. No pinpoint of light showed in the deepening gloom. Rising to bend and peer through the other window, no man-made glimmer was detectable, but she already knew that - had thought about their isolated position often enough. Reaching for matches, she struck one, holding it to the mantle and turning the black knob. With a familiar quiet hiss, yellow light flooded the little caravan, and immediately the windows became opaquely black.

Sharon started to speak again, but stopped. Her parents were watching each other in a kind of challenging stare, both with suppressed smiles, eyes locked as if all else around had disappeared.

"Mum!" Sharon tugged at her mother's sleeve. The boys

261

watched, waiting.

Jan looked at her daughter, back at Dad, then moved to draw the caravan's small curtains with slow deliberate motions before sitting down again. Sharon was still waiting for an explanation; the boys were obviously expected it too. Should she tell, Jan wondered?

"It's your father, he insists the curtains should always be drawn before turning on the light."

"Why?" Stephen murmured the word into his chest.

"Dad says, if you draw the curtains first, people can't see to shoot you through the window. Do you remember the cowboy films when we used to have television?" Jan rolled her eyes upward, tossing her hair with a sigh; throwing head back in a soft laugh as the children cast curious glances towards their father.

"That street lighting may never be carried out," Gordon smiled back at Jan, changing the subject rather than try to justify his in-built cautiousness. "There's a meeting later this week in St Hilary, to see if the scheme gets local approval. I shall go to listen."

The matter was forgotten as they continued to eat, but when the meal finished, Jan spoke again.

"How are we doing for money? I know how much is left, but will it be enough. Can we finish this year? We didn't expect to."

The children, about to leave table, paused on hearing their mother's question, and turned with interest towards Dad.

"The season was good, we took more than I believed possible. Some material prices, the roof timbers for instance, were very keen. Certainly all the main work will be done. If we're careful with the finishings, it's possible."

The street lighting meeting took place at seven in the evening. Parish meetings had a reputation for being totally uninteresting and were said to be attended only by Councillors, though no doubt one or two members of the public must from time to time have shown up. They were usually held in the old Schoolroom at St Hilary, separated from the church by an ancient cemetery. Some wag once suggested it was questionable whether the occupants of this plot or the Councillors themselves, were more alive.

It was surprising therefore to find difficulty in parking, and even more to discover that the meeting already had standing room only. It turned out to be a rowdy gathering, perhaps the first occasion for some time that the population had objected en-mass to a local event. Gordon might have been worried had he known that another such meeting would one day concern himself! People seldom go out of their way to show approval; only for protest when things look like going wrong, can they be persuaded to give up an evening most would have preferred to spend elsewhere. A large attendance is seldom a good sign for those wanting to do something new; and so it was with the Council's St Hilary to Relubbus, street lighting scheme.

The Cornishman later referred to 'a crushing majority' against the plan, and that was no exaggeration. Speaker after speaker stood up to oppose the idea and sent the Council's spokesman away to think again. This mass of humanity swept through the doors on their homeward way, largely happy with the outcome but not entirely confident; well aware that Authorities did, on occasion, ignore local opinion. That of course, might not be entirely a bad thing, otherwise no one would ever be allowed to build anywhere, for change is invariably unpopular; but would it happen in this case?

"How will it affect our site?" Jan asked, on hearing about the meeting.

"If we ran a site for those who want lots of activity, clubs, evening entertainment and so on, the lighting would definitely be an advantage, but the people we appeal to are looking for the country, the more rural the better."

Jan nodded, "Mum and Gramp don't want them either. Audrey says they've lived in a town most of their lives, had enough of lights shining in their windows all night."

* * *

The plasterers left early one afternoon in late January. They completed the floor finish of the room to be used as an office, working backwards through the doorway, finally closing the door, suggesting it be locked and no one enter for a week while the floors hardened.

Jan prowled round the outside, peering through every window low enough to reach, nodding her head in satisfaction but returned to the caravan, a pensive expression on her face.

"Do you really mean we can't go inside for an entire week?" She asked in slightly incredulous frustration. "Surely you can at least work on the upstairs bedrooms?"

Gordon looked at her in surprise.

"I know you're impatient but what would I do? The upstairs for instance, the floor boarding is already done, and the framework for the walls. We need big sheets of fibreboard next, that's not even ordered yet, the house needs to air first, they change size too much under damp conditions."

"Well what about drainage and plumbing?"

"All outside drainage is finished and I can't touch the plumbing inside until the floor hardens. I've those few loads of topsoil, it's too early for grass seed but I can spread them, that will take..." he paused estimating how long, "probably three or four days. Then we can enter using slippers. The bath and loo can be chosen when you want, plenty of storage room now; in the toilet building if they come before the floor is hard."

Jan brightened at the prospect. "Pity my old sewing-machine is stored with the rest of the furniture, Audrey has offered to pay for our curtain material."

Equally impatient at the hold-up, Gordon immersed himself in topsoil spreading. Happily, Robin and Blackbird had not deserted the area in spite of a lack of any activity causing soil disturbance this winter. They were unlikely to leave, this was their territory, but the continuing presence was pleasing all the same. At Jan's insistence a break was taken the following afternoon for that promised trip to choose a bath.

Harvey's of Hayle, the local builders' merchants had only re-opened the showroom just before Christmas, their previous one having been destroyed by fire. Entering the building, Jan strode around with renewed vigour, her spirits lifted as Gordon supposed all women's spirits were when presented with the opportunity to spend relatively large amounts of money. Having considered the dozen or more designs and colours displayed, she chose a turquoise bathroom suite. It included a plastic bath, a basin with pedestal and a toilet pan with matching seat; not drastically expensive but good quality, something she would not feel compelled to change after a few years.

Gordon spoke to the salesman, checking the trade discount, making a note in his pocket book then mentally deducting it from the money still available. He had taken little part in the selection other than to look carefully at the price tags and definitely to rule out the large triangular corner bath that Jan had paused at, as she said, "just out of interest." On a sudden whim, a passing doubt, she inspected the entire display again, returning to the turquoise set.

"Yes! I definitely like this one, you do agree don't you?"

It was hardly a question. A negative response might have inflicted another hour of looking. It was, in any case, quite a good buy, a reasonably pleasant shade and no obvious installation problems.

"It will match your complexion," he muttered, nodding agreement.

She responded with mock offence, taking a threatening step towards him, but nothing could repress her happiness at the major step forward that this purchase represented.

"Just for that you can buy me a kitchen as well!"

A special half-price offer on pastel blue and white kitchen cabinets had caught her attention. The sizes needed had already been worked out, she had them written down. After inspecting the cabinets carefully, Gordon took out his book and wrote down the details. Another good buy he thought, though naturally displaying a proper reluctance, shaking his head.

"OK, but I should have listened to my mother, she warned me about women like you, always trying to pinch a chap's last penny."

"Pinch it! I couldn't squeeze it out of you with a cider press, it's worse than getting blood out of a stone!"

They were both grinning broadly at each other, on a little high with the purchases, and more with the progress they represented. Gordon reached for her hand, pulled her gently behind a tall kitchen display and their lips met briefly, a more satisfying clinch prevented by the surprised looks of a salesman entering from the rear.

As often happens with special offers, the kitchen cabinets did not include worktops, and those available were both expensive and poor quality. Instead, they bought a complete eight foot by four foot sheet of Formica surfaced plywood, with the splendidly optimistic title of Beautyboard. It would be sufficient for all the kitchen worktops with enough left over to make new shelves in the toilet buildings. The old shelves, cheap plastic-covered chipboard, had swollen at the edges due to water penetration. A small sheet of matching Formica provided material to cover any cut edges. Thermoplastic floor tiles and curtain rails for each window were also ordered, and fibreboards for lining the upstairs bedrooms, this item to be delivered later. Each purchase was carefully noted down in the book.

Signalling goodbye to Billy Warren and Mike, two of the sales team, they left the showroom, walked to the mini-van and climbed in. The vehicle had become a little smoky but still functioned reasonably well. This trip had been both successful and satisfying; they sat back, in no hurry to turn the key.

"That is everything, isn't it?" Gordon asked hopefully.

"No I want Persian carpets for every room!" Seeing him gulp in air and swallow, Jan laughed, "Scrooge! Don't worry. Yes, I think that's all, except the curtain material, and Mum's paying for that. Wouldn't take long to reach Penzance from here. If we get the material, she's offered to start making them."

Harvey's showroom lay right alongside the A30; they drove out, and off to Dingles in Penzance, near the Humphry Davy statue. A roll of orange Draylon, a new material by Courtaulds was purchased, then dropped off at Jim's bungalow on the way home.

Back in the caravan, the pocket book figures were totted up while coffee brewed.

"Are we broke yet?"

"Nearly. Need a good Easter. Should last until then if we're careful."

"How much has it cost altogether now?"

He opened the account book, took a loose sheet from the back and added the amount spent that morning.

"Approximately £3,240, foundation to finish, including this morning's materials. Not too bad."

Three days later, Gordon opened the house door and discarding his boots, entered carefully wearing only socks, bending to test the floor with a thumb nail. It seemed fine. He turned, beckoning to Jan who stood outside holding two pairs of slippers. The interior felt both cold and damp, windowpanes opaque with globules of moisture. Jan opened every window and fanlight, announcing the intention to do so each morning unless it rained, and to leave the fanlights open all night except in the unlikely event of frost.

The children, at school during the day, now made a dash to the house every evening, even though tea was usually waiting. Mum allowed it, knowing well that insistence on tea first would cause gobbled meals in an impatient hurry to finish. Gordon had started plumbing, hanging various doors and other carpentry jobs, but still awaited arrival of their recent purchases. It seemed that Dad never worked hard enough. Dashing back to the caravan after looking round the house, Sharon passed a resentful remark.

"You haven't even finished the door to my room yet!"

Stephen screwed up his face in a gesture of disapproval but said nothing, while Christopher asked, "Is that *all* you've done today?"

However, the arrival during the following afternoon of both bathroom suite and kitchen units, caused many Ooh's and Aah's! In the single act of delivering the goods, the lorry driver got far more appreciation than fixing all the pipework and carpentry ever received.

Explaining how much work the bathroom and kitchen would entail, Gordon was trying to instil a little sense of proportion into the children's expectations, when Jan interrupted.

"Speaking of plumbing, did you know there's been an official warning of water rationing? I never thought we'd be affected by electricity cuts."

"Rationing? Who says?"

"The Water Board, Harry Blight, the coal strike as you know has caused power problems. The Board moves water around with pumps and if the electricity position worsens, he says water may be rationed. Will it affect the site?"

"We won't suffer if it's just pressure drops, pressure's always good in a valley; it's people on the high ground who suffer then. If they actually go round turning off the mains, that's when we would be affected. How many buckets do we have?"

"Not many, most are dirty; with cement mainly. I could try to clean some up. You're thinking of water for flushing loos?"

"Yes. They're bound to give advance notice of any cuts. We can tell people to top up their water carriers beforehand, and not to plan showers for that time, but toilets must always be available." Gordon paused, thinking. "Perhaps it will be over before we get busy, if not I'll buy a couple of dozen new buckets. Christopher and I can fill them and leave some in each toilet building."

"Hope it is over. By the way, did you know Princess Anne is coming to Penzance in May, on the eighth, her first ever visit."

* * *

The walls were still damp. In winter, with no heating to hasten drying, they might remain so for some time; decoration must wait! Work concentrated instead on a host of other tasks. A gas cooker, full sized but second-hand, seen advertised in the *West Briton,* was purchased, collected and installed in the kitchen. There were more doors, skirting boards, waste pipes to connect, putting floor tiles down and curtain rails up, and all the time the children seethed with impatience. Finally the walls were ready, or rather Jan insisted they must be ready, for painting with emulsion. Having discussed it with Gordon, she offered the children a choice.

"You can choose any colour, as long as it's white."

The boys didn't care what colour, bare plaster would have suited them, but Sharon really fancied her room with coloured walls.

"Every room? Does my room have to be white too?"

"Yes. It's cheaper and quicker to use all one colour."

"I could paint my own."

The boys pretended to fall about laughing at the idea, Stephen making a face and Christopher hiding his head under the tablecloth to protect himself from splashes. Sharon reacted immediately, back straightening, chin up.

"I'd do a better job than you!" She suddenly lunged forward making a grab for Christopher's head under the tablecloth, ending up on top of him on the floor. The cloth, which fortunately had been empty, lay crumpled between them.

"Hmm," Jan cleared her throat as both looked up expecting trouble. "There is another reason for white. It reflects light better."

They failed to understand, frowning, at a loss.

"Did you forget? There's no electric." She paused while it sunk in. "There won't be gas lights in every room either, not like in the caravan. Candles work best with white walls!"

Towards the end of February Gordon drove to South Heath in Buckinghamshire to supervise loading the furniture still stored at his parents' house, mainly in the loft. It was good to see them again. Ivy and Frank were delighted when various beds, chairs and other pieces, disappeared into the removal van. By early afternoon all items rested compactly stacked but nowhere near filling the wagon's cavernous rear. The vehicle left, its driver expecting to arrive at Relubbus approximately mid-morning the following day, but Gordon stayed for an early farewell tea. Idle chatter took on a nostalgic turn as Ivy talked about her young days when starting their own butchery business, and of Frank driving thirty miles to Smithfield market in London early in the mornings for meat. Going farther back, she spoke of her young childhood in a cottage near the pub overlooking Hyde Heath common, living with her Grandmother who was born in the 1870s.

"People used to come from miles around to see the bonfire on our common. Every year we tied wet blankets over the thatch on bonfire night, because of the sparks. The village men built up a huge stack of branches, bigger than our cottage, using tall ladders and starting early in October; they had time in the evenings then, even though working days were longer. No television, not much gardening needed either, not at that time of year. Youngsters would drag bits of tree from all over the common.

"On the night, we children ran wild; people were everywhere, so many strangers come to watch. We could do anything that night and get away with it, no one could tell; too many children in the crowd. Life was normally strict, took good advantage while we could. When the bonfire burned down, the common itself came alight. Not just the children lit it, men did too. The gorse burned so bright, you could see it for miles. Get into trouble now if you did that. The common these days is sacred, reserved for men's cricket. It used to be the children who played there; cricket, football, anything they fancied - safe from houses and windows. Men had work to do, gardens to dig, vegetables to grow. It's not the children's common any more. You dare not cut a branch for a wooden sword, or make a tree house, or have a camp fire now. But in those days, after bonfire night passed and everything burned, it grew up young and fresh; always looked better afterwards, after it recovered," Ivy sighed, spreading her hands in a gesture that might have said "That's progress!"

Talk turned to children Gordon had known, his childhood girlfriend Audrey and a whole classroom of remembered pupils from the local village school; Ken, Brian, Michael, Micky, Peter, boys he had played with, scrumping cherries from Jim Howell's orchard. Finally, he took his leave, climbing into the mini-van, hoping the overworked engine would hold out and expecting to complete the three hundred miles by midnight. During the visit terrible storms had swept the country. He worried about Jan and the children on their own, glad the valley offered protection, hoping the worst would miss them.

The wind died down towards the Cornish border on the final leg of the return journey, but signs of storm damage appeared here and there, with broken tiles and tarpaulin covered roofs in some towns and villages. The occasional uprooted tree appeared, one on a roadside verge, but more on bends where the headlights picked out wide tracts of adjoining land.

He arrived in Relubbus later than expected; it was almost one o'clock and a mist lay along the river, something rarely seen. No one seemed sure why, but fog was almost entirely absent from the valley. Sometimes a sea mist would creep in on one coast or another but it seldom reached the village.

This present mist hung, intermittent thin flat layers low across river and road, horizontal cobwebs that came and went, continually appearing and disappearing, translucent white in the headlights, the air between sharp and clear. A strange eerie homecoming, an omen perhaps? He sought a reason, a logical explanation, as the little van hurried on, cutting the lacy wisps without resistance. Approaching the caravan, a fox ran off, illuminated in the vehicle's lights. Jan must have seen the glow through the curtains, for she came to the door. Pulling to a halt, he entered quickly, slipping arms round her and the children.

"We're so glad you're back! What a terrible storm. Lightening, lashings of rain; the caravan rocked! The radio spoke of structural damage all over the country."

"We slept in Mum's bed!" Stephen sounded happy enough, even pleased with the situation.

"Yes, it's true. They came in for over an hour at the height of the thunder. It was unnerving, I was glad of their company; we thought at one point the caravan might turn over. If it hadn't been raining so hard we planned to carry mattresses across and make beds on the house floor. Gave that idea up in the end, sat up with hot drinks instead. It lessened gradually, the wind eventually dropping right away, but we waited-up until you arrived!"

Regardless of lost sleep, morning found everyone up early, well aware this was *the* day; furniture arrival day! If it came early enough, they might even sleep in a real house tonight. Breakfast, taken leisurely, developed something of a holiday atmosphere, relaxed yet expectant. The children talked continually, about their rooms, which carpets went where, what furniture would each have, what other forgotten items the stored boxes might yield, hardly able to contain themselves, their naturally contagious exuberance embracing both parents. Chatter ranged from subject to subject, the meal extending, no one in a hurry, absolutely no work likely until the removal wagon arrived, which could be either minutes or hours away. Jan, pouring her second coffee and making extra rounds of toast, hummed a tune, obviously happy.

"You realise this may be the very last day I ever cook with these rings, just lunch and tea to go," she heaved a great sigh of contentment.

"Don't be too sure! I may need more than one day to get the carpets fitted and furniture arranged."

Four heads came up immediately, regarding Dad with disfavour. No way were they waiting for carpets, no matter how much the furniture needed moving later.

"After all," Jan raised her eyebrows, "what else are husbands for?"

The children nodded agreement!

"They're not much use anyway," Sharon moved across to her mother's side in support, followed by Stephen, who stared hard at Dad, muttering the single word, "Lazy." Christopher was sure he could do it if he were married.

Gordon suggested that perhaps, being so useless around the home, he should go off working down the site and leave it to them. He rose, making to depart.

"Oh no you don't. You're not wriggling out of it that easily." Jan spoke with force and determination, stepping smartly in front of the caravan door and barring the exit. She received again, immediate and total support. It was four to one, with everyone laughing; a family charade, using up time, dissipating the tension of waiting.

By ten o'clock the furniture still had not arrived. Jan looked out through the window and along the empty road yet again, noticing with pleasure the bright orange curtains that now hung at every window of the house, then made coffee for the third time. Not a stroke of work had been done by anyone all morning. At a quarter to eleven, when the van finally came into sight, a great cheer arose from the children.

The system had already been arranged, chatted over and discussed a dozen times in the waiting period. Mum would direct the removal men while Dad attempted to lay at least the lounge carpet as furniture was taken into other rooms. The carpets were not new, only the ones from their old house. None in expensive wool, just acrylic by Cyril Lord, bought at cut price before he went broke, and really strong, probably last for ages. These shapes were not prefect, some edges required cutting to fit, others would show a broad strip of plastic tiles at the edges, but they were thick and to the family, luxurious. As he hurried to fix the carpet, the children ran around shouting to each other in excitement. G-Plan table, chairs and matching sideboard disappeared down the corridor, bound for the dining room. Bedside tables, chests, wardrobes and the beds themselves, were hoisted up the narrow stairway. Streams of cardboard boxes appeared, passing by, en-route to their various allocated places. All the time little feet ran to and fro, watching, checking, directing; triumphant calls ringing out "That's mine!" each time some article destined for a particular room was sighted.

With the first carpet in position, others still tightly rolled were placed in the office. These would be laid later.

A shout drifted in through the doorway, "Gordon! Where do you want the billiard table?"

"In the office!"

Two men carried the three-quarter-size table into the house, legs separate, taken off for the move; more boxes and other smaller items followed. As the vehicle emptied, Jan made more coffee, this time for the men before they left.

The removal van departed shortly after midday, watched by the family standing grouped outside the house. When it disappeared behind bushes far down the track, the children looked up at their parents, barely holding themselves back. This was the moment dreamed of all winter.

"Well, what are you waiting for?" Jan asked, motioning towards the door.

Dad, standing behind her, shook his head and with a hand signal indicated that their mother should enter first. Seeing the youngster's attention switch, Jan swung round, but Gordon had changed both stance and expression. He now stepped backwards, arm held out inviting her to be first. Christopher copied the motion, Sharon and Stephen quickly following suit. Jan was taken aback. Though certainly never taken for granted, it was seldom the entire family spontaneously displayed such feeling, offering her pride of place. Making a little curtsey, she led the way.

Knowing the cooker to be tested and working, the children insisted lunch be prepared in the house, and with Dad's help, hurriedly carried everything necessary in from the caravan. This would be no grand celebration; available food precluded anything too special, and with the time already approaching one o'clock, something fairly short in preparation would also be appropriate.

"I'll do my best, but I'm not accustomed to a full-sized gas cooker!" Jan warned.

Quality would hardly have mattered, sitting round a full sized table on proper chairs would almost have been sufficient, but the meal proved passably fair. With four instead of two hotplates, a bigger oven and a grill, much more became possible. While quite simple, the meal with three different vegetables was more elaborate than usual. A dessert of pancakes with cherry pie filling and Cornish clotted cream on top, added a distinctly special touch.

They could sleep in the house that night, Christopher suggested. Again Jan was doubtful.

"The beds might not be aired."

No one wanted to listen. Anyway, Sharon argued, it was almost March, the weather reasonably warm and they all had their own sleeping bags. Mum relented after token resistance, the house was chaotic anyway, a little more would hardly notice, the carpets would get lain and the mess sorted eventually. The move was completed that afternoon, three children willingly tripping back and forth bringing bits and pieces into the house under their mother's direction.

Jan crossed back to the caravan after tea, intending to make one final check that nothing had been missed. It lay starkly empty. She stood, suddenly still. A sadness filled her, looking round the forsaken kitchen and lounge, gazing down the narrow corridor to their deserted bedroom; not a wisp of clothing or a personal item anywhere. Bare and abandoned - where were the laughing voices that used to echo round these small rooms, particularly at meal times? She remembered the children's joy at being tucked into the three tier bunk for the first time; breakfast with the French doors wide open to the morning sun; evenings crowded together round the now cold stove. That rip in the worn carpet was where Sharon had tripped with a tray full of food, and the cupboard door that hung half open; Gordon

275

never did get around to fixing the catch. Her eye rested on a number written on the wallpaper where the phone had been. It triggered memories of a film she had once seen about an airfield, deserted after the war, scribbled notes on the wall from a bygone age. Was this her own past that she looked at now; good carefree times, gone, never to be re-lived? A small tear ran down her cheek.

CHAPTER 16

It's Cold

"Brrr." Jan rubbed her hands together, rose from the arm-chair and walked into the hallway; re-appearing to resume her seat dressed in a coat.

Sitting across the lounge reading a grass-seed pamphlet, Gordon glanced covertly up under raised eyelids, concealed a smile and pretended not to notice. Subtle hints had been flowing all morning, getting steadily more direct.

At breakfast it had been, "Doesn't the milk keep cold? In *this* house we don't need a fridge."

"Just as well because in this house there's nothing to run one on!" he had thought, but remained silent.

Later she brought him a coffee made with cold water, and in reply to his comment had responded with surprise.

"Goodness, it does cool down quickly in *this* house."

Hinting was something he did himself - frequently. How many times had she warned with mock severity, "Stop hinting and say what you want!"

The reversed situation was amusing; should he play his fish just a little longer? Yes, perhaps, though he could never see her unhappy; anything she wanted he would do in the end, even if she still refused to ask outright!

For late February the exterior temperature was moderate without being warm, but inside the house an unfriendly cold dampness dragged heat from the occupants' bodies, leaving them unsettled, uncomfortable.

The materials were ready, or at least most of them. An old second-hand 30,000 Btu solid fuel boiler bought for £20 now rested in the basement, manhandled there with the help of three dustmen on their weekly rubbish collection; a friendly compensation for always helping load the cart on Thursdays, getting them on their way more quickly. A stack of radiators rested against one wall in the hallway, all carefully sized from heat-loss calculations for each individual room. Long lengths of copper pipe and hundreds of fittings waited in the service passage of the second toilet building where the workbench still remained.

Installation, the missing ingredient, was all that separated the house from warmth and comfort.

Since October, Gordon had worked almost non-stop, every daylight hour and all weekends; his only three respites during that time, Christmas afternoon, the journey to supervise furniture loading, and yesterday morning while awaiting the removal van's arrival. The remainder of the previous day had been spent sorting out, moving pieces of furniture and generally making the place habitable. The other carpets had not been laid, for it seemed sensible to complete the heating system first; but that was not planned immediately - Gordon had announced his intention of taking a little time off.

He had certainly earned a day or two of relaxation, Jan knew that, and felt unable to ask outright for more work immediately. But the little hints, they just slipped out somehow. Shrugging, she moved across, reached for a handle and swung the window wide. Wind rustled papers on the sideboard; one took flight, rising, wafting like some magic carpet to settle below.

"What's that for?" Gordon asked, with an almost straight face.

"Just trying to let in a little warmth." She said it with a wide-eyed innocent look, just a hint of a question hanging in the air.

He smiled up at her and rose to his feet, stretching.

"OK. You win! I'll do it! I'd better, before you get really desperate."

Jan's expression of surprise changed rapidly to indignation, "You knew all along?" She pointed an accusing finger and seeing him nod, continued, "You knew and you let me go on!" The finger was still waving.

"You should stop hinting and say what you want!" He watched her mouth open, then pause, recognising the phrase she so often used herself.

For a second they hesitated, then were together hugging each other, her arms pulling him forward, his hands running up and down her back touching those sensuous places she liked him to rub.

After a while they stepped apart but remained close, facing each other, still holding hands. When he leaned forward, kissed her cheek softly and whispered his love, she stepped back with feigned surprise.

"Love? Oh? I was just trying to get warm!"

Holes through the floor! That must be the first task; two under each radiator for the half-inch copper pipes. Certain openings had been left at the time of concreting, the biggest for a trapdoor providing alternative means of escape from the basement, to meet fire regulations. Two others, for the chimney flue and the four-inch soil pipe, were provided simply by nailing an empty bucket and a paint tin to the decking. Pity provision for heating pipes had not been similarly made, but precise location of these smaller holes could never be assured in that way.

Drill through the concrete, that was the only answer! Exact positioning required the holes be made from above, essential anyway to avoid spoiling the floor finish. Hitting downwards should obviously be easier too, but the concrete proved exceptionally hard. For some reason this sign of quality was not greatly appreciated, and another severe drawback quickly unfolded. Boring was achieved with a hand-held hammer and a chisel, the latter constantly rotated - how else without electricity? Unlike a power drill however, this hand method did not lift debris from the hole while work proceeded. As each hole deepened, a layer of dust, sand and shattered stone particles lined the bottom, cushioning to a great extent the force of the blows.

A vacuum cleaner would be nice. One came with the furniture, but no power to run it. The solution, arrived at by trial and error, proved simple but messy. Gordon stuffed the flexible end of a bicycle pump down the hole, giving it several quick pushes. Dust and small stones showered into the air, clearing the bore. It worked brilliantly. The chisel penetrated with twice the speed, but very quickly the debris accumulated again. When Jan walked into the room some time after, she stopped dead, eyes opening wide.

"The abominable snowman I presume?"

He rose, crossed to the mirror, and saw an off-white figure reflected by the glass. Removing the goggles, worn to protect eyes from small flying fragments, left two clean circular patches on otherwise obscured features.

"Looks more like flour than snow."

"Yess?" She drawled hesitantly, stepping back, inspecting him, head tilted one way then they other. "Perhaps not snow - but definitely abominable!"

The children, on returning from school that day, heard the noise immediately the house door opened. They came in, put down their books, rushed straight to the source of the hammering - and pulled up short just inside the room.

"Ooh! Why are you all white?"

"It's the new fashion."

They dashed off to find Mum in the adjoining room.

"Have you seen Dad, he's all white, you can hardly see him!"

"Yes. Big improvement, don't you think?" She knew very well that he could hear.

The children had not known work would start that day, and at tea were full of questions; at least, Christopher and Sharon were. Stephen mostly just listened, his approval or disagreement indicated by a nod or shake of the head as he ate.

"Will it work better than the caravan?" Christopher asked, his sceptical tone clearly detectable despite the distortion of a mouth filled with food.

"Having our boiler in the basement, seven feet lower

than originally planned, offers great prospects. It will increase circulation power considerably and..."

"Why?"

It was Christopher who had interrupted, but clearly the others wondered too. A certain amount of disbelief was evident in all the expressions; doubt which Jan encouraged, nodding approval of her son's question. Gordon looked round the ring of faces, thinking how to explain.

"When things get hot they expand. You've seen hot air balloons with people in the baskets, that's how they work. The air heats up and expands, expanded air is lighter, and being lighter it rises.

"With our heating, one pipe leaves the top of the boiler taking hot water to the radiators. This water loses heat as it passes through those radiators and eventually goes down another pipe, back into the bottom of the boiler. By then it's much cooler. So, we have two pipes rising straight up from the boiler, one filled with lighter hot water, the other full of heavier cooler water. Naturally the heavier water sinks and pushes the lighter hot water up the other pipe. That's how gravity circulation works, circulation without a pump that is." He paused again, working out how to continue.

"Vertical pipes, they are the key! The longer these pipes, the bigger the difference in weight between the hot water and the cool water they contain, so the better the circulation. Since it's in the basement, our boiler will have very long vertical pipes. That's good, because with nine radiators a gravity system needs all the help it can get!"

Sharon was unsure. "Why does the water get colder going through a radiator, the radiators at school are quite hot!"

"It's heat leaving the water that you feel. Remember when it snowed and Mum made you coffee? You couldn't drink it at first, it was too hot, but you held both hands close to the cup, warming them as the coffee gradually cooled? Water in the radiators will cool in the same way but you won't notice, because it's constantly reheated by the boiler - or it will be if the system works!"

281

Both Christopher and Sharon nodded, but seeing a blank look on Stephen's face, their father paused and decided against mentioning the other things that had been done to improve circulation. A heating engineer would consider them crazily expensive anyway, but normal installations had electric pumps! Fortunately, heavy external wall insulation would prevent any unpleasant coldness from these surfaces. Radiators could therefore be on inside walls, shortening the main circuit, which would be in one-inch copper pipe, enormous by normal standards. Long easy bends should reduce friction losses, and swept tees would encourage better flow to radiators, hopefully resulting in satisfactory circulation everywhere; but would it actually work?

Over the next days, Gordon hammered on, knocking holes, mounting radiators, knocking holes, cutting up lengths of pipe, knocking holes, joining up the pipework, knocking yet more holes and eventually testing the system for leaks.

Daylight was failing as the final joints were carefully examined. The family were torn between lighting the boiler immediately or waiting for the following morning.

"Won't make much difference in the basement, it's dark down there anyway." Jan suggested.

"Light it now!" Sharon urged, but Dad thought otherwise.

"Don't worry, there's no school tomorrow - you won't miss anything! I'd rather wait until morning. When those pipes get hot, leaks may appear which don't show yet. And there's that old boiler, we can't be sure it's OK. I prefer to have it working for a day before we go to sleep with it alight."

Jan made a grimace to the children, they shrugged, knowing their father always tended to expect the worst; they were all used to it.

"Why?" Jan wondered, not for the first time. "He *will* take risks sometimes; selling up and coming down here for instance, and working the dangerous face of those waste heaps. He even climbed to the top of that half-fallen tree, cutting off the upper branches so it wouldn't damage other trees on the way down. Why is he so careful with details? Treated timber, stronger concrete, better joints, larger size screws; if he puts one in the wall for a picture I bet it would hold an elephant!" Sighing, she turned to him in exasperation.

"You're certain leaving them all night won't be a disaster? Don't want me to sit up on sentry duty do you, in case a single drip of water falls somewhere?"

After breakfast, when the pipework had stood fully charged overnight and still showed no sign of leakage, five people descended the narrow basement stairway, early sunlight from above fading as they went. Turning the corner, a single candle held out in front pushed back the gloom, their own huge shadows flickering on the wall behind. Entering a thin dim passageway a dark opening loomed on the right; Sharon, bringing up the rear, quickly moved nearer the candle. She had been down before, though not often since the basement's completion, and each time had felt that same apprehension when looking into the blackness of those underground rooms where the feeble candlelight failed to penetrate.

Turning another corner, the dark portals of two further rooms showed dimly ahead. One more turn and they entered an opening to the left, a doorway like all the others, with no door.

Before them, primed for firing, sat the boiler. In all their minds, one question. Would it work?

Gordon stooped for a sheet of newspaper, crumpled it to a rough cylindrical shape and touched the underside on the candle. Kneeling before the open ash pit door, he waited as the flame flickered, died down then grew again, a little ring of faces fading and glowing in unison, dark outlines deepening on the wall behind. When fire engulfed this makeshift torch, the flaming end was thrust forward, lighting paper and kindling wood inside the boiler before burning itself out on the ash pit floor. The room returned to candlelight.

Again they waited. The whisper of sound grew to a roar, hot air rushing up the short length of metal flue leading to the main chimney, wood crackling as it caught. Levering up the hopper to drop the first coals in, allowed flames to jump through the opening, flames very bright in that dimly lit cellar. Another five minutes passed; more coal added, the fire well established.

"We can go upstairs now, I'll come down later and top up again," Dad turned towards the darkened doorway but felt Jan's gently restraining hand.

"Not yet."

Her hand fell away, returning like the other, round the children's shoulders. The darkness was changing; no longer coldly threatening, but warmly inviting as growing sensations of heat emanated from the boiler, the first heat anywhere since they moved to the house. Candlelight no longer seemed so dim either, eyes acclimatising to its yellow light.

Eventually the little party did climb the stairs, squinting at the sudden brightness, to go from room to room turning on each radiator. It had taken four days to complete the system, two of them knocking the necessary holes.

All the heaters worked. The upper bedroom ones, being slightly sluggish, were modified immediately by the simple expedient of placing a large pair of grips on the relevant pipe and giving a good squeeze, squashing the copper slightly to restrict the flow, forcing more in the other direction. That worked fine. Later when the house felt warm and dry, something more conventional might be done.

When all radiators were piping hot, Gordon's insistence that they be turned off and allowed to cool, met a hail of protest. The children, at Jan's whispered suggestions provided a barrage of reasons against any such move. However, he insisted, determined to establish the circulation time, and closed the valve leading to the radiators but left the hot water system operating. Half an hour later when the heating circuit felt completely cold, he returned to the boiler room, placed the candle to shine on his wrist watch, and opened the valve again. With one hand on the return pipe, he watched the time tick away, waiting! At one minute fifty seconds the pipe suddenly became warm, then too hot to hold. Some pumped systems took almost that long; a very satisfying result.

After a few hours of flat out heating, the house already felt warmer and dryer. At lunch, everyone commented on the better atmosphere. Dad, well pleased with his achievement, found his stock in the household had definitely risen.

"What job will be the next?" Sharon asked.

"I'll lay the carpets, but that's it. The house is as good as you get this year. Must concentrate on the site now, should have started weeks ago."

The discussion, as they ate, turned to those jobs still required and Christopher raised the subject of that drain smell that came every spring.

"That reminds me," Jan interrupted. "You remember the pile of newspapers I kept in the caravan, the ones laid under the children's mattresses to help absorb condensation? Browsing through before throwing them out, I came across the local paper for December. The District Council has applied to County Planning for a sewage works at St Erth. You don't think that smell will reach us too, do you?"

"No. At least I'd be surprised; it's three miles away. Did it say how big, what area it would serve?" Seeing Jan's shaken head, he continued. "Normally, sewage works don't smell very much, unless something is wrong."

"What can go wrong, what is a sewage works anyway?" Christopher spoke as he ate, looking to his father.

"A sewage works? Er... You know our septic tank, where dirty water from basins and toilets flows in at one end and how clear water seeps out at the other? Well, in towns they can't all have those; too many people. In coastal areas, town sewage is normally carried out to sea in a big pipe; they call it an outfall. Really, it should be treated first, so nothing nasty floats on the surface, but in many places they don't bother. That's what a sewage works does. Dirty sewage flows in at one end, passes through a series of tanks and filters, and out from the other end comes the final liquid, pure water - well, it's supposed to be pure.

"There's an old tale about how sewage works were commissioned in Victorian times. The chief engineer took a champagne glass, filled it with the liquid from that final outlet, held it up to the light, took a sip, then drank it down with a show of relish. Supposed to demonstrate its purity, show his confidence in the filters. Good way to create a shortage of engineers if you ask me!"

Christopher and Sharon nodded, but Stephen looked puzzled, so his father tried again, speaking directly to the young lad.

"People only like to swim in really clean water. Cornwall needs lots of tourists, they bring in money. You know; that's how *we* get money to pay for our food. That's why they're putting in a sewage works, to make the sea nicer for people."

"What makes them go wrong?" Christopher prompted, repeating his previous question.

"Tomatoes for one thing! Early sewage works always had trouble with tomato plants springing up everywhere, clogging up the filter beds. Tomato seeds are unusual, when you eat one it isn't digested, or so some specialists say. It comes out unharmed and when you pull the chain, floats down to any sewage works and starts to grow strongly. Very nourishing stuff, sewage - for plants anyway. I don't know of any other seeds that cause trouble. Mind you, during the war, sewage works near American airforce bases used to..."

He stopped, swallowing, and looked sheepishly at Jan, realising he'd made a mistake. "I don't think you want to know about that."

"Yes I do!" Sharon insisted, fork half-raised to her mouth.

"Mum would disapprove, and I don't think I want to explain. Forget I mentioned it. It's a grown-up thing."

Sharon, consumed with curiosity, was about to insist on a proper answer, but stopped at a sharp glance from her mother.

"This is not a suitable subject to discuss while eating lunch. Talk about something else!"

Later that night, after they retired, Jan lay awake. Even with the boiler turned down, the bedroom was much warmer; it made her feel... relaxed, good. She turned over carefully, straining to see the sleeping figure lying next to her, faint moonlight filtering through the curtains. His head was just visible, a dark shape outlined against the white pillow, a face without definition; but she remembered it so well. It was he who had made this new life possible, not alone to be sure, the whole family had helped, but he had taken the brunt of the work. And he had done it for them, for all of them, but particularly for her, to make her happy - she knew that, and felt a great love inside. She wanted to caress him, hold him to her but he was asleep - it would be unfair. Snuggling closer, she let a hand fall on his bare leg, moving it gently upwards, touching but almost not touching, caressing with fingertips, not meaning him to waken, but some part of her hoping he would. The hand reached a pyjama top and hesitated, descending again. He lay on his back, legs apart, she could just reach one knee. The fingers, with a mind of their own and with great tenderness, drifted upwards again, stroking, barely touching the inside of his thigh, noticing with pleasure that the hairs here were softer. Something warned her to go no higher, to stop; he might wake. The moving fingers brushed a thicker, more luxurious growth, silky, curly; then the warmth of soft flesh, changing, tightening under her touch. His breathing had altered; now she *must* stop!

She didn't, couldn't. Even when sure he was awake, aware of what she did, the hand stayed, moving tenderly, lovingly.

It was all of an hour later when they finally lay, close together, her head on his shoulder, hair across his bare chest, neither yet prepared for sleep.

"What did American airforce bases do to sewage works?"

The question was asked with idle languor, not really

caring about the answer, about anything.

"Blocked the pipework."

"How?"

"Well not with tomato seeds - something else that doesn't degrade - rubber. Used to stick to the bends and build up; so many you see. Common problem, everyone knew about it, all the construction engineers anyway."

"Rubber? Where from?"

"Don't know if I should tell you, you're too young!"

"Too young? Thank you. But what... you don't mean...? Must be gossip, however many would it take?"

"Thousands, or so it was said. Gossip as you say, but they were young men away from home and supposed to have a way with the girls."

"Didn't it happen at British bases, were our boys less red-blooded?"

"Something they put in the tea."

* * *

A few days of flat out heating banished all sign of dampness. Jan revelled in the new level of cosiness. The children too were content with privacy, plenty of room to store their belongings, and now their own radiators; and yet - all was not so normal!

Though warm and relatively spacious, there remained the matter of electricity, the nearest half a mile away, the cost of bringing it in entirely beyond reach. It was not just an absence of fridges, vacuum cleaners, food mixers and the like; these were luxuries not experienced in recent years and therefore hardly missed. Such things they considered trivia, though Sharon in particular yearned for a television. One problem however, had to be solved - lighting! In the caravan, gas lamps had graced every room. Not so the house! Candles forever was not a terribly appealing thought. Something had to be done!

Copper pipe from the big red gas bottles, entered through a hole in the outside wall. It re-appeared in a corner of the kitchen, a foot above worktop height and connected to the cooker close by. A little ingenuity with pipework quickly provided a gas light directly above. Knocking a slender hole through the wall, sufficient for a tiny copper pipe half the diameter of a pencil, provided a route to fit another similar lamp in the adjoining bedroom. Though Sharon made a great play of the circumstances that led to only her room having a proper light, it resulted purely from geographical chance, not favouritism as the boys' objections implied.

For the rest of the house, gas lighting presented too much installation difficulty, too time-consuming with the new season now approaching, and a certain amount of fire risk if placed near the sloping fibreboard ceilings in the roof bedrooms, one of which the boys shared.

When darkness fell, both newly-fixed gas lights were turned on and lit. The family sat, not in the lounge with its comfortable armchairs but round the dining-room table, since that room was an extension of the kitchen and received a share of illumination from the gas light over the stove. It was not very bright but thanks to entirely white-painted walls, proved just sufficient to read by.

Sharon rose, stretched, and made a big point of picking up a book. Taking it into her own bedroom she lay back, body propped on a pillow against the wall. Her lamp, being directly above, shone powerfully down on the book, making reading easy. Deliberately she left the door wide open, raising her head, casting a haughty look of superiority and disdain at Stephen as he passed by with a candle on his way to the loo.

She was still flaunting her brighter light later, when Stephen again lit his candle to go upstairs to bed. Reaching the threshold of the dining room doorway, he could see both into his sister's room and back at the rest of the family.

"Sharon shouldn't have a better light than we have!" he claimed loudly.

"Girls are more important!" Her quick, emphatic reply, was particularly unhelpful.

Stephen looked ready to throw the lighted candle at her,

including the saucer to which it was stuck with its own melted wax. Watching him leave, hearing the exchange and warned to expect the worst by her young son's body language, Jan stepped in quickly, bending over to rest a hand on the little lad's shoulder.

"Perhaps girls are more afraid of the dark; boys are braver," she whispered.

Stephen's face changed, the little head rising proudly. Readjusting his hold on the candle, he marched off along the corridor without a word. Jan, catching Gordon gazing at her, winked as she turned, following to tuck the youngster in. Content now with the arrangements, Stephen stomped up the stairs, his stance and demeanour calling to her clearly.

"I'm not afraid of nothing!"

"Anything," she corrected her thoughts, realising the chosen words were those her young son would likely have used.

For the other rooms, the temporary solution devised over the next few days was hardly more sophisticated than the candles that it partly replaced. A series of stout screw-eyes provided hanging points in the centre of each ceiling. A single Tilley lamp, operating on pressurised paraffin, could be hung from any of these with the aid of a meat hook. Unlike the translucent frosted shades round the gas lights, this oil lamp had clear glass and therefore appeared brighter, its incandescent mantle burning an impression on the retina if viewed directly. However, in the bigger room the radiance spread wider, diluting rapidly with distance. At its brightest, the light was adequate, but remained constant only for short periods. As the pressure dropped the power would fade, the light gradually dimming until Dad rose again to recover lamp from ceiling and pump in more pressure.

There was only the one portable lamp. If anyone took a bath after dark, the rest returned to sitting in the dining room, illuminated more weakly by the gas light over the stove. Should a knock at the office door occur during such a time then someone, usually Dad, removed the lamp from the bathroom ceiling, striding off with it, leaving the bath's occupant in darkness. Such little inconveniences, which some might call hardships, usually caused a good deal of laughter, particularly from the children. They were now thoroughly satisfied with the new lighting situation and with the house in general, barring a small reservation relating to not having a television. Sleeping arrangements were very satisfactory. Christopher and Stephen came to an amicable sharing agreement in the large bedroom upstairs, consoling themselves that it was bigger, something quickly pointed out to their sister.

Sharon however, far from being upset, referred to her smaller room with pleasure.

"It's not so big but it's my very own. And it's nearer the toilet!"

The children were all in bed, and so far as one could tell, fast asleep. Jan turned off the gas to Sharon's light, and crept upstairs to check that Christopher had doused his candle before falling asleep. Now she lay back in a soft chair, both knees hooked over one arm, facing Gordon, a book resting unread on her lap. She watched him turn a page and read on, noticing the dark stubble starting to show on his face.

Suddenly he looked up at her. She made no attempt to avert her eyes; knew he was aware she had been watching him. He displayed no surprise. Did he sense it and look up expecting to meet her gaze? They watched each other without speaking. After a while her eyes broke away, wandering idly round the room.

"It's a good job, the house. I didn't think when we started in October that we'd live in it this spring." She paused. He was smiling, pleased to have made her happy, she could tell. "Why did we have to live in a caravan to really appreciate a house? I enjoyed the caravan mind you, but we've done well, or rather you've done well?"

His only reply was a little motion of the hand, waving away the credit; he had often said he could never have managed without her. That was true enough, she too had worked hard, they had done it together. Happy, pleased to be in a real house again but somehow slightly nostalgic for those first days in the valley, she sighed, expressing her feelings slowly.

"Less that three years ago we had nothing, just the little caravan. It was fun; an empty site, no services and hardly enough money to get started. Now, after only two seasons, we've moved three times, have a regular trade and our own house without any mortgage. No wonder I feel good!"

Sure enough, sustained efforts *had* borne fruit! The house was complete; warmth, space, comfort, even a full-sized oven. But at what price! The absolute priority given to its finishing had excluded all other work. Such single-mindedness was understandable and necessary for more than their own happiness. The messy jumble of building supplies that deterred many visitors last October, had diminished only slowly during the winter as materials were used up. Additionally, their own caravan, which could not be disposed of until they moved to the house, had grown increasingly tatty. Had such scruffy disorder persisted into the new season, few visitors in their right mind would have considered staying. Presenting a tidy and attractive entrance before opening day had demanded all efforts be concentrated on the house. Hence, the site itself had experienced virtually no progress since the previous autumn.

Homes of another sort were now the immediate problem; the nesting season approached. They badly needed more room for visitors; bookings already flowed in - well, trickled fairly fast. Clearing a sufficient area for extra pitches, removing gorse and other shrubs big enough to nest in should be done quickly before eggs were laid. Filling could follow later, the site would normally be empty much of each day in the months up to Spring Bank Holiday. First however, a day must be spent spreading grass seed on that already topsoiled area. This was rapidly done and as no further lorries had yet appeared with more soil, clearing the next bush-choked section was quickly commenced.

Jan's almost constant help with the inside jobs only emphasised the sudden change as Gordon swung back to more solitary days working remote from the house. The change, as any change of task is apt to be, was enjoyable enough. A certain relaxing quality accompanied all simple work connected with the land. Dry stone walling, spreading soil and particularly this grubbing up of gorse; all were physical, requiring little concentration, but his mind roved restlessly again. "Must have input," the little grey cells demanded! A piece of rotten wood falling from a tree triggered thoughts of apples, Issac Newton, gravity, weight-lessness and space travel, in quick succession. Later a large old sycamore leaf lying on the ground, conjured pictures of Adam and Eve, followed immediately by an image of Jan in Eve's costume.

"A survivor from autumn?" He glanced again at the leaf, then argued with himself, "How can it be a survivor, it's fallen, it's dead; a corpse from autumn perhaps!"

He heaved out another root - hours passed - it was difficult on occasion to remember how time had slipped by. Where were his feathered companions? Some blackbirds and robins migrate, they can leave for warmer climates in winter, or may have migrated to Cornwall from farther north. Most, however, remain in one place, defending their territory throughout the year. Had his own friends left?

The pair soon returned, though neither was constantly present. Usually one or other would appear shortly after work started, often both; and either or both might fly off for varying intervals. As days passed their rapport re-established, the behaviour pattern of each clear to his circumstantial comrades. Both birds knew that each root extracted would be tossed in a pile, they also knew he would check their position before throwing it. Trust and confidence were features of the partnership, all contributing, all receiving rewards; two in food, one in companionship. He continued to chat to them, or with them, the difference no longer clear. When the birds were absent, he chatted instead to bushes and trees, modifying unspoken answers to suit their life cycle; but interaction with the birds was more satisfying. Looking at Blackbird, he tried to recall their last conversation.

"Oh yes, religion. If religion is good, why does it so often cause conflict and wars"

"Is it Religion, or intolerance of differences that cause the friction? Suppose The Lord wanted to carry The Word to birds instead of humans. Why not? We too are His creatures. Probably He would not feel the need; birds, blackbirds in particular, are rather splendid characters, without man's tendencies of evil. But if He did send messengers to the birds, He would hardly send an eagle to pass word to a blackbird; the blackbird would be afraid to stay and listen. To convert a finch for instance, a finch would be sent, and the teachings would relate to goodness in the lifestyle of finches, to the environment of finches.

"My point is this, though the messenger and message may be different in order to be relevant to those receiving it, it does not necessarily come from a different source. These various messengers, you may say prophets, or Messiahs, might in human terms be considered brothers; brothers from one Great Father. Therefore for you a Christian, to insult the Islamic or any other religion, is unthinkable. You would perhaps, insult your own God. This would explain the similarity of religions in that all are based on goodness. Goodness depends on circumstance at least to some extent, so you should not expect all teachings to be identical.

"Think also that if He was prepared to vary the message to suit the circumstances of His various flocks, would He not also wish to alter the teachings as passing time changed those circumstances. Acts that were once good may not always remain so beneficial. With passing time and changing conditions, other actions may become more appropriate? Is that why He gave us brains, so we could ourselves make modifications; guided by kindness to the entire animal kingdom, including, of course, the feathered varieties?"

Gordon was slacking. He realised that, suddenly becoming aware he had stopped work, daydreaming, gazing idly at the bird still near his feet. The slightly chill breeze, late winter's parting gift, made him shiver, previous sweat now cold between the shoulders. He was half standing, half leaning on the pick, gazing round in a vague sort of way that without doubt the children would have called laziness.

Chapter 17

Comics

"There it goes *again*. Damn!"

The engineer, when moving the telephone from caravan to house, had fixed an external bell high on the front gable wall so calls could be heard from outside.

On the run-up to opening day Jan had her own chores, but chores restricted by that telephone. Incoming calls at this time of year were usually bookings, and bookings were too precious to miss! Both toilet buildings needed a thorough internal clean and repaint; partly the odd chip and blemish from wear and tear during last season and partly from having lain empty and unheated over winter. She worked on them before coffee each morning, a time when the phone rang less often, but even so some interruptions had to be expected.

The bell echoed loudly across the site. She had just dipped the brush in again, leaning over on the stepladder; there remained only a small patch to reach the corner. Half a dozen more strokes and the final section would be finished. Stepping to the floor, dropping the pot down, two quick strokes of brush against rim removed excess paint and she was away, racing to the office, rubber gloves torn off and dropped as she ran, abandoned to be picked up later. The bell rang on, "Damn thing!" The thought was unintentional; they did need the calls. "Don't stop!" Her hand reached the door and she was through, grabbing the receiver. "River Valley Caravan Park!" The words came out breathlessly, causing an explanation, one well rehearsed on previous callers, and the inevitable apology.

"Oh no. No trouble. I was coming in for coffee anyway. You were just the excuse I needed."

Having taken the details, she rang off and picked up an envelope, copying name and address in more legible writing. This one had been OK. Those that stopped ringing as the office door opened, they were really annoying. "Blast!" she had said explosively, on the last occasion; it hardly seemed enough. Stronger language might indeed be generated if later in the season that bell rang out over a crowded site in the small hours; a switch in the office should avoid that - provided someone remembered to turn it off each night.

Returning to paint the small remaining piece, completed the first building; fresh, smart, ready for visitors. Turning on the water was planned for a week's time when March began, though no caravans were expected so early.

Jan moved to the second building. Spider's webs around the high windows above the loo's were prolific, having accumulated since the site closed in October. No spiders were visible but she knew where they hid, had seen them disappear before. Above each toilet, about head level, hung a black cistern with hanging chain. It was through a hole where the chain lever entered that spiders scuttled to safety, hidden and protected, clinging to sides and top well above the water line. When painting during the previous spring, she had persuaded Gordon to remove a lid. Inside in a mesh of threads were several silken nests, some of them old, testifying to long use.

Holding the lid carefully, he had pointed, balancing with only one foot on the stepladder so she could climb up alongside. Crouched in one corner, sat an enormous spider, at least she had thought it enormous, certainly by English standards. Nearby was another, slightly smaller. She focused more closely; it had no body, just legs still attached to the web, a skeleton.

"That's the male. She's eaten him." Gordon had said. "That's where the old saying comes from."

"What old saying?"

"How does a male spider make love?"

"No idea." She waited. "Well go on. I know I'm going to regret this, but how do they?"

"Carefully!"

A little fist punched his midriff, he wobbled on the steps, tilting the lid and the large spider dropped on a silken thread to the floor. He had leapt down, intercepting it, chasing with a finger, first in one direction then another. When it would run no farther and stood exhausted, he had dabbed a tiny blob of white paint on its back and carried it outside to a nearby tree.

The following week when the cistern lid was again lifted, there sat a large spider with a tiny blob of white paint. They decided then, that it was not worth the effort. A quick dust round once a week with the broom would remove all the webs; the spiders could stay, they must help reduce the fly population - had to live on something.

Smiling at the memory she prodded a new looking web gently with the wrong end of the broom, seeing if the owner would come to investigate, but no spider emerged.

At ten-thirty, Jan returned to make coffee which they usually drank together in the house now, again to avoid missing bookings. Sometimes she hated that phone; even to go into town, arrangements must be made for one of her parents to stay in the office. When she asked for such help, Audrey would sometimes walk down if the weather was fine, though more often Jim came in his car.

At coffee they discussed the coming season, how the entrance yard's new appearance with a house instead of a caravan might affect trade, and certain feelings of concern over money, with hopes that a good early season would improve the situation. A trade magazine arriving in the post claimed more tourers had been sold, cheering news! It also contained an interesting article on a site owner prosecuted by his local Council for taking caravans outside his permitted open period.

"Lucky to get the chance," Jan suggested, "Think what a few site fees would do for us right now - and who would know?"

With Gordon departed for work again, much remained to be done inside. Stored furniture had accumulated grime, its wooden surfaces needed cleaning, surgical spirit then teak oil seemed best; some upholstery also needed attention. Had the various pieces been arranged in quite the best way? Certainly that billiard table spoiled the office. It stood in one corner, taking a major portion of the room; shots could only be played from two sides but the children liked it.

"Pity it's so big," she thought, "restricts the space, makes the room look smaller than it really is."

Fortunately it had top covers, four polished mahogany sections converted the playing surface to a table on which she laid tourist pamphlets in an attempt to make it appear an intentional part of the office.

"Somehow I have to persuade the rest of the family it should go!"

* * *

The park's third season was upon them and fortunately the threat of water restrictions had disappeared. With the strike over, coal again flowed to the power stations, removing electricity shortages that had threatened the water board pumping equipment. The last day of February saw all painting complete and the site ready for visitors but turning on the water was not planned until the following day.

Unexpectedly, towards evening a caravan appeared along the track, Christopher spotted its approach.

"Caravan coming!"

Jan rushed to the window, wiping flour from her hands on a tea towel, reaching round to untie her apron.

"Run and find Dad."

When Christopher arrived breathless with the news, his father listened in surprise then hurried towards the entrance, happy to have a customer so early. As he jogged along, the article on a site owner prosecuted for opening out of season came to mind and a nagging suspicion beset him. Visitors in March were rare enough creatures, but on 29 February?

Remarkable! Rounding the corner, he slowed, walking towards the new arrival, smiling but with a certain reserve. Were they genuine or Council Officers in disguise? A youngish man wearing casual clothes emerged from the car; that meant nothing, a Council Spy would dress casually, wouldn't he?

On a flight of fancy, a trick of the mind, the chunky sweater and slacks disappeared, replaced by bowler hat, furled umbrella, and pin-striped suit.

"Is something wrong?"

"Er... No." Gordon realised he had come to a stop and was staring; the question jolted him back to reality, to the visitor, still casually dressed, before him. "It's just that we're not officially open yet. And there's no water turned on." The water had been an afterthought, an excuse.

"You're the sixth site we've tried. I suppose we'll end up in some car park overnight. When do you open?"

"Tomorrow."

The man raised a hand tentatively, palm up, "Couldn't you...?" he hesitated.

Seeing the gesture, Gordon knew what he wanted to ask. Should he let them? After all, better here than in some lay-by or car park with no toilet and nowhere to put their rubbish; surely the Council would be reasonable? Again a mental picture grew: the Council Chamber at Penzance, sometimes used as a law court, himself standing in the dock. The room was alive, full of people, of Councillors, all in judges' wigs. The public gallery too was full. Council Officers stood around in dark clothing, one wore a mask and rested muscular arms on a large headsman's axe, the sharpened edge of its curved blade glistening in the light. Across the face of this axe was writ in Old World letters 'Ye Planning Department'. Three gowned figures sat on the high rostrum a coat of arms clearly visible behind. Below, a figure dressed entirely in black took the floor, a man of importance, for a hush descended over the chamber. His harsh voice rang out, "How do you plead!"

"It was only one night, sir." The accused shrank back.

A black arm slowly extended to point at the dock.

"Hang him!"

The arm swept in an arc to a gallows in the corner, its noose swaying lightly as heads around the room nodded in unison. A single "No" barely audible across the hall was drowned by shouts of ascent, "Aye hang him!"

The scene faded. Gordon shook himself mentally, coming back to reality, trying to show no outward sign.

Chunky sweater, still standing before him, shifted uneasily from one foot to another in the awkward silence. The move was too real, the anxiousness, the patience; he must be genuine - or a most consummate actor? "Risk it, let him stay, put the poor man's mind at rest..." The impulse flashed through Gordon's head and he had almost resolved to agree when that little doubt crept back, "or should I?" Seeking to allay those suspicions, to test the visitor, he spoke up in a confidential tone.

"The truth is my licence doesn't really allow me to open until March, which is tomorrow. The Council might have spies out..." While speaking he watched the visitor carefully for any sign, a crafty glance at his companion perhaps; a sinister laugh; the unconscious rubbing of hands together in anticipation? One could scarcely expect anything more explicit, no warning like, 'anything you say will be taken down and...' Oh no, none of that; that would be later.

Gordon drew a deep breath, lecturing himself, "Stop it, you're being paranoid. Of course he's not an Official!" Suspicious thoughts pushed forcefully aside, he turned to the man and spoke.

"Sorry, just working out the details. Water's not really a problem, that could be on in half an hour."

Tension eased from the visitor's face. "We can stay then? No hurry for the water. We'd like to shower later if that's possible, but no hurry."

The chap looked so pleased. Gordon nodded, smiling, convinced but some part of his brain, as always, framing the answer with care.

"Park your caravan, we're allowed winter storage. When

301

the water's on, try out any of the facilities, but you're not officially in residence until midnight, OK. Of course, I've my own work to do, shan't have time to check. Pay in the morning, when we're legally open."

A good deal of scurrying and turning on of water taps, soon had one toilet building usable. Did this premature arrival presage a bountiful season ahead? It certainly seemed to. Weeks passed and more visitors did come. Following the adage 'It pays to advertise', the Caravan Club Handbook now sported a whole page on River Valley, complete with map and lengthy text. Those extra pitches would be needed!

No sign of growth yet showed on the recently seeded soil, but the section set aside for adults without children lay ready for use. First referred to as the 'Old People's Area' it was diplomatically changed to the 'Adult Only Area'. Here, seed sprinkled during the previous September now showed richly green and should prove popular, particularly at peak season. For all the lush appearance, being in its first year this grass remained tender. More time to become a dense turf would have been beneficial, but it must make the most of the next few months, for by peak season these pitches would be needed - provided all went well!

Selecting grass seed had proved a vexing dilemma. Temptation was strong to use a cheap mixture, mainly rye-grass, but rye was notorious for requiring much cutting. What of other grasses? Most books on the subject in the library were for farmers, boasting only of the maximum nutritious growth yielded in a given time. Nutritious growth meant lots of mowing, not at all what was required!

By delving into various magazines, asking seed suppliers and sports-field groundsmen, it eventually began to emerge that certain grasses should definitely be included, but opinion differed widely on how much of each to use in the mixture. For hard wear, use some rye-grass, not any old rye-grass, a prostrate growth style like S23, and a good proportion of finer grasses including some Crested Red Fescue, Smooth Stalked Meadow Grass and Brown Top. Other grasses could be added for specific purposes, like Timothy, said to be good for drought resistance. Clover to fix nitrates could also be important, particularly in the thin layers of soil being laid on site, where artificial fertilisers might tend to wash away.

The compromise mixture finally arrived at was 40% S23 rye-grass, 40% Creeping Red Fescue, 10% Smooth stalked meadow grass, 10% Brown Top and a touch of wild white clover to improve soil conditions. A coating designed to repel birds but not harm them, helped lessen losses to finches, yellow hammers, linnets and other seed eaters with their thick stout beaks, all plentiful in the valley, drawn by its abundance of gorse and other seed sources.

A family decision to use only fertilisers and avoid dangerous weed-killing chemicals on site, would lead inevitably to extra work keeping weeds at bay, but babies could then crawl with confidence on the grass.

Research, much reading and burning the midnight oil as the saying goes, (it really was oil, or sometimes a candle, but seldom as late as midnight) revealed a bewildering array of factors affecting the growth and quality of turf.

Gordon, studying the book on grass care, paused thoughtfully. "Sod!" he muttered, gazing into space.

Jan looked up in surprise. He never used bad language, what was the matter?

Seeing her head jerk and the startled expression, made him realise the word had been spoken aloud. He smiled, explaining.

"It's what we need, a dense, tightly-knit sod and you've no idea the care needed to keep it that way. Cut regularly, don't cut too short, encourage the earthworms that aerate it, watch out for crane fly larva, use Sulphate of Ammonia to keep it acid because weeds thrive on lime rich soils, use Sulphate of Iron to suppress any moss... it's unending. The book is right though, we do need to treat the moss. Could you stop in at Monro's at Longrock next time you go to Penzance, pick up a hundredweight? I'll write the name down."

Constant rolling by car wheels the previous year, before

the new grass could become well established, had created conditions in which moss thrived - and it had! Patches that showed yellowy green among the grass, were already growing again after a winter lying dormant.

Jan nodded agreement, she had wondered what he would do about the increasing problem. A visit to Penzance was overdue anyway, put off for lack of funds. Sharon needed new clothes, her existing ones hardly fitted any more, but the house had taken priority, nothing non-essential had been bought since the end of last season. However, early visitor numbers were promising; certainly enough to justify something new for her daughter, something modestly priced!

Sharon sat in the mini-van beaming, wriggling with the thrill of the occasion. She knew already that clothes were to be bought, a rarity in itself, but there was more! Soon after breakfast on this fine Saturday morning, her mother had announced the two of them would go to Penzance for an outfit, but had refused the boys' request to come.

"No, this time it's just us girls," Jan had insisted, "and we don't want you fussing and fretting while we window-shop. You stay behind, make yourselves useful here."

Sharon had loved that, the special treatment, an outing with Mum exclusive to herself and from which the boys were barred. Later there would be the tale to tell, slowly, making them wait, and new clothes to display! Thinking of it she breathed a deep sigh as the van sped along, now well on their way. Entering the top end of Marazion, they slowed, glimpsing St Michael's Mount, and on down past the Fire Engine, narrow streets still largely deserted.

Driving up Market Jew Street in Penzance, the young girl glanced quickly from side to side, watching the various displays of clothes. As they passed Lloyds' dome and onward she expected a turn to the car park, but her mother drove on to Alverton and into a side road where parking was free. Walking back together, the pair stopped at every dress shop window, descending the main street on one side, returning on the other. It was Causeway Head where they finally made the purchases, a little nondescript bargain shop with a temporary look about it. Though the clothes were not well displayed, a host of garments took Sharon's eye. Many she would have liked were too dear, but the blue long-sleeved jumper and a grey gymslip type dress that were finally chosen should go well enough together. About to leave the shop, she pulled her mother's skirt, pointing tentatively to some scarlet ribbon hanging by the door.

"What would you do with it?"

"For my hair, Mum."

"Would you use it now it's short?"

"A girl at school wears one, her hair is shorter - looks good too."

Some ribbon was bought and on the journey back Jan stopped at Monro's for sulphate of iron.

"I can put it in your car boot but be warned, this stuff stains. Anything the powder touches, goes brown. Can't be got off!" the salesman cautioned.

"Fine. I've an old sheet in the boot, we use it for carrying cement. Just drop the bag in, my husband can lift it out."

At home, the boys were off somewhere, but Dad, seeing the car return, came in for coffee.

"You're early," Jan commented. "Thirsty, or come to check how much money we've spent." It was clear from his expression that her intuitive probe had scored a bull's eye. Although he recovered quickly, professing not to understand, she was well aware of his continuing concern.

At Jan's instigation, during coffee the two girls discussed a series of increasingly expensive clothes that they just might have purchased, chatting over what extra accessories would be needed to match, and where *did* the money go so quickly? Seeing Dad run a finger round inside the collar and tie that he often wore during the season to present a better aspect to visitors, Sharon was unable to control a small snigger.

"Hm! Where is it then?" He rose, not pleased to have his leg pulled about so serious a matter as money, and stalked off towards the car, knowing the moss compound must be in the boot.

Mother and Daughter watched the large plastic sack hoisted into the service passage, saw him rip the top open with one savage stroke of a knife, fill a bucket with the fine powder and stride off round the block.

"I don't think he's very happy!" Jan pursed her lips in a pseudo-frown at Sharon and they burst into quiet laughter, taking care the sound would not carry to where he had disappeared.

Only a light wind blew, but it gusted unpredictably. The fine powder was being spread by hand; thrown in an attempted even covering, it wafted around freely. Never mind, this stuff was harmless, not poisonous like some chemicals. After two hours, a slight drizzle unexpectedly prevented the last area being finished, though he persevered, using up what remained in the already part empty bucket.

The boys had returned when the rain started, and were sitting in the office listening to Sharon's tale of the morning in Penzance. She already wore her new outfit. Mum leant against the billiard table, also listening and answering the odd question, when Gordon came into sight.

"Watch!" Jan pointed as he went to the service passage and tossed the bucket inside. To the children's absolute delight he was brown from head to foot; hands, clothes, face - everything with a deep tan. Their jubilation increased when Jan insisted he undress in the garage, dashing to fetch clean trousers and a jumper, throwing them to him, together with a plastic dustbin liner for the stained clothes. Closing the door she beckoned the children nearer.

"You know why he's brown?"

The little faces looked at each other, shrugged, and back to Mum, waiting for an explanation.

"He's been spreading powder to kill the moss. It's called Sulphate of Iron. Really it's a type of powdered iron, and you know what happens to iron when it gets wet." They were still mystified. She turned to Christopher, "Don't you do an experiment at school where you put a shiny iron nail in water and leave it there. What happens to it?"

Christopher, his white, short sleeved shirt and faded jeans long past their best, leaned back on the billiard table, eyes lost in thought. Suddenly his face lit up.

"Yes, I remember. It goes rusty."

She nodded, seeing the thoughts ticking over in her son's mind.

Christopher hesitated, then started doubtfully, "You mean Dad's..." He stopped, looking up at his mother who nodded encouragingly.

Sharon saw a smile spread across her brother's face. It annoyed her, knowing he'd worked out something she didn't understand, something that was fun! Why should Christopher be first to know? She reached for Jan's arm, shaking it to get attention. "Mum! Tell me!"

But it was Christopher who turned to his sister, smiling even more broadly. "Dad's gone rusty! That's what the brown is. It's rust!"

They were hardly able to believe their luck! Gordon could hear them giggling with glee as he stuffed clothes in the plastic sac, pushed the door open and made for the bathroom. The children, jumping with curiosity blocked his passage. Stephen squeezed to the fore, Sharon let him, conscious of her clothes, but wanted to feel her father's skin. When he knelt down, she stretched out an arm, careful her new dress should not make contact, and gingerly felt the skin of his face. Just as the finger touched, he passed a quiet comment.

"You do realise it's contagious."

For an instant Sharon hesitated, absorbing the words, then leapt backwards with a little scream, falling on the carpet, adding hugely to the boys' enjoyment. Gordon smiled at her alarm, but simultaneously a foot appeared from nowhere, rested an instant on his shoulder as he knelt, and with a heave, sent him sprawling. Jan blew out her breath in a little snort and a nod of satisfaction, turning to her upset daughter, arm held out.

"We girls must stick together. Come on."

Having pulled Sharon to her feet, Jan dusted one hand against the other, in her usual 'that settles that' gesture, and the two females, turning on their heel, stalked away.

Gordon headed again for the bathroom, cries of "Rusty" from the boys, ringing in his ears. Nor was a thorough wash the end of the matter. Rub as he might, the stained skin would not return to its normal colour. He was quite sore before admitting defeat. It would have to wear off, like a suntan. The clothes, equally resistant, were not discarded, but kept in reserve for specially mucky jobs like future re-applications of sulphate of iron. Next time he would certainly wait for a windless day. Re-use would undoubtedly be necessary, since this particular chemical suppressed rather than killed moss. A mercurial based moss killer would be more effective but they absolutely refused to have it on their site! Never mind, this treatment should suffice for a time.

Due to a continuing shortage of topsoil, there was now a considerable area of hardstanding. Last season, during one wet spell, many people had chosen hard ground from preference, but for the greater part of the year the weather had been dry. Then, it was grass the customers wanted, hard pitches remaining nearly empty apart from the occasional thirty-five foot plus, motorcaravans. These excessively heavy vehicles had, in general, been pleased enough to find a surface they would not sink into.

* * *

Audrey worked in her garden planting more annuals in the wall. She liked being outside; villagers stopped to talk as they walked by taking their dogs for exercise. Not so many had come in the last few weeks, dry May days increasing the dust clouds following cars up and down the stony track to the site, covering anyone on foot in a fine white powder. Many caravanners waved as their cars passed by, Audrey lifting an arm in response. Jim, who pottered around helping, waved to everyone, unconcerned if he knew them or not; even to arriving foreign caravans which for certain he had never seen before.

Sometime after ten, Jan appeared. At weekends early

in the season, she liked the walk to pick up Audrey's news-paper, leaving Sharon to mind the office and take telephone calls. Jim came over to greet her, then as he wandered off to shoo a crow from bread put out for the smaller birds, the two women stood talking.

"I washed your sign again this morning," Audrey motioned towards the riverbank. "Not the one on the garden wall, the dust doesn't reach that so much. We need a shower to damp it down."

"Rain's bad for visitors," Jan shook her head. "Is Jim's leg any better in all this sunshine?"

"He pretends it is, but it's not really. Wish he'd sell the car. Don't want him crashing like those people in the village last month."

"Are they better?"

Audrey shrugged. "No idea. The ambulance took them but I've heard nothing since. You seem quite busy this year although you're not leafleting."

"The weather probably. Yes, we are well up, I was surprised, but it doesn't mean much. Early trade is too sparse, even a handful of extra visitors make the figures look good. Everything depends on the main weeks. Your wall is a picture, maybe that's helping."

"I want it nice, Princess Anne might drive by on her way to Penzance next week. What would you do if she visited the site?"

"Pass out with surprise probably - would be great though wouldn't it. Mind you, I've had royal connections before." Jan's smile broadened. "I've sat in the Queen's seat - you remember? I was in junior school and Dad was a policeman on palace protection duty. He took me to see horses at the royal stables one day; the Coronation coach was there. I ran over to it, he opened the door, lifted me up and sat me inside. I was too young to really appreciate how special that was, sitting where a Queen might sit, or rather a King at that time. It seemed hard and lumpy, I remember asking why the King couldn't afford something more comfortable."

Audrey nodded, gazing nostalgically across the garden,

309

looking at but not seeing the flowers, recalling those days long past. Would Relubbus ever become really famous; it was such a small village. How many sovereigns had clattered across Relubbus bridge on horseback or by carriage in bygone years when this road was the main route to St Michael's Mount?

* * *

The children, as growing children will, had become competitive in their display of knowledge and ability; a contest at which Stephen, being so much younger, seldom found the opportunity to shine. Each evening, five o'clock to six o'clock was designated homework time for the older two, though it seldom took that long to finish and on many evenings there was none.

Stephen made a virtue of seldom having homework but was nevertheless envious of the status and attention that Christopher and to some extent Sharon, garnered from both parents in connection with their studies. Early attempts to annoy his brother and sister by distracting them had quickly taught him that such tactics only brought disapproval; neither his mother nor father were prepared to tolerate such behaviour.

As a result, if either Christopher or Sharon had homework, Stephen found himself a quiet pastime, often drawing, or whatever interested him at that moment. However, he pushed his luck to the limit, searching for ways to irritate the older pair right up to the very moment when they started, and again after they finished.

One evening immediately following tea, the children were sitting down relaxing. Stephen sat idly turning the pages of *Beano* while his sister, next to him at the table, browsed through her *Bunty*. Sharon rose, leaving the room for a moment, returning to discover Stephen had both comics, one in each hand.

"Give it back!"

"No. You've got homework to do!"

"You can't read two comics at once!"

"'Corse I can. Got two eyes haven't I?"

Actually, he could read neither properly, but the underlying quickness of wit left both parents trying to suppress chuckles. They pretended not to notice the developing argument until eventually, to stop a stand up fight, Jan intervened.

"Stephen, give Sharon back her comic."

He looked up, defiance on his face, but at a stern glance from his mother, grudgingly complied.

Shortly after, dead on the stroke of five, he spoke again, not loudly or to anyone in particular, not even lifting his head, speaking gruffly down at the table.

"It's homework time! Sharon ought to stop reading comics."

Sharon continued to read ignoring the comment, deliberately finished the magazine, turning back to the front page, scanning idly through again then cast it to one side and took up her pen. Jan said nothing, preferring where possible to let them sort their own relationships. She noticed Gordon give Sharon a sly wink while he marked Christopher's spelling mistakes in soft pencil.

Among the early visitors were several old friends, caravanners who had come in previous seasons and had made the site their home in the west. It was great to see them again, several felt like part of the family. New faces too were appearing, drawn by the quietness of the valley; some were quite knowledgeable on the countryside. The titbits of new information they offered re-stimulated the family's study of natural history. This interest, necessarily suppressed to some extent in earlier years by pressure for progress, now blossomed. With Jan no longer leafleting, life had become easier. The site was not yet busy and this, coupled with an absence of TV, left much time for reading in the evenings.

Birds had always been watched for, but when restricted to ornithology many weeks could pass without chalking up a new sighting. Flora however, provided a rich source of fresh discoveries, many natural to the valley but previously unnoticed, others springing forth from imported topsoil. Not all were desirable.

A visitor popped his head round the office door one evening to speak of a new plant.

"I spotted a hemlock, it's on the topsoil heap near where you were working this morning."

Gordon wondered if it had been intended as a pun, 'spotted a hemlock' for the plant was usually recognised by the spotted stem. In spite of a temptation to keep it as a curiosity, the plant was disposed of. The hollow shaft, ideally pea-shooter shaped, might easily tempt some youngster to put the tube to his mouth and no one seemed sure just how potent the juice might be.

Besides flora, moths appeared regularly in the toilet buildings. All colours and sizes were found during morning cleaning, attracted in by the lights overnight. Really large ones were carefully removed, since lady visitors in particular found them frightening. Pulling the door open, Jan walked out one morning with four clinging to the extended fingers of her left hand. A woman about to enter, stepped back in alarm. Jan stopped, holding out her arm to display the creatures, unmoving and dormant during the early daylight.

"How could you?" the woman asked with a shudder, stepping back a further pace but intrigued all the same by the moths' size and immobility, and even more by Jan's obviously pleasure at their presence on her hand. She leaned a little nearer, "They won't fly at me, will they?"

"No. You're quite safe! These are night creatures, only fly in the dark - unless they get badly disturbed, that is. Even then you get plenty of warning. They vibrate all over for some time before flying, kind of warming up their engines ready to escape." Jan paused extending her arm towards the reluctant but fascinated onlooker. With her other hand she pointed to three, their wings almost touching each other in spite of widely spread fingers.

"These are Poplar Hawks, quite common, usually the

first to appear. This one," she indicated the moth on her thumb, gently pulling away one fore-wing to show pink ribs of colour on the body and matching pink markings on the under-wing, "This one is a Privet Hawk, it's early, we usually see the first in June."

The woman reached out a hand towards the nearest moth, but, unable to bring herself to touch, withdrew it again.

"What will you do with them?"

"Gently hide them, probably on an ivy-covered tree trunk some distance away and hope they're not attracted straight back by the lights tonight. They won't fly anywhere until dusk."

The loan of South's *Moths of the British Isles* from their old friend, another Gordon, Gordon Blythe, known to the family as the Orchid Man, proved invaluable. The thousands of illustrations in this series of three books had so far never failed to reveal the name of any new specimen found.

Also in the toilet buildings and equally abhorrent to some ladies, were those spiders hiding in the cisterns. These were less easy to identify. Bringing one to the house in cupped hands, Dad placed it on the floor in the middle of the lounge, showing Christopher how to study them with a hand lens.

"No need to hurt it, just chase it round the carpet with a finger. Like this." It raced away, to be diverted by a strategically placed hand, then off in another direction and another, until quite quickly it stopped. "Spiders are fast for their size, but only over short distances. Once it's exhausted, you can lift it onto your hand to study with a lens. You need to be quick, they soon recover."

Sharon, when offered a chance, declined.

"It's not coming on me! That's from the toilets, you don't know what all those legs may have trodden in!"

Under the lens it did look somewhat ugly, but really there was nothing terrifying about the creature. Spiders are Arachnids; they have eight legs, not six like an insect. The book *World of spiders* from the New Naturalist Series helped

313

with the family name, but there seemed no popular comprehensive guide with colour photos of the kind that made Lepidoptera so interesting.

Pursuing the family's growing interest in nature, Gordon sat in his wicker rocking chair one evening. The warm climate and heavy work frequently combined to cause perspiration; wicker helped to ventilate and cool much more than modern foam rubber upholstery, the small light chair had become a favourite. Seated comfortably, he produced a knob of wood the size of a small pencil box; a discarded end cut from the roof timbers last December. With a Stanley razor-knife he commenced whittling away, offering no explanation or reason.

The children exchanged glances and Jan began to breathe more deeply, the way she did when coming to the boil. A small pile of shavings grew steadily on the carpet, odd slithers tending to fly outwards for some distance. He said nothing, just whittled on with a happy smile.

An electric air of expectation hung over the lounge; Jan's lips tightened into a thin line. The children concealed grins, hid them behind hands or with down-turned faces that looked up obliquely under eyelashes. Something must happen, it was inescapable - just a matter of how long.

"I hope you're going to clear all that up!"

Jan, normally so difficult to rile, had finally risen. He must be careful, or she would escape!

"Me? No, it's women's work. Men do the heavy jobs and all the thinking."

Success! He dodged the cushion and just managed to lay down the knife when she was on him, pulling his hair; it was still firmly attached but he might end up bald quite young, like in the next ten seconds.

"You are going to clear it up, aren't you!" she forced the words out between clenched teeth.

He rolled her over onto the floor, trapped one arm behind her back and held the other wrist. Reaching out with his free hand, he stroked her hair and whispered indulgently.

"There, there. It's wrong to lose your temper," a favourite expression, used often. Eyes flashing she struggled and heaved just as all three children piled in, on Mum's side naturally but as she was underneath, nearly squashing her in the process. Eventually he was dragged clear by force of numbers and the need to avoid hurting anyone, and found himself looking upwards into Jan's face about six inches away. She was sitting astride his abdomen, hair tussled, skirts awry, holding down his arms with the aid of the children.

Not seriously trying to escape, he reached forward, making to kiss her cheek and though she turned away smartly, there was a smile on her lips that suggested now might be a good time to surrender.

"I give in, let me up."

"Not until you tell us what you're doing with that piece of wood."

"Couldn't possibly, it's covered by the Official Secrets Act."

She released his wrists, leaving them to the children, and grabbing handfuls of hair again, tried to knock his head against the floor. The hair might be well fixed at present, but with the treatment it was getting the whole scalp could not last long.

"Okay! Okay! It's a robin."

They let go, giving each other knowing looks and little nods of the head, with glances towards the figure still lying prone on the floor, glances with a clear message, "He's flipped his tiny lid."

"Yes, yes, of course it is. We should have realised." Jan said it for them all, in a tone of utter disbelief that Dad, digger of trenches should do something artistic like carving. Nothing more was said. The whittling continued and time passed. To his surprise as much as anyone else's, the wood did begin to resemble a Robin.

From little acorns giant oaks do grow. A new hobby was born. Over the weeks a succession of other birds followed the robin, the latest one a buzzard carved partly from memory, partly from a photo of the one they had helped over a year before. All were life sized, some later painted, others left in a natural finish.

This hobby had always been one for the end of the day, not being allowed to interfere with other work. Lighter nights and more visitors left less time for carving, but often late evening found another wooden bird slowly emerging. The family, sitting together drinking a late coffee before the children retired to bed, had become quite used to it.

"You shouldn't use that knife towards you!" Sharon chided, one evening, in her 'mother knows best' voice.

"Why not?"

"It's dangerous, you'll cut yourself!"

"Who says so?"

By this time everyone had turned to watch. The boys hesitated, equivocal, torn between two desires, unable to achieve both. To prove Dad wrong would be great but that would mean supporting Sharon, admitting she was right. Jan, however, had no such scruples, quickly siding with her daughter.

"I say so! Anyone with half an ounce of common sense knows that."

The boys nodded. Now the argument lay between Mum and Dad, they could happily take sides.

Gordon regarded the four, all smiling, convinced they had won. He rose, moved to a central position and sat on the floor.

"Gather round, I'll show you something."

Jan pulled her chair closer, the three children sat in a ring on the carpet.

"Look, this is a Stanley knife, notice it's very short."

"Short or not," Jan interrupted, "that razor blade is sharp enough to cut deeply into flesh."

"Watch. See how I hold the knife hand, clasp it close to the chest." He paused, demonstrating, wrist pressed hard against his body. "The danger with a knife is if you slip. What will be cut if I slip when using this blade towards myself? I'll show you." The knife jerked towards the mottled

316

jumper, but it stopped short. "There! See. It won't reach. So long as I keep the wrist tight against my chest, I'm safe. Look if I use it the other way, outwards. The blade can only move in a small arc, maybe four inches. I just have to make sure of two things. Firstly my other hand must be beyond that four-inch arc, so if it slips nothing is in range. Second, the wrist must stay tightly in contact with the body. That's where the control lies; all motion must come from the wrist! If the arm starts moving, someone will get hurt."

A stubborn resistance to belief could only be overcome by letting them try for themselves, first with the blade retracted, adjusting the grip to achieve the proper position, stressing with each one the importance of moving only the wrist, keeping it in firm contact with the chest. For further emphasis, they were shown what could happen if the arm swung free, still with the blade retracted, and finally were allowed to extend the cutting edge, satisfying themselves completely that it would not reach the flesh. Jan looked on doubtfully, allowing the experiments to proceed but with some reluctance.

Teak was the most enjoyable wood to carve, it had a wonderful oily feel but for some reason blunted the blade more quickly than other types of timber. Often it tended to be cross-grained, whereas mahogany always seemed straight and though lacking the oily texture, was also pleasant to carve.

Other woods, almost any seasoned timber available, were tried. Oak proved very hard, Elm hard and soft according to the growth rings making it difficult; Beech, Sapele, Sycamore and several others were also quite good. Balsa, while quick, was not satisfying, giving a poor surface; useful though for things like the Poplar Hawk and most other big moths, which being night flyers would remain still for hours in the lighter evenings, provided one could finish before darkness fell.

CHAPTER 18

Jan's Dutchman

"That desk you want, there's a firm advertising over near Truro. Office equipment, new and second-hand it says; mentions desks." Flicking through the *Western Morning News*, Jan had noticed a small display advert. "If you want one before we get busy, better go this week. Jim will mind the site."

She hoped he would go, Truro was a good shopping centre, the boys needed one or two new clothes. They were at school but she knew the sizes; neither Stephen nor Christopher ever showed a true appreciation of shopping anyway. On the point of suggesting a walk round the shops together while in the town, she hesitated thoughtfully. "He'll be in a hurry as usual, probably refuse, say there isn't time. I could suggest clothes are cheaper in Truro, that would make him come but he'd still want to hurry. Better find an excuse to go alone on another day, buying clothes is a thing to be enjoyed not rushed; might find something for myself. Pity Saturdays are so busy or I could go then and take Sharon, she loves shopping."

Jan was still standing unmoving, gazing towards the river lost in her thoughts when Gordon asked urgently, "What's the matter, have you seen something?"

"Er... No, just wondering if Jim would come down this afternoon." It was not entirely untrue, that thought had also occurred.

A quick phone call and Jim agreed, his car appearing shortly along the road. Leaving him in charge, they set out; Praze-an-Beeble, Camborne, by-passing Redruth, through

318

Chasewater, on to Truro. Of the several desks displayed, a dark brown, discoloured and slightly disreputable one was chosen in spite of Jan's disapproval, and slid upside-down onto a blanket in the rear of the little green van.

"It's not *that* bad," Gordon insisted. "I can paint it if necessary. This one is the best size, it will just fit beside the billiard table, exactly how we want."

"It isn't the size you like. Don't pretend to me, I know! It's the price. Twelve pounds, no wonder it's rubbish."

Arriving home, this desk when eased sideways through the office doorway, did indeed fit the allotted space ideally, but it looked poor. That evening the children needed little encouragement to pass unfavourable comments.

"It's horrible, Mum. Why did you let him buy it?" Sharon demanded.

"I tried, but couldn't stop him. It was cheap."

"Looks it!" Christopher agreed, casting a sceptical eye over the piece.

Sharon nodded, as if her mother's last word explained everything.

Dad glared back at the family, "You can stop carrying on. There's nothing a little work won't put right - look fine when I've finished with it."

The following day with the desk outside again, tentative experiments using sandpaper began the refurbishment. As luck would have it the coating was brittle, some cheap dark brown varnish that sanded away with relative ease. Underneath lay good English Oak. Cleaning a bit here and a patch there revealed that the edges, the frame and all four drawer fronts to be solid timber; the working surface made of some cheaper wood veneered with oak.

Unwilling to commit his full time to the desk, Gordon prepared one side, then sloped off to complete a length of dry stone wall that was being extended. At tea that evening he asked for the children's help; a request that had been anticipated.

"I told you," Sharon sighed to her brothers amid groans and a fresh outburst of adverse observations. Once the work had started however, and the attractive wood grain began to appear, this criticism diminished.

"There, I knew you'd enjoy it once we got started."

Dad's comment was met with a further howl of hostile remarks but now delivered with derision and laughter, amid smiles as the family sandpapered busily together.

Though never an expensive piece of furniture, not an antique or anything spectacular, the quality was nevertheless surprising; certainly worth a great deal more than the twelve pounds it cost. Having spent a night in the garage while a new coat of clear varnish dried, it made a very presentable and spacious desk when reinstalled in the office, ideal for signing in new arrivals and dealing with customers' needs. That was good, because the season's start was promising.

For the purpose of comparison with the previous year, numbers in each ten-day period were recorded on a graph. Visitors for the first ten days of May were nearly double those of the 1971 season, increasing from twenty-three to forty. While giving a great boost to the ego, making everyone feel terrific, there was little real significance, for it represented only four caravans on site each day.

Trade was expected to pick up later in the month but while new arrivals were still few, Gordon pushed on with the filling of new areas, using Max whenever the site was empty. At other times, like in the morning before people left for the day, quieter jobs made good use of the time. A shed was built, working silently, using a rubber hammer to bed the concrete blocks down rather than tapping them with the end of the trowel. This large lean-to, sited against the Ladies side of the second toilet building, was constructed almost entirely with materials left from the house. It would store gas bottles that had become a nuisance in the service passage. The mower and other tools could also be stored there, keeping the site more tidy.

Spring Bank Holiday did see the hoped for influx of visitors. An absence of leafleting had not sent numbers tumbling, to everyone's great relief. The reorganised road system at Scorrier had been checked again as holiday trade built up, but in spite of increasing traffic, no sign of a queue had appeared. The nearest regular hold up on the A30 was now thirty miles away, at Bodmin; too far, most of the traffic would be turning off for Newquay and other destinations.

"Think yourself lucky I'm here to cook," Mum reminded the family at tea. "This would have been my first weekend sitting at that roadside if they hadn't altered our junction."

"It's good to have proper cooking." Christopher looked sideways with a grin at Sharon.

"You didn't have to eat my food last year - or ever. You can always fend for yourself!" Sharon's retort was automatic but without force; she was confident enough not to care. "I like cooking but it's nicer having Mum home."

"Glad I'm appreciated. We seem to be doing OK at the moment..." Jan hesitated turning to Gordon with a question, "d'you think it will affect us badly later in the year?"

"I hope enough people know the site now, and we understand more about advertising. That's the key, good adverts and spend more on them when we can. Even the limited extra money this year is producing results," he paused, unsure, extending one hand palm upward with a shrug. "Mid-season? Who knows? Probably numbers *will* fall but it shouldn't be too great a disaster, at least I hope not, but it could still happen. That's what I've been trying to warn of ever since our junction was changed Stop spending so much money, kerb your expensive tastes, at least until we're sure about the main season."

"Expensive tastes? I already manage on a fraction of what every normal housewife gets. When do I ever waste money? And we're not going back to luncheon meat and mash!"

Sharon moved to her mother's side, "All the other girls at school have lots of new clothes, these are my first for a year!"

"OK, didn't mean you don't do well, but we have to survive next winter. All I'm saying is, let's not get carried away just because we're a little up at the moment. We'll know soon enough if the peak period fails."

He was on the defensive, Jan could see that, she had wondered why he seemed so concerned about money lately; he never stinted with materials while building the house. True, their bank balance was virtually zero now, but with the season ahead that had not seemed important. Could they really be in trouble again? Surely the end of leafleting would never cause trade to collapse to that extent - would it?

A proper reception room to greet arriving guest and the absence of the family's old caravan, recently sold cheaply just to get shot of it, these things must improve confidence on arrival. So far it certainly had seemed to. People were booking longer stays right from the start, rather than taking a few doubtful days and adding to their booking later. Another helpful point, evenings were now so light that no caravans were arriving after sunset, a fact which concealed the remaining substandard feature. Much earlier in the year, those coming to reception after dark had been surprised and often amused by the lantern swinging from the ceiling; certainly not a confidence-building feature. Seeing it may have prompted some to wonder if the toilets were similarly primitive. The weak light had just reached to reveal three children, sitting in semi-darkness in the adjoining lounge, patiently awaiting the lamp's return. If the visitor was known to them and conversation looked like being prolonging, either Christopher or Sharon would light a candle enabling the resumption of their games. Fortunately now, nearing the longest day, arrivals in darkness no longer occurred. Surely all the improvement since last year would outweigh those missing leaflets?

* * *

Jan had a new task, showing recent arrivals to a pitch; a duty she seldom performed and really preferred to avoid. It was not just that this left the office and phone unattended, though the need to hurry back each time was a factor. Her aversion to pitching stemmed more from a different source - the occasional encounter with difficult people that required

322

a firmness unnatural to her character. However, the task was unavoidable, since a plumbing problem had arisen. To be honest, this shortcoming of the system had existed before but had become more noticeable recently. Whether from declining efficiency of the gas boilers or from visitors generally rising expectations was unknown, but several detrimental comments had been passed in the current season. It concerned a tendency for shower temperatures to change when anyone used a hot tap at the basins. Such fluctuations were not surprising, since both basins and showers flowed from the same water heater. The solution had been to buy an additional gas boiler for each building, changing the pipework so the existing system worked only the showers, leaving all basin taps to be separately fed from the new boilers. Expensive, but it should cure the problem! Gordon had been working at it all morning and would need at least until nightfall to complete the job. One building at a time was being tackled, a temporary sign outside the door requesting "Please use other toilets."

Jan therefore, found herself not only greeting the customers, but showing them to a place. Already three had arrived. The last, a caravan from Holland, had really wanted to pitch on top of the waste heaps, but there was no route up except by foot.

"We go abroad mainly to camp on a hill," the man had said in excellent English. "There are no hills in Holland except in one small part of our country."

In the end he had accepted a pitch on area three, just downstream of the house, choosing it because that area was now reserved for families without children. He expressed some amusement when seven paces were carefully stepped out from an already sited caravan to ensure a six-metre gap.

"It's fire regulations, don't you have that on the continent?" Jan asked.

"Oh yes. I believe it is a law, but nobody pays any attention, particularly in France where we normally stay."

The couple reversed their rather long caravan into position, its back against a hedge that separated the area

323

from the river, the big front window looking across the open site. Shortly afterwards another tourer was pitched in the same area, seven paces again carefully stepped out to maintain the proper spacing.

It was when passing by an hour later, leading a new visitor to an area farther on, that Jan noticed the long caravan had turned sideways, much reducing the room available to the adjoining units. Apart from being unfair, this well and truly infringed the spacing rules.

"Why do they never do that when Gordon pitches them?" she muttered to herself. "This is the part I hate. I'll have to tell him - but later."

She walked on, leading the new arrival, deliberately finding a pitch round the corner out of sight, and stayed talking longer than necessary, knowing she must speak to the Dutchman afterwards.

Remembering the note left on the office door read "Back in five minutes," Jan waved a goodbye and left, turning the corner to stride purposefully forward. Coming level with the offending caravan and about to turn across the grass, a thought occurred.

"This could take some time, I've already been away more than five minutes, I'll pop to the office first, make sure nobody is waiting."

Feeling better, she strode on, disappointed on rounding the toilet building to find the entrance yard empty.

"I'll just make a coffee, might not get another chance."

Quickly entering the house, the sense of relief was palpable as the door closed. Carrying her drink through to the lounge, she sank back in an armchair. Tension that had built up over the misplaced caravan further relaxed as she sipped the hot liquid while idly watching the empty track and bridge. It was unusual to drink alone but then, extra cups of coffee were not normally taken.

"Don't know why I made this one," It was a lie, pushing aside the real reason, refusing to acknowledge it. For a time the watch on the road continued in hopes that another visitor would arrive and demand attention. When all remained quiet, an impulse suggested that perhaps Gordon would leave his plumbing and speak to the Dutchman.

It wouldn't do! Face set with determination she rose, walked to the doorway and hesitated, looking round at the empty coffee cup. What about the washing-up? Almost giving way to the temptation of another delay, she grasped the door handle, stepped through closing it behind and strode off, hurrying on round the corner, along the straight, then cut across the grass. The Dutchman appeared in his doorway with a folding table, obviously intending to set it outside as continentals so often like to do.

"You can't have your caravan that way round," Jan spoke while still a stride away, shaking her head.

The man straightened up, surprised. "Why not?"

"It's too long, you don't have the proper space each side."

"Oh. The fire precautions. I promise to be careful."

This was going to be difficult, Jan sighed, had felt in her bones that it would be.

"We take the regulations seriously, inspectors come round to check sometimes, but it's not only that. It's not fair on your neighbours, you're too close; they should have plenty of room too you know." She breathed deeply, it had been an effort but the man now looked thoughtful, he flicked a glance in either direction at the neighbouring caravans, the owners of which were fortunately absent. Their presence would have made Jan feel even more self-conscious. She hurried on, "Another thing, your big front window; it points straight at the other caravan. In England people don't like that, it makes them feel they're being watched, overlooked, that their neighbours are nosy."

The Dutchman's wife had appeared, descending from the caravan doorway and spoke with concern. "They never said something. The gentleman, he friendly... seem quite friendly."

Jan smiled, more at ease with a woman. "Politeness can be a disguise, to mask real sentiments. The English don't show their feelings too much, never wave arms about like the French for instance. They're more reserved but they

325

like a certain amount of privacy, particularly the older generations. Your neighbours are older, most people on this area are, they choose it because these pitches have no children and they like the extra quietness." Jan stood, trying not to let her discomfort show, hands held tightly together at waist level in front.

The Dutch woman nodded thoughtfully, reached out in a friendly gesture and touched the back of Jan's hand with her fingers, patting it gently as she spoke. "We turn. Thank you for explanation."

Leaving the caravan, crossing the broad grass area on the way back to the office, Jan had the feeling that their eyes were following her and felt jerky and ungainly as she strode on, but forced herself not to look round.

* * *

The little green van showed its age. Ribbons of rust had surfaced in places, a haze of oil smoke following its passage. Audrey felt the image deplorable for a quality site, and having persuaded Jim to agree, took Jan to task on the matter.

"Sell it and buy a proper car, something smart."

"We can't - sentimental value!" Jan's joking response masked the real cause. However, remembering how hard the little vehicle had worked, pulling the overloaded caravan on that long initial journey, carrying untold bags of cement, towing the old horse drawn mower, she paused, reconsidering. Nothing else remained from that first year - there *was* some sentimental attachment. "Can't afford to, that's the main reason. Spent all our money on the house, hardly had enough for food at one point. A car must wait, I hope Mini keeps going!"

However, having made up her mind, Audrey was not so easily deflected, her reply, simple yet unarguable.

"Trade the van in, we can find the difference. With all the work Gordon put in, our bungalow cost less than we expected. Pay us when you feel rich."

So the mini left, replaced by a Vauxhall Viva in glacier blue, brand new, collected while the children were at school. They felt like toffs climbing aboard for the drive home, convinced no better car graced the road. On the journey they smiled at each other in pride, captivated with the quiet, smooth ride, the space and comfort. What a change after the oil smelling, noisy, bumpy, but courageous little van. Jan sighed, leaned back into the soft seat shrugging her shoulders forward in a little shudder of pleasure, wondering if film stars felt like this when wrapping a new mink coat around themselves? "We wouldn't have felt this way before. New cars used to be something normal, you just worried whether it was newer and bigger than next door's. We think differently now, know a luxury when we see it. I'm so glad we moved." She sighed, pushing herself even deeper into the seat, "I hope some nice young couple buy the mini and care for it properly. I won't forget how well it did."

The children, knowing the car would be waiting, came dashing along the road at a gallop, Christopher slowing his pace so the others could keep up. Stephen could remember no vehicle other than the mini-van. Even so, the change was greater for Christopher and Sharon, who always sat on the floor behind, whereas Stephen normally travelled on Jan's knee. Now there were seats for all.

To celebrate, they left Jim watching the site, drove the children to Porthleven, about seven miles from Relubbus, and walked along the beach as far as Loe Bar, a natural sandy dune that held back the river Cober from the sea. During the last war, a German plane was said to have crashed into Loe pool, an extensive freshwater lake behind the bar, but no trace of the machine was ever recovered.

Driving to and from the site on odd days over the following weeks, Jan felt sure the caravanners' reactions were improved when they saw her alight from the new vehicle. One long-stayer and some who had been in previous years, walked across to congratulate her. Life was good! She liked their expanding diet that the last few weeks had brought, more variety and better quality but not extravagant; no prime steak or out of season fruit. The children had more new clothes, not a great number and certainly not enough but they were all healthy and reasonably intelligent. Stephen perhaps had the fastest brain of all.

"He ought to," she thought, remembering the scrapes he got into. "He's used less of it than the others."

Resources had not yet recovered much and reasonable care was still needed with the spending, but looking to the future it was possible to feel what some would call "Quietly Confident."

June saw numbers decrease on the previous year but only by three percent, not the substantial drop that Gordon had feared, a worry that had made him ultra cautious with money. In spite of the worst June weather for many years, life had become busy again. Not that the work was strenuous yet, although occasionally it was, but the days were long. At frequent and unpredictable intervals some person or task would demand attention, often several at once, with the occasional unexpected crisis suddenly creating a rush of action.

The pace picked up gradually, most days seeing arrivals exceed those leaving, until the commencement of school holidays brought another grand surge, visitors pouring onto the site in a wave over that first weekend. Meals were eaten hurriedly again, activity ran at a fast tempo, unsustainable over the longer term but now, and no doubt for the next few weeks, their lives were supercharged, exciting, a constant challenge. Few visitors realised how near the edge, the limits of patience, tact, endurance, or even sanity, two people running a big site can come. But neither would have changed places with a Monarch.

The children were enjoying themselves again, perhaps even more this season, for although their help was still sometimes required, the necessity to stay regularly on call had passed. Now that Jan was available, no longer leafleting, the youngsters were free for most of each day to play with their friends.

"Does your father sell water-carriers?" the woman asked casually as two girls sat animatedly swapping tales in a visiting caravan. Sharon looked up at her new friend's mother, shaking her head. "No, there's a place at Scorrier, about twelve miles, or Bennetts the gas suppliers in Penzance might have some."

"OK thanks," the woman nodded. "Ours is going green inside, I've tried several things but it won't come out. Don't like using anything strong, it might affect the water afterwards. Lock the caravan if you go out Sally, we're off down the river path for an evening walk to St Erth; take an hour probably."

The parents departed, leaving the girls together. As the footsteps faded, Sharon leaned across, speaking in a whisper.

"I know how to clean that water carrier. Let's do it as a surprise?" Seeing her friend's nod, she rose making for the door, peeping out, then signalling Sally to wait. Once the two parents were out of sight, Sharon opened the door wide and went outside, leaving her friend to lift the half-full water carrier. With the door carefully locked, she led the way towards a stony area that no soil had been available to cover. Reaching it with Sally still struggling along behind, they moved past some small bushes that screened one side.

"Put it down and take off the top."

"What are you going to do?" Sally asked, lowering the narrow-necked container, taking off the top and laying it on the ground.

"Fill it with stones, ones about pea sized are best."

"Mum will go mad!"

"She won't know. It will be clean - really. But don't tell her how you did it. Say... say we filled it with Cornish Piskies and they scrubbed it clean!"

The two girls gathered handfuls of stone, feeding them carefully into the top.

"The water's terribly cloudy." Sally sounded doubtful.

"Wait 'til we finish, it's going to look much worse. Don't

329

worry, I know what I'm doing - we do ours this way."

After a few more handfuls, Sharon screwed the top back on tightly, lifted the carrier and shook hard, passing it after a time to her friend, telling her to keep shaking. Eventually the stones were tipped out, but the container still appeared dirty. Sharon knew Sally was concerned.

"It's OK. Let's find a tap. My turn to carry it."

"Now it's empty!"

Sharon grinned at her friend's exclamation. "You *are* slow, thought you'd notice *much* sooner; a lot easier to fool than my brother. We used to fetch most of our water from the river. Sometimes when it was my turn, I persuaded him to fetch the full ones; pretended he's so big and strong. My Mum does that sort of thing to Dad all the while; you'll just have to learn like I did! Here's the tap. Watch."

The carrier was part filled, shaken and emptied, then the whole operation repeated. "There! See that - sparkling. I'll fill it right up for you." Seeing Sally's mouth open and her finger point, Sharon laughed, "You're learning! All right, we'll carry it together."

When the carrier rested again on the draining board of the caravan, the water inside showed clear as crystal.

"Now remember, don't tell them how it's done! They'll think you're brilliant, but once they know the trick you won't be so clever any more. And they'd tell the other Mums too. We can get all the girls onto this, make them promise not to let their brothers know; we don't want boys looking intelligent, do we?"

The two grinned at each other, eyes bright, delighted with the plot, eager at the prospects it held.

This season, more continental visitors were finding their way to the valley. One morning, while Jan dashed out to give a pre-lunch freshen up to the first toilets, Gordon was on a ladder speedily cleaning windows. He had reached the three small panes on the entrance side of the toilet building nearest the house, when a woman approached and made straight for the Gents.

"I think you've chosen the wrong side," he called down to her from the top of the ladder.

The lady hesitated, a bewildered expression furrowing her brow.

"Non. Other one is cleaning." She pointed to the building in which Jan worked, the words heavily accented, obviously foreign, and started to push open the door.

"You are definitely using the wrong door." Gordon insisted, shaking his head.

The lady said something in a strange language, speaking so fast all the words ran into one, waving a hand in the air, and turned determinedly back to the door. What could he say? She was halfway inside when he tried again.

"It's for the men!"

She stopped, backed out, and looked up somewhat sheepishly, her cheeks with slightly more colour than he remembered.

"Pour les hommes? Ah..." She faltered, "The men? Yes?"

He nodded, trying to keep a straight face as he pointed to the other door, but in attempting to say 'Ladies' lost a grip on his expression and a strangled chuckle escaped. Fortunately, the woman had a sense of humour and herself burst into laughter, reddening prettily and quickly walked round the ladder to disappear through the correct door.

It was Jan who, on hearing the tale later, suggested the outline of a lady and a gent, the continental toilet signs, should be painted on the doors. Cardboard stencils, cut out that evening, provided a means of marking the outlines in soft pencil. Screwing a rubber doorstop to the end of an old hammer shaft, Gordon used it the following day to support his wrist as he had seen signwriters do. The figures were painted after lunch when most visitors were out; black Valspar gloss ensured quick drying.

Subtle changes were taking place in the two older children, particularly Christopher. With the arrival of the summer holidays, he had finished at the junior school. September and older companions beckoned. Whereas the previous summer his friends had been almost exclusively boys with just the odd girl to raise Jan's eyebrows, now each week he was seen frequently in the company of at least as many girls as boys, the faces changing as weeks passed. He was becoming more useful too, more able to hold his own with the customers when circumstances required.

A man approached the office one morning while Gordon was out clearing a partially blocked drain. Christopher listened as the man complained to Jan about dog mess near his step, and how a well-run site should see that dogs were kept on a lead.

"I can move it, Mum, if the man shows me where it is. I'll get a bucket and spade."

The lad ran off, returning quite quickly to accompany the visitor, listening to his continued grumbling without comment. Arriving at the caravan, the man pointed.

"There. Who lets their dog run free? Lazy, that's the trouble. If they own a dog they should walk it properly, along the riverbank; wonderful walk, no excuse for letting it soil other people's doorsteps!"

Two other couples had come over from nearby caravans to watch and to listen. Christopher could tell from their expressions they were not pleased and that they agreed with the little speech. Bending over, he pretended to inspect the dropping closely, poking it suspiciously with the spade, then turned to the small audience.

"Doesn't look like a dog - badger more likely; I'm sure that's a beetle casing... Did you know there are badger's in those banks over there?" He pointed to the grass covered sand heaps, quickly picking up the offending dung on his spade and placing it in the bucket before anyone could make a closer examination. "I'll remove it. Wonder if they've got cubs?"

When he left, the group of people were talking happily together, objections to the dropping forgotten. Moreover, when another appeared the following day, one of the same caravanners gently removed it himself, calling in at the office, quite proud of his actions, as if it was a privilege.

Sharon, two years younger than Christopher, was also becoming interested in boys, not yet with a desire to make close friends among them but more the wish to make an impression, to be considered smart. In her little tartan skirt, long white socks and blue jacket-like top, she took some pride in her appearance and smiled shyly under her lashes at a few.

Stephen, at six, was still the one who said least and got into trouble most! Though seldom the outright leader, it was Stephen's ideas that often motivated the unruly bundle of boys and girls roaming the site. This was not one cohesive band, its size varied constantly with the changing numbers on site as visitors came and went, and as new friendships were quickly made and just as quickly broken. Often smaller groups formed, created mostly by the geographical position of caravans, a nearby pitch creating a more convenient friend. But nothing remained static. Various groups formed, joined together for a while, only to split again and be off on their own separate pursuits. Jan noticed that when many children were together, combining as one large noisy unit, there was often roguery afoot. Under these circumstances it was frequently Stephen whose ideas directed the band, though he still tended to remain cautiously inconspicuous, allowing others to do the shouting. She was suspicious therefore when what must have been the entire population of five to seven-year-olds and a few outside that range, ran noisily across the bridge and on towards marshy ground on the east side of the river. She tried to locate Stephen, caught a glimpse of his small light-haired head in the centre of the crowd, the seething mob of young bodies pushing, jostling each other around him like bees round the queen. This was a cheerful swarm, an air of abandon, of total accord with one another, no sudden fights or disagreements, its members all happy and united - a very ominous sign! When such a pack had but one mind, it was invariable a mind set on mischief.

"Ah well," Jan thought, "whatever they're up to at least it's off the site. Over there, the most they can do is get covered in mud."

She watched for a while as this band dispersed over the adjoining soft ground like ants from a disturbed nest, dashing this way and that, gradually disappearing from her view. A customer arrived at the office and the youngsters were forgotten.

Over near the margins of the marsh, children were hunting, many now with a muddy coating to shoes and socks, some had even removed their footwear, leaving them on some nearby solid ground. They were searching for frogs. While Stephen was not exactly in command, many were turning to him for advice, shouting questions which he answered with no more than a pointed finger or a sweep of the arm. Eventually a frog was located, captured and passed to Stephen, the rest now tightly bunched around. Much whispering of plots followed, schemes that no one must overhear, heads shaken in small arguments, others stretching to watch for passing adults. One small girl held out a hand to receive the frog, withdrawing it quickly at the last moment and shrinking back. The pack sought another volunteer and finding one half-willing, pushed her forward. The girl, short, dark-haired, took the small amphibian from Stephen, one hand under, one over to prevent its escape, and the plan was underway!

The young procession crossing the bridge and back through the site was marked by a very different demeanour. When a little face tries to look angelic and behave as if all was well in the world and butter wouldn't melt in its mouth, then watch out! When a whole bunch of small children behave in this way, some trying to whistle, looking away when an adult passed, sneaking sly glances under unruly hair; then without the slightest doubt, devilment was afoot.

The crowd rounded the toilet building. One girl slid into the Ladies, to reappear quickly with a thumbs up sign. Immediately a path opened in the young ranks. The girl with the frog, hidden in their midst, slipped forwards and into the building in an instant. Nor did she remain long inside, returning as the bunch made off to fade into a small copse of willow not too far from the door.

Jan first became aware of a problem when two women approached the office at a run, one serious, even upset, the other disabled with laughter, totally unable to do more than point in the direction of the toilet building. The straight-faced lady turned to glare at her friend, who dissolved into more floods of laughter.

"Stop it, Alice. It wasn't funny!" She spoke with stiff dignity, turning to Jan. "There's a frog in one of the ladies loos. I thought someone had forgotten the chain so I pulled it. What looked like a... you know; well, after the water stopped flushing it bobbed to the surface and croaked at me. I nearly..."

She didn't finish, cut off by a further helpless wail of merriment from her friend who collapse against the office billiard table gasping "She never knew they could answer back!"

After a while the laughing woman recovered and Jan accompanied them back to the Ladies, taking rubber gloves with her. There, in the third compartment, swam the frog. She reached in, lifted the creature clear and carried it to the nearby bushes, realising now, the cause of the young children's earlier quest. Kneeling and lowering her hand to the ground, she regarded the glistening, slightly slimy skin. "Hop it!" The frog obliged.

At tea that evening she related the story to Christopher and Sharon, then turned accusingly to Stephen. The lad, his little satanic grin hardly disguised, stared back defiantly, lips tightly compressed, saying nothing. Jan studied the small roguish face, those tousled curly locks, one flopping downward, and wanted to cuddle him to her. Maintaining a stern expression was difficult but he was naughty enough already without further encouragement.

Stephen never did pass a single comment on the incident, but Jan learned from one of the other mothers that it had indeed been his idea. It had been Stephen who made the initial suggestion and led them to where frogs might be found. Jan revealed this information at tea again the following evening but the lad still regarded her silently, admitting nothing. Christopher and Sharon were little help either; far from condemning the behaviour, they viewed their younger brother with new respect.

Walking round the site in the darkness just after eleven o'clock that evening, Jan stopped at a vantage point commanding the main areas.

"I haven't walked round with you at this time for ages, getting up so early we're usually preparing for bed by now. Don't all the little lights in caravan windows look super?" She squeezed his arm.

They sauntered back slowly towards the office, but she passed the door, pulling Gordon on towards the bridge. He followed until they stopped in the centre; she pointed, "That's where Stephen found the frog," then turned back towards the house. Lights from lounge and kitchen shone, soft but visible through unlined orange curtains, a warm, welcoming, almost sunshine colour. Every room in the house, all ten windows but not the hall door, had identical curtain fabric, all from that roll of material that Audrey paid for but Jan had chosen.

"There!" she said, "I told you they would look good to visitors coming back late at night! Pity our lights are not better so all the rooms show. Wish you'd put that curtain rail up at the hall door."

In the preceding year, while Jan had still been leafleting, it was Jim rather than Audrey who had come to the site most weekdays, minding the office for an hour or two when the children were unable to do so because of school. Many a booking had been saved because Jim was there to answer the phone while Gordon hurriedly cleaned toilets or cut the grass, or whatever else might be required on any particular day. Even with Jan now at home full time, her father still frequently called in, helping here and there, liking the chance to meet old friends and make new ones. Many people got to know Jim and often visited his bungalow to partake of the offered hospitality, usually including a sizeable nip of Scotch to which Jim himself was partial, though he seldom liked to drink alone.

Today Jan needed to go out, she knew her father would cover for an hour at midday; Gordon must manage alone for the rest. The journey would be long, unusual in the busy season, to Par forty miles away, the only place for digger spares. Although not used in mid-season, periodically the excavator was started, perhaps once a fortnight if it was lucky! Running the engine for ten minutes or so when most people were out, maintained it in good condition. Extending and contracting each of the rams kept the rods coated in oil, otherwise their shiny steel surface was apt to rust. When this had been done on the previous day, oil trickled from one of the pressure pipes. It continued to drip slowly and needed replacing. She intended to take advantage of the journey to bank a handful of cheques so could not start too early, and to call at cash and carry for toilet rolls and bleach. Lunch would definitely be very late. Two rounds of egg sandwich had been left in a plastic bag.

Mowing was still done with the old Haytor, the engine driving the blades but all forward motion achieved by muscle-power alone. As the site expanded, now nearly four acres of grass, the time required for a full mowing had increased considerably. Fortunately the grass grew slowly in midsummer. Nevertheless, each caravan that departed left a green patch, which shaded from the sun, had grown taller as the length of stay increased. One such patch, particularly tall after a three-week stay, was to cause a small problem.

No sooner had the caravan left, about mid-morning, than two others arrived, travelling in company. On his own now, Gordon locked the office to show them round, offering a choice of position. The chap in the second caravan, tall and rather thin, was very relaxed, easy to please and liked all the pitches. His was the better caravan and the newer car, but he happily left the choice to his friend.

"I like them all," he said. "Spacious pitches for mid-season, not like the one we just left. You choose."

His friend however, less easy to please, went from one area to another, none quite meeting with his approval. Having learned that some people liked to assert themselves, Gordon moved on without rancour to show yet another pitch, idly wondering if the stout form waddling along slightly ahead was a heavy drinker or just enjoyed good food. He toyed with the idea of withholding the next pair of empty pitches, telling the new arrival that they were booked already and so not available. Something led him confidently to expect that under those terms, they would be the very pitches this customer would demand. But he resisted the urge; it would be a bit mean. Perhaps it had been a long difficult journey.

Rounding the corner, Gordon made to pass by the pitch where the previous caravan had just left, but by chance, or more likely sensing it was not being offered, the man pointed, "That will do. I like the big tree behind."

"That one's not available. I have to mow the grass, then it will need a week to recover. I never put a caravan exactly where another has been, that's why we don't have marked pitches."

Seeing determination come into the man's face and sensing trouble coming, Gordon sighed. "He's happy now there's something to argue about. I *should* have refused him one of those other pitches. If I had, they'd already be settled!" He glanced back towards where the caravans had been left, way in the distance, now obscured by trees, wondering if the wives ever had any say.

The stout man cleared his throat, squared his shoulders and adopted what might have been intended as a macho stance. "I'm not worried by a bit of grass; that's the place for me!"

He marched off towards it. Gordon turned questioningly back towards the tall friend who had followed throughout looking slightly amused. This man shrugged his shoulders, unconcerned. They grinned at each other and followed the determined steps of Mr Difficult.

"OK. If you park one each side of the used area, I'll mow the grass later. Leave me plenty of room, and there must be six good paces between the caravans - that's fire regulations." Gordon hesitated, then trying to inject a little humour into the situation added, "If one of you catches fire, it won't spread to the other... so you can move in together."

"I'd rather burn!" A laughing voice whispered faintly behind him.

Jim arrived about eleven-thirty; most visitors were away at the beach. Quickly cleaning the toilets, Gordon dragged out the mower and pushed it towards the long grass patch he had promised to mow between the recent arrivals. On turning the corner, annoyance surged at finding the difficult customer had parked right on the very edge of the uncut patch.

"Damn!"

Both caravans were empty and the cars gone; a quick trip to get their bearings probably. "Off to trouble someone else?" The thought came spontaneously as he pushed the mower into position and started the engine, mowing close to the caravan but still not quite catching all the long grass. The other caravan, the one owned by the tall, more congenial friend, had thoughtfully been pitched with the proper spacing and lay well clear.

An hour later, after Jim had departed, Mr Difficult came storming round to the office.

"There's grass all over my caravan! It won't come off!"

He stood there, just outside the door, feet planted firmly apart, the picture of an outraged citizen.

Was this one of those people for whom only confrontation made life worthwhile Gordon wondered, looking at him and weighing the best response.

"I'll come as soon as my wife returns. Must stay in the office until then."

The man hesitated, uncertain, then turned and stalked off.

On Jan's return, recounting the story in detail elicited little sympathy; she laughed instead of showing concern.

"One of those, is he. You should have showed him that pitch first, insisted he stayed there. He'd definitely have chosen somewhere else then. Go and see him."

Jogging down the site, Gordon rounded the corner and even before reaching the caravan, the man emerged from his doorway.

"Look!" An accompanying gesture said, 'See what you've done!' The stout figure stretched out an arm with one extended finger, moving it forwards then back again, indicating the shiny, light coloured aluminium sides to which a few small flecks of grass adhered.

"Should wash off." Expecting a substantial amount, Gordon was amazed the fuss should be over so little. Caravans often arrived with more dead flies sticking to them than this one had grass. A movement to the right caught his attention as the tall amenable travelling companion came into view.

"Terrible, isn't it!" There was mock alarm on the broadly smiling face.

Gordon liked this man and felt a certain sympathy. Turning back to the stouter friend, he stood for a moment, tempted to make a rude suggestion but decided to offer something sensible.

"Wash it down with a soft cloth and some Fairy Liquid water. Do wonders for your hands."

The last words were added without thought, no doubt from once seeing the advert on Jim's television. How did it go? 'When hands that wash dishes are soft as your...' He couldn't quite remember what they were soft as, because the chap in front of him looked about to explode.

The tall friend behind was trying to speak, hampered by a fit of laugher, but managed with difficulty to pull himself together long enough to get the words out.

"It needed washing anyway. Do let me feel your hands when you finish Les." And he subsided again, helpless, unable to continue.

Gordon couldn't help smiling, it was good, there should be lots of laughter on a holiday.

Les' expression changed from anger to indecision, then unable to resist, a little embryo grin fought to get out.

His friend fell, knees on the grass, pointing up at the emerging smile, tears running down his face as he spoke in gasps.

"Careful Les. If that gets out, your chin will fall off."

Try as he might however, Les could not suppress it, and shortly all three were laughing together with abandon. Two heads poked from separate caravans as the wives looked on in amazement.

"How do you think we've done so far?"

Jan, gazing out over the river, turned at Gordon's voice. He sat in the other armchair, a small drawing-board covered with papers and notebooks on his knee. Life was slowing; more time to take stock and relax.

"Seems to have been busy, difficult for me to say, I was away at the roadside most of last year, it's different now, being here all the time. I would guess this season has been nearly as good... No, it was better! Must have been! I saw that sneaky grin cross your face."

He nodded agreement, looking down to where his finger marked a spot in a list of figures. "Up to the end of August, we had 3,706 caravan-days last year, that includes the tents too. This year it's 4,487, quite a good improvement. River Valley's fame must be spreading!"

It was certainly good news, moreover, as additional people came to know the site, recommendations were bound to increase. On the downside, expenses were also escalating; everything from insurance to toilet rolls had risen and would almost certainly continue to do so. No great fortune appeared in immediate prospect, but the family felt content not to have everything at once. It should only be a matter of time before finances substantially improved - shouldn't it?

Chapter 19

Blackberries and Judy

Blackberries were in season again; the children picked them regularly, helped occasionally by their parents now business demands were slackening. Some fruit found its way into tarts or pies, mixed sometimes with apple from the single tree on site, served normally with custard but occasionally topped instead by thick Cornish clotted cream. Over the past years, what with economies and restricted cooking facilities in the caravans, it had become normal not to have a second course at meals, except on rare occasions. This practice had continued now they lived in a house, so the appearance of a dessert, and particularly when it included cream, elicited much praise and delight from the children.

However, most blackberries continued to be converted into bramble jelly. Reliance on this type of jam in earlier years had given the family a taste for it. In spite of the new cooker, there seemed no better method of preparation than that previously used in the caravan. The big pan was still hoisted onto the kitchen stove, although now it boiled more quickly. One morning a batch had been cooked and strained off into various smaller containers - mixing bowls and Pyrex dishes mainly. The residue hung in muslin to drain for a short while, yielding perhaps another half pint to be returned with the other juice and an appropriate amount of sugar to the big pan. This mixture was re-heating when Gordon arrived for coffee.

"Thought you were off to the hairdresser."

Jan, reaching for a wooden spoon with the intention of stirring the juice again, stopped in mid-movement, alarm on her face, neck swivelling towards the clock.

"Damn! I'll be late!"

Hurriedly changing clothes, she prepared to rush into town, pausing to issue instructions.

"It needs about twenty minutes but the time varies quite a lot," she paused, seeing the blank expression on his face. "Listen!" She thumped one fist down on the worktop in irritation, casting another hasty glance at the clock. "I know you're not paying attention! What are you thinking about!"

"I was wondering why you put on new lipstick and powder your face to see a hairdresser?"

She glared at him in exasperation.

"In case I meet a good-looking chap I can run away with! Now Listen! I'll start again because you didn't hear a word, did you!" She said it explosively, daring him to answer.

He hesitated, smiled at her and spoke slowly, as if reading something recorded in his mind.

"It needs twenty minutes, but the time varies," he paused, correcting himself, "varies quite a lot."

"Grr! I hate you! How can you always do that? I know you weren't listening!"

"I always listen to everything you say, dear." He said it earnestly with just a hint of a condescending smile.

She took a deep breath, clenched and unclenched her hands, lifting the spoon she had intended stirring the mixture with as if to strike him. He smiled back blandly, waiting.

"Grr," again the sound rumbled under her breath and she continued, trying to put it simply as if instructing a child, hoping he would get it right and wishing she could stay to finish the task herself.

"To test if it's done, use two spoons. Take a very small quantity in a teaspoon, then holding a tablespoon upside down over the sink, drip a spot of the liquid onto the back. You follow?"

He nodded.

"If the liquid runs off the cold spoon, it's not done, so

343

let it cook a little longer. If it's ready, it should set on the spoon and not run off. You can pour it into those jam jars while it's still hot. I'll be some time; want to shop while I'm out - save a trip later in the week."

He had his instructions and off she went. Nothing difficult, the timer was set for twenty minutes, something about not trusting him to remember she had said. Anyone would think he let his mind wander!

The time passed quickly as he sawed and planed away at a temporary workbench in the basement, producing a new set of footstools for children to stand on - for use in front of the basins in the toilet buildings. As fortune would have it he just heard the bell and wondered for an instant why it rang. Of course, the bramble jelly; he hadn't really forgotten, would have thought of it any minute - probably.

There had been no need to hurry back to the stove, to leap up the basement staircase three steps at a time as he did. Although boiling merrily away, the first sample tested ran straight off the spoon. It wasn't ready.

Two hours later matters were starting to get a bit worrying. Where was Jan? Help! The stuff would still not set on the spoon; she had definitely said it wasn't ready until it did. The colour had changed as time went on, getting darker and darker. No sign remained of the super deep red colour seen at first. It had become what could only be described as a dirty black; a dark, sullen colour with perhaps a faint suggestion of brownish maroon. And another thing, there was less of it. The level in the pan had gone down by nearly a third. It was time for action. He must make a decision! Mustn't he? Or should he wait a little longer? Yes, why not? Just another five minutes. If the stuff didn't set by then - straight in the containers with it.

Fifteen minutes later the mixture continued to simmer, and still no Jan! Peering again through the window, the track lay empty. Turning back, he reached for the gas tap, hand hovering doubtfully, then grasped the black knob and twisted.

Gradually the bubbling subsided and after a short

cooling period, the dark mixture now somewhat thick and syrupy, was ladled into the waiting jars.

When Jan finally returned the full containers were standing in a line ready for capping, a pile of previously cut plastic disks and elastic bands waiting nearby. He warned her they were still hot.

"Can't be, I've been out for hours. It's a funny colour." Her hand reached out confidently to lift one.

"Ouch!" she dropped it quickly.

"I did warn you."

"How long did you boil it for?"

"Only two and half hours."

"Two and a half hours!" Her voice rose an octave with incredulity, total disbelief. "You forgot it, didn't you!"

"No. I..."

"You must have!" she cut in, not giving him chance to explain. "I should have known you would. You're useless!" But she was laughing. Jan looked so good when she laughed.

"You didn't say that last night."

"Well perhaps not entirely useless," she agreed as they hugged each other, "but you must admit you go off in a world of your own sometimes."

Never admit anything!

"Certainly not! If a chap could get a word in edgeways I'd explain." He stopped, not actually offering an explanation. She'd ask if he waited long enough - would never be able to resist. The pause lengthened as seconds ticked by.

"Well go on then! Explain! If you can."

"I did exactly as you said, tested it on a spoon but it never set. Must have tried it twenty or thirty times and each time it ran straight off. In the end I took decisive action and tipped it into the jars; that was just before you came back. Anyway I think it may be all right. I'm sure it will keep."

"Keep! Certainly it'll keep - probably forever! That jam will set so hard no one will ever get it out of the jars!"

Relating the tale at lunchtime, Jan found the children less amused than expected; other things occupying their

345

minds. The holidays were over tomorrow and Christopher would start his first day at the senior school.

In the morning, Sharon and Stephen saw him go, enviously watching as he strode up the road for the school bus to Penzance. Sharon had even deferred to his new stature at a small argument during breakfast, backing down to his new seniority by agreeing to call him Chris instead of Christopher. Both parents had waited at the doorway to wave again as he disappeared round the bend in the road, hoping he would settle in well, and had been fascinated by the facial expressions of their two younger children.

"It's extraordinary," Jan commented later, "how much this week has changed the relationship between them. Did you see the longing in their faces to be old enough to go with him?"

Gordon nodded, slipping his arm round and pulling her close. "Have you ever thought how many people spend their first years wanting to be older, and the rest of life longing to be younger. I think the change occurs at about eighteen."

She nestled closer, head on his shoulder, forehead resting against his cheek. "You're being very profound, do *you* want to be eighteen again?"

"No, couldn't risk it."

"Risk it?" Her face tilted, puckering in a quizzical expression.

"Didn't capture you until we were twenty-one. Who knows if I should be so lucky again?"

She stretched up, softly touching her lips on his.

* * *

Blackberries were not the only natural fruits in the valley, hazelnuts too, abounded. The children had collected them by the bucketful in previous Septembers, particularly in the first year when food was so short that living off the land to the greatest possible extent had been a necessity. These nuts, rich in vitamin E, added welcome variety to the restricted food range. They had been enjoyed by all except Sharon.

Gordon spoke to the three children at coffee one Saturday morning.

"I need a bucketful of nuts, not in their husks, just the shells. Can you fill one by lunchtime?"

"A bucketful without husks is millions!" Chris's voice held dismay.

"I don't eat nuts, I shouldn't have to help!" Sharon immediately objected.

A storm of intended protest was clear in the boys' faces but their father's raised hand, one finger extended, caused them to pause.

"These nuts are not for eating."

Argument forgotten, the children waited attentively, expecting an explanation but none came. It was Sharon of course, who spoke first; he expected she would.

"What are they for?"

"Fill the bucket, then watch!" Dad rose, leaving for work again, pausing in the doorway to address Jan. "By the way, the tractor cushion is falling to pieces. Could you knock up a new loose cover, something really tough? Won't need a cushion this morning, I'm stone walling. Don't sew the back up, so the cover will slip off." And he was gone.

Returning at lunchtime, the children met him at the door displaying a bucket filled to the brim with brown hazelnuts. He nodded, patting Stephen's head but the young lad shook off the hand and stepped backwards, not prepared to be treated as a child. As her father made to enter, Sharon moved in front of the doorway,

"We've collected them, now what are they for?"

"All in good time," he turned to Chris who stood holding the bucket. "Bring them inside." As the group entered the house, Jan appeared with the finished cushion in her hands. Gordon took it from her, eased the new outer casing off the old foam rubber inside, and signalled to Chris.

"Tip them in here."

As the nuts tumbled in, Sharon and Stephen drew close to watch. Jan, standing to one side, anticipated what would be required.

"Why didn't you say it was only the outer casing you needed? Now I suppose you want me to sew it up before we eat." Seeing a nod of affirmation, she shrugged holding out a hand. "OK, lunch is stew, it can have a bit longer. Give it here."

Chris lifted the sack like cover, passing it to her. The job was quickly finished, a double row of stitches pulled tight in strong thread.

"There, it's finished." The new cushion was passed over. "Can I throw the old one away now?"

"Wait until I try this for a few days first."

She had expected the reply, knew his reluctance to throw anything away. Last time an old donkey jacket was finally tossed out at her insistence, she had seen him rescue it from the dustbin later and secretly hang the disreputable garment in the service passage.

"Might be useful for working down trenches," he had blustered, on being challenged.

She wouldn't ask again about the old cushion, just dump it one day in the bottom of a bin, hidden by other rubbish. As the children watched, Dad turned the nuts round a few times getting the feel, then tossed them on his chair and sat down.

"Is that all they're for?" Sharon demanded, voice rising. Taking several quick paces, feet stamping in annoyance, she stood before him with one hand on her hip, staring with disapproval.

"Yes. Bean bags are used by some tractor drivers, supposed to be more comfortable than foam in hot weather. Nuts will last longer. And these are for free!"

"Only because we collected them." Sharon objected as the boys moved in to support her.

"What else are children for?" Gordon asked as the ring of young faces surrounded him accusingly.

Jan swivelled towards the window, hiding her face. How often had the family asked him, "What else are Dad's for?" when they wanted something done.

Loose cushions were always used on the digger, to be

taken in at night, for it stood out in all weathers. Sitting on the machine after lunch, the seat seemed fluid, unstable. This first impression was false. After a short time the nuts moulded themselves pleasantly into shape, moving only slightly with changing positions. The new seat proved so extremely comfortable that the idea was extended to the office chair, and later his armchair received similar treatment. One of the year's last visitors, an old friend, was ushered into the lounge one day for a chat, something time seldom allowed during most of the season. He chose the wrong chair, lowered himself into the seat and rose again like he'd sat on a cat.

* * *

"Judy is a wonderful creature." The woman patted the animal's back. It continued browsing, ignoring the owner's attentions.

Jan looked at Gordon and back again to the somewhat unkempt figure; black hair with white patches, matted and muddy in places, and purposeful horns sweeping sharply backward. They approached a step nearer and Judy's head came up, turning over one shoulder to regard them critically. After a moment the head returned towards the grass, pausing to shake in a peculiar twisting motion before it resumed munching. Was it a fly, or a dismissive shake showing disapproval of its visitors?

The woman, seeing their doubts, reached out again to stroke the coarse hair of a flank.

"Goats are not much trouble to look after," she promised persuasively. "They give lovely milk; it's so easy to do."

They wanted to believe her. She briefly demonstrated, letting both try while explaining how. It did seem easy, if a little awkward, the goat tending to move about, upset perhaps by strange hands? White liquid first trickled, then squirted as techniques improved, to disappear wastefully into short tufted grass below. When satisfied, the woman attached a rope round the goat's neck and passed it over, taking the agreed sum in exchange.

They had bought themselves a new, twice-daily source that should solve the problem of keeping milk fresh without a refrigerator. Gordon turned for the car, pulling on the rope but the goat had no intention of following, digging in its hoofs and straining backwards.

"Use the horns," the woman advised.

She was watching with a faint smile on her face, a Mona Lisa smile that hinted at knowledge she was not prepared to reveal, an ominous smile perhaps. Had they really made such a wise decision? Moving hand over hand along the rope until within range, Gordon grabbed a horn and held on as Judy tossed her head from side to side in a vigorous attempt to dislodge the hand. Gripping tighter, he was slightly surprised at being able to retain a hold, and proceeded to tug the struggling goat, half pulling half lifting, towards the waiting car. Quickly opening the rear door with one hand, he stepped in, dragging the resisting animal up into the rear floor-well. There it stood, sandwiched between the front and rear seats, trapping him in the far corner. Slamming the door behind them, Jan ran quickly round the car, climbed in and started the engine. Looking back to wave as they drew away it was disturbing to see the woman leaning against a small tree, chuckling at some jest she had not thought fit to share.

On the way home the goat behaved reasonably well, though Gordon, wedged in a corner of the back seat, never once released his firm, two handed grip on the horns.

Unloading the goat afterwards, Jan watched in amusement as he struggled, hampered by the confined space, heaving strongly, attempting to push the animal backwards through the now open door. Stopping to rest for a moment, an upward glance caught her grinning at his efforts. Indignantly he glared back, took a deep breath and heaved again, not prepared to be laughed at for being bested by a goat!

"Why don't you leave it to me," she suggested as the animal stubbornly resisted.

"Go ahead!" He spoke with a snort of derision, letting

go of Judy's horns, tossing the lead rope out through the open door and sinking back into the seat to watch.

Instead of walking round behind the animal for the rope as expected, Jan opened the other door.

"Lift your legs," she ordered, and seeing his feet swing up onto the rear seat, called, "Come on Judy!"

The goat stepped calmly forward, jumping to the ground next to her.

"It just needs a little common sense." The words were tossed over one shoulder without a backward glance, as Judy followed towards a grassy area, trotting at heel like a faithful dog.

Having tied the lead rope to a nearby tree, Jan returned, walking towards Gordon who now leant on the car watching. Brushing hands together in her usual gesture of success, she paused beside him, speaking quietly from the corner of her mouth, accent somewhere between the typical American detective and Connery's Bond.

"Some of us have it, some..." She shrugged, leaving the rest unsaid, and with a long sideways gaze from under lowered eyelashes, departed into the house, hips swinging from side to side in a grossly exaggerated manner.

Sharon and Stephen arrived home from school, dashing along the road, well aware of the expected new arrival. Discussions on buying a goat had continued for weeks, recurring each time the milk went off, which without a fridge was frequently. Gordon had been reticent, cautioning every-one of the time and effort caring for an animal would entail. Approval from the children however, was unanimous.

Three cries of, "I'll look after it," had rung simultaneously across the table that very morning when Dad again warned, "We may buy one today. Are you sure about the extra work needed to care for it properly?"

Now, pelting across the bridge, they arrived breathless at the door.

"Did you buy it?" Sharon gasped, eyes shining at the nods of confirmation, head turning to scan the areas nearby.

"Where?"

Jan, slipping on a cardigan, pointed in the direction of the second toilet building, both parents following behind as the children sped off. When they caught up, the youngsters were standing, eager but dubious, as Judy strained towards them at the full extent of her tether.

"Can we touch? Is it safe?" Sharon edged closer but offered no move to actually make contact. "Those horns...?" she didn't quite know what to ask about them, but stretched out a tentative hand, snatching it back quickly when Judy reached up exposing teeth as if to nibble the fingers.

For once Stephen lagged behind, his usual reckless tendency to dash straight in deserting him. The goat, after all, was nearly as big as the lad.

Jan smiled, nudging Gordon. "You'd better go and help."

He stepped forward, taking hold of a horn and kneeling beside the goat. Following their mother's lead, the two children moved to the other side. Gingerly at first, they patted and stroked the coarse hair, gaining confidence as Judy exhibited no objections; seeming in fact to enjoy all the attention. Watching the goat's expression as he knelt, Gordon recalled the way someone else reacted when his own fingers ran across her back.

After a while Jan announced her intention of returning to the house, to be there when Chris arrived home. Expecting the children to stay with Judy, the parents moved off but had taken no more than a couple of steps when Stephen followed behind. Jan smiled down at him.

"Tell Chris," he said quietly.

That was all, but Jan understood. He wanted to be first with the news. Sharon had heard too, and looked from goat to departing group, torn between staying and missing out on the revelation of Judy's arrival. She hesitated, half rose to leave, changed her mind and knelt again to stroke the black neck - then stood once more, looking with indecision to where Stephen had disappeared. Turning back to pat and rub Judy's head affectionately, she resolved to stay. However, the torment of not knowing what was happening at the house was too much. Suddenly she took off at speed in pursuit of the other three.

The small family group stood on the bridge for perhaps five minutes waiting, idly watching the fish, facing upstream towards Relubbus, the direction from which Chris would appear. At first sight of the approaching figure, Stephen sprinted up the road, gaining a head start while his sister pointed, arm outstretched, "There he is!"

The little lad glanced hurriedly behind as he went, fully expecting to be overtaken by the faster Sharon. Jan however, had laid a restraining arm on her daughter's shoulder, bending over to whisper in an ear.

"Don't you think it would be nice for a change to let Stephen tell him. You're older and a girl should learn to show restraint."

Sharon nodded reluctantly.

"Boys find a certain reticence more interesting," her mother encouraged, smiling to see mixed feelings cross the youthful face. Boys were still an enigma; she was in no way attracted to any of them but as was natural to young girls, terribly concerned to make a good impression.

"Reticence? Sort of being quiet, being left out?" Sharon glanced at her mother doubtfully, turning away, uncertain, ostensibly watching her brothers now walking together along the road.

"Sometimes it pays not to join in, to pretend you're above such things; just stand quietly, perhaps the merest hint of smile on your face, as if you know."

"Know what?"

"Never mind, doesn't matter what, that's for them to imagine; gives you that air of mystery, makes them wonder."

The boys were coming; Sharon nodded again, looking at her mother thoughtfully.

Stephen led Chris round to Judy, the rest of the family following not too closely behind. Unlike his younger brother and sister, Chris strode straight up to the goat, scratching its back and head, allowing Judy to rub her side against his leg.

"Is it real milk?" Sharon asked her mother warily at tea

later.

"If you mean is it cow's milk, yes it is; a pint I bought this morning. There's not much, use it sparingly. Judy kicked the pail over while I was milking, so there's none of hers. My technique must need improving, I'll try to be more gentle."

The children had departed for school the following morning when Jan suggested to Gordon, "Hold the horns while I milk."

This certainly seemed to help but at one point Judy, standing on three legs, attempted to kick the pail with a hind hoof. Only an adept movement from Jan, snatching the bucket clear as it tipped, saved most, but not all of the contents. They deemed it wise to tether the goat until it became used to the valley, to prevent it wandering off and becoming lost. Tying the rope to a woody stem within reach of plentiful grass seemed easiest.

Now in September, when booking calls were almost non-existent, Jan had returned to the practice of taking coffee to where the big machine was working. She paused, flask in hand, to check on Judy and noticed two small saplings nearby had been entirely stripped of bark.

At tea that evening, the children gazed suspiciously at half glasses of milk beside steaming plates of beans on toast.

"It's Judy's?"

"Yes. Would have been more but she tipped the bucket again." Jan paused seeing Stephen lean forward to sniff at the liquid.

Chris lifted his glass and took a sip, then a swallow. "You can't tell the difference!" He grinned at the others in pleasure, his voice holding surprise.

"We should milk her early tomorrow," his mother suggested. "We need to - no milk otherwise. I've hardly enough for hot drinks this evening. If we do that each day, breakfast milk will always be fresh but someone must walk her first, let her eat a little. Might make milking less difficult; arrange it between yourselves."

To an extent their hopes for Judy were justified. Over

the next few days, milking apart, she proved just as the woman had said 'not very difficult to look after', though it was necessary to move the tethering position regularly. Goats' appetites were legendary, and this one proved no exception; she would eat almost anything. That included her undesirable habit of chewing bark. After those first two saplings were destroyed, it became imperative to tether Judy in places that prevented her reaching small trees; larger trunks seemed comparatively immune. Original thoughts that she could one day run free, choosing for herself what to eat, had to be discarded.

Other things were learned too. While the goat could be tethered to gorse and would eat those prickly tops with apparent relish, it was also gifted with a special knack for getting tangled, winding the rope round anything in sight, including its own legs. This could easily be overcome by staking Judy on a long tether in the centre of a grassy area, leaving nothing with which to become entangled. However, a chapter near the beginning of the goat book revealed that feeding solely on grass was unsuitable. Some roughage formed an essential part of the diet, helping with body heat and preventing the formation of a wad of cold wet grass in the stomach, so difficult for the animal to break down. Sometimes Judy was tethered on grass alone, but given at least three walks a day where she feasted on bramble, ivy, gorse, young twigs and other suitable roughage, with enthusiasm.

Chris, having taken to the goat from the start, did the majority of this walking and regularly moved the tethering point to fresh places. One day, when passing an area where gorse bushes were being uprooted, he paused to speak to his father, allowing the goat to browse the prickly tops and the entwining blackberry leaves.

"Dad, Judy really likes brambles. Whenever I walk her, no matter how much she's eaten, she always gobbles up the leaves."

Gordon paused in his work, looking down at his son, as Judy reached up to delicately nibble another leaf from between the surrounding barbs.

"A goat will always eat a little more if it's different, rather like young children. If mum served an enormous lunch, then unexpectedly produced ice cream afterwards, Stephen would eat some more, wouldn't he?"

"We all would - you should try us!"

"I'll bet! Perhaps that's why children are often referred to as kids?"

"Will Judy have kids?"

"We hope so. Must visit the Billy first, but not until she's in season. You should watch; if she bleats a lot and holds her tail high, it may be a sign."

Mid-autumn saw the start of a more solid return to removing stone from the heaps; a constant task, scheduled to last through winter and beyond. Some of this work had been done sporadically earlier in the month at times when the handful of visitors were out for the day. A few loads of topsoil had also arrived, hijacked by the simple expedient of stopping lorries on the road, offering drivers a small commission for bringing it to the valley instead of the intended rubbish tip. Several other newly levelled areas still awaited such soil, and more would be needed for planting along the tops of dry stone walls to form terraces as work proceeded. Perhaps a few further lorry loads would appear, Jan had noticed in the paper that Goldsithney, a village two miles away on the route to St Michael's Mount, was to have a new village hall. The site for that would need clearing. Whatever was planned for the soil, a word in the right ear might divert the odd load, even if only the last one at night with the driver in a hurry to get home. It would add a most welcome touch of variety to the winter's work. This year too, maintenance tasks on grass, in toilet buildings and odd jobs around the house all required attention, offering the prospect of further short breaks from relentless clearing and filling routines. These diversions, welcome as they might be, would inevitably limit the number of extra pitches for next season. However, pressure to expand no longer controlled their lives. Any shortfall in caravan places should not now threaten failure, just postpone perhaps the possibility of a lounge carpet that properly fitted the room.

* * *

"Well apart from money, how have we done, can we improve anything for next season?" Jan addressed the question mainly at Gordon, though she glanced also towards the children.

They were seated, not in the house but on a grassy clearing high above those parts of site so far in use; a small glade surrounded on three sides by trees, with views over the valley towards the southeast. The season was dying; not officially, the site remained open for another week but only four caravans were left. A sign stuck to the office door instructed any arrivals where to park but that was only a precaution placed there at Gordon's insistence.

With the children at home for the weekend, Jan had decided to take advantage of the warm sun that shone down from a cloudless sky into this sheltered retreat and onto the picnic now spread between them. Only the topmost branches of the surrounding trees moved in a light breeze, the odd autumn tinted leaf floating down. It was early for tea but the sun would be gone in an hour.

"Improve?" Gordon responded as they ate. "Yes, I think so. Certainly I don't intend to be idle over the winter. It will never look really good until the terraces are finished. That means moving more mine waste, building dry stone walls; what else did you have in mind?"

"The roads." Jan frowned. "People dislike the dust, could we spray them with anything?"

"Only tarmac would last - expensive. Too much yet but yes, we do need it. I don't know when."

"Several of my friends have asked for hair dryers. One doesn't want to come back because we've none." Sharon offered, turning to her brothers for support.

"None of the boys have said anything," Chris shook his

head, "but some complain how far away the taps are. Boys usually do the water carrying."

Jan nodded, turning to Gordon. "The taps are a long way from the new pitches, you'll have to do something soon, before you get much farther downstream."

"I can easily put more taps on the toilet buildings but I'd rather fill and level a bit more before extending the water main; I can do the whole pipe in one go then. Hairdryers are out, they need electric and you know it costs too much. Eventually perhaps - but we may have to choose between power or tarmac for the roads. We'll need a lot more seasons to afford either. People don't seem too worried, do they? Most like the valley, at least they say so when we talk."

"Sure, most do appear happy, satisfied with what we offer. They particularly like our showers. One woman described them as being torrential!" Jan smiled, pleased at their success. "But they do ask a lot of questions. It's difficult sometimes, particularly if the place referred to is local; you're ashamed to let them know you've never seen it. Don't you find that when you talk to people?"

"Um yes, mostly when I'm seeing them in. I usually stay chatting, making sure they're satisfied and comfortable - unless we have a queue waiting, that is. They do ask all sorts of things, as you say. The flora and fauna questions are getting easier, but the others... Ah, well, no need to worry; if you don't know the answer, change the subject." Gordon directed his attention to the children, "Sometimes, if it's a difficult question, I start speaking, then break off abruptly, look towards the office and say, 'that's Jan calling, must be a problem, I have to go', and I dash off. They never realise I didn't have a clue. It's not always advisable to reveal your ignorance!"

"My friends ask a lot too," Chris agreed, "but usually I know the answers. When I go out in other people's cars we visit places, and the boys at school talk a lot on anything special in the area. Mostly I've seen or heard of the things that get asked."

Dad looked at Sharon and Stephen, seeing them both

nod in agreement with Chris, and realised that the children probably did know more about the area than either parent. Bringing his mind back to the subject in hand he asked, "What about cheaper things? What would help without costing much?"

Jan pursed her lips, thinking. "A few more hooks in the toilets, I've heard some comments that there aren't enough - and the dustbins keep getting knocked over, can we stop that? "She turned to the children, inviting suggestions.

"My friend had a dog." Stephen offered.

"Yes?"

"Took it to the toilets with him each morning."

"Well?"

"Nowhere to tie it. People grumbled if he took it in."

The meal was largely finished, and the sun declining, shadows from the taller trees had already crept out to cover the cloth spread on the ground between them. Shortly the family rose, reluctantly making their way down the steep slope and back to the house.

* * *

"They have an emu!"

"Who has an emu?"

"This new exhibition in Hayle, like a zoo for birds, it's called Bird Paradise." Chris explained. "Can we visit it, you said we need to know about these places? It's not actually an emu..."

"Probably a sparrow!" Sharon interrupted with derision.

"You needn't come. It's like an emu, one of my school friends went last week."

"Never mind the arguing," Jan cautioned quietly. "We'll go if you persuade your father. He'll be back shortly so think how you're going to do it. Try to be a bit more subtle than just asking outright or he'll refuse; you know he doesn't ever like to stop working."

The children looked at each other blankly while their mother strode over to the stove, checking on the evening meal, before turning back to sit down at the table.

"No ideas? Then listen, this is what I suggest."

She outlined the strategy; they listened. At one point Chris protested that his friend had never said anything like that and he had no idea if they were any good.

"Do you want us to go, or not?" his mother demanded.

Shortly after, Gordon arrived slipping off muddy boots on the office step and the family sat down together to eat and to chatter.

"This new bird place," Sharon asked in a lull, "do you think many people will visit there next year? The girls at school were all talking about it."

The four watched Dad's expression, trying not to make it obvious, Mum casually suggesting a visit. A frown indicated immediate resistance. Jan caught Chris's eye and gave a faint nod.

"It's got thousands of birds," Chris responded, "and an Emu. One of my friends has been there. He says it has the most fantastic loos!"

On Saturday morning, the whole family prepared to climb in the car. Surprisingly Gordon chivvied them along, offering encouragement rather than the reluctance normally shown when working time was lost. Three children on the back seat cast sly glances at each other, smothering giggles. Quickly the five miles to Hayle were covered.

The displays actually consisted of perhaps a hundred different birds in various generously sized enclosures; all looked very contented with life. The display of colourful feathers was impressive but after the first dozen, any attempt to remember the names was abandoned. Gordon's efforts to find the super loos were unsuccessful, deliberately diverted at every turn by Jan, hesitantly backed up by the children. Towards lunchtime, Sharon wanted a loo herself, and whispered to her mother, but Jan urged, "Don't you dare! We'll be off shortly, you wait. Dad will only start searching again if you disappear."

"Well, we found the Emu." Gordon unlocked the car for the journey home. "What was it called... a Wattled

Cassawory? Your friend seems to have got it wrong about the loos though!" He glancing suspiciously at Jan who gazed innocently skywards.

"Must have mis-heard," Chris mumbled, looking down. "Perhaps he said Owls, not loos?"

"It may have escaped your attention but there aren't any Owls in the collection either; parrots, macaws, cranes, flamingos, even a bird of paradise but not an owl anywhere." Seeing Chris shrug and ease his weight uncomfortably from one foot to another, Gordon reached over to lay a hand on the boy's shoulder. "Don't worry, I can guess whose idea it was. Let that be a lesson to you about girls!"

The following day another caravan arrived, but two left, reducing those on site to three. It was only to be expected towards end of season. The day was sunny and mild with little wind, and neither of the visitors seemed inclined to leave the site. Gordon chose to spend time quietly trimming back trees overhanging some already completed areas rather than starting the digger engine. He wondered if any of the visitors would wander over to talk but none had done so and he worked on alone all morning.

Just before midday, missing company again, he chatted to Robin who had flown up to investigate. The bird perched as always, slightly sideways on a tall stem close by, almost within reach, head on one side, watching man and ground simultaneously. Recounting the previous days visit, Gordon asked, "Why don't cock robins have better plumage than female robins, like those exotic tropical birds."

"Hm! Hothouse plants. They need the help, the fancy feathers, just to pull a hen. Personally, I have more trouble fighting them off - natural charm you know. Find difficulty yourself, do you? Try a beard."

Thoughts terminated as the bird flew off, no doubt to cadge an easier meal from one of the remaining caravans. Watching it go, he stroked his chin, remembering the thick black beard he had once grown, and how Jan had detested it.

CHAPTER 20

Must be a way

Looking after Judy was taken seriously. Continued reading revealed a goat's usually robust health could be damaged in several ways. Two books borrowed from the library proved helpful. A relatively cheap one by Jefferies and the more expensive volume, *Goat Husbandry* by Mackenzie. For a start, re-using the same patch of grass with too short a break between might cause heavy worm infestation, so recently used tethering positions must be avoided.

On soft ground the books said, hooves may tend to suffer and require trimming with a knife. An answer had been found to that problem, too. A goat is made for hilly, stony terrain, it likes to climb; the soft centre and hard exterior of each hoof makes it so sure footed, happy to stand on any raised surface. A rock left nearby, even though relatively small, proved irresistible to Judy and was frequently climbed on. This hard surface, together with many walks along the site's stony, rather uneven roads, helped to keep her feet in passable condition, though they were inspected regularly and any long outer edges trimmed with the same Stanley knife used for carving birds.

Judy was one of the family now, deserving every care. Extensive reading compensated, at least a little, for a sad lack of experience with farm animals. She was no offspring of champions. Certainly not, no pedigree this one, but a 'Heinz' - that is to say, 57 different varieties; hardly affectionate like a dog but quite endearing in her way, gazing up with television eyes, the pupils rectangular, little beardy pieces hanging below the chin. Many goats were de-horned at birth but fortunately, not this one, for she looked more proud, more grand and natural. The sturdy horns curved up, slanting back and outwards nearly a foot long; excellent handles, ideal for a really good grip. Judy adored being rubbed around the neck, behind the head or having her back groomed, standing with legs firmly planted, solidly still, quite obviously enjoying the sensation.

However, improvement so far as milking was concerned, proved non-existent; yet it would have been very painful had this regular process ever been neglected. Hand milking was not difficult, provided the animal would keep still. Both Jan and Gordon could now do it well but as the teats were short; three fingers and a thumb were the most he could bring to bear, while she could use a full hand.

"What makes Judy so difficult?" Jan asked. "Was that why the woman laughed when we bought her?"

Gordon shrugged. Quite possibly, but difficult or not, they all liked the animal and wanted it to stay. There was a certain dignity to the way Judy never let herself be dominated.

"Perhaps my hands have been too cold. Hold her a minute, I'll warm them on the hot tank before we start, then try on my own without help again." Jan trotted off to return shortly after, hands clasped together preserving the warmth.

The big question was, would Judy now stand still? Her answer, definitely No! Warm hands or not, it was feet in the pan, kick backwards, then push forwards, head shaking, that large pair of horns swinging about dangerously. Jan sighed in exasperation.

"I might as well not have bothered, you can have them cold next time Judy my girl!"

The pan, one of several utensils used for milking, was taken inside and rinsed; small stones and dust from the rough surface had flown up in the tussle. Starting again, Gordon took the head as Jan milked but Judy kicked her back legs, upsetting the milk again.

"Let Chris hold the head," Jan suggested from her

kneeling position. "You go round behind and stop the hind legs moving."

This worked for a few minutes but Judy overcame the restriction by kicking backwards with a front foot.

Sharon and Stephen joined in, lying flat on the ground, grasping a front leg each, hanging on with both hands and all the force they could muster. Judy was having none of it! She sat down on her udders by throwing her weight backwards, even though all four feet were held immobile.

There must be some way to keep her upright and still! Gordon, continuing to grip both rear legs, changed position to place a shoulder against the goat's backside, preventing her collapsing onto the bucket. At last Jan was able to milk away merrily.

Judy, however, was not to be beaten. Cocking up her short tail, she placed several dozen little spherical deposits on that restraining shoulder to the absolute rapture of the family's younger members. Jan stopped milking, whisking the bucket away and fighting to keep a straight face.

"Don't move!" she gasped, rising. "Let me sweep those in a dustpan. If they fall to the ground here in front of the house, they'll walk in every time the door opens!"

Sharon and Stephen were rolling around on the stony surface, Chris bent over with mirth. Only Dad retained his hold, unable to move without disturbing the little deposits. As Jan passed the goat's head, she stopped to speak and give it a pat.

"Good girl Judy. Well done!"

The children, copying, tried to pat and congratulate Judy in their turn, hindered only by tears of joy running down Sharon's cheeks and further fits of laugher that rendered Chris totally helpless. Stephen, always happier with actions than words, executed a little jig of jumps in the air while holding his nose between index finger and thumb, an action quickly imitated by the other two. It was to be repeated all that evening whenever Dad came near, regardless of the fact that goat droppings, very like those of rabbits in shape only bigger, hardly smelt at all.

Over time milking became easier but Judy periodically reasserted her independence, taking advantage of any drop in vigilance of the restraining hands. While the weather was dry and evenings light, milking normally took place outside the house. However, mainly for the convenience of Sharon and Steven who lay stretched out diagonally on the ground restraining one front leg each, the little ritual moved indoors as autumn progressed, into the hall in front of the two part reeded glass door where the light was passably good. Even here, Judy manifested occasional displays of temperament.

In a sudden tantrum one evening, Chris struggled to retain his grip on the horns as she pulled wildly from side to side. Sharon clung on valiantly but failed to hold the front hoof and Stephen found himself pulled bodily across the floor.

Sensing victory, Judy pushed strongly backwards, treading on the milking pan rim. It spun over, swilling the contents on Jan, the hall carpet, the walls, everything in reach! Lunging farther back, Judy overbalanced Gordon whose shoulder still rested against her hindquarters, and rammed him with a shattering crash, against the lower glass door-panel, some twelve inches behind where he squatted! The whole onslaught took only seconds.

As Gordon struggled to regain equilibrium, his weight resting unbalanced against the door's solid mid-rail, Judy turned to look over her hindquarters, a satisfied expression on her face! Now unrestrained, she stood quite still surveying the chaos around her, making no attempt to move. If goats could smile, this one was certainly doing so!

Fortunately the whole pane had shattered as one and fallen outwards. Gordon, intent on regaining his hold, thrust himself forward, grasping the goat, holding her backside while endeavouring to stand. Only then did he think to examine his own posterior, surprised to find no damage, not even a cut trouser. Chris took a new grip on the horns, Sharon and Stephen grabbing a foot each - but it wasn't necessary. Judy offered no further resistance that night.

Content with the mess now surrounding her, she stood serenely still and at peace as wind whistled through the broken pane. Jan, wet and uncomfortable with milk still dripping from her chin, reached under to squirt a few last streams into the now empty pan, but milking had been substantially complete before the incident occurred.

The carpet must be taken up and washed; sour milk would smell truly awful after a few days, though a goodly proportion had already been absorbed by Jan's clothing. As an afterthought, a final touch to underline further her independence, Judy again cocked up her tail, adding a liberal sprinkling of small round brown spheres to the mess for good luck. The children, now recovered, were beside themselves, showing immense admiration for her achievement! Jan and Gordon smiled at each other as Chris led their temperamental but very loveable goat out; Judy following behind him without the slightest difficulty.

"You promised to fix a curtain rail over this door," Jan commented as she carefully picked tiny splinters of glass off the hall carpet before rolling it up to wash. Fortunately, most of the pane had fallen outside.

Gordon nodded, it was not the first reminder but the reeded glass had no real need of a curtain; it could wait. He worked on, repairing the door panel with a square of plywood cut to fit in place of the glass, and fixed a thicker sheet onto the inner face, using over a dozen screws to make a really secure job.

"Let her try to get through that!" he muttered, as Jan washed milk stains on the wall.

"Haven't you made a lot of work for yourself when you come to put the new glass back in?"

"We're not having glass any more. It can stay like this forever!" He turned towards her, waiting for an argument. She stared back at him, down at the door again, then turned to stalk off with that *We'll see*, look in her eyes.

Having cleaned up and decided the hall was not a suitable milking parlour, she pushed for an alternative arrangement. Next day they milked on the workbench in the basement. A pronounced improvement - Jan could now stand upright on the job and little rope ties fixed to the bench were pulled round Judy's rear hooves preventing her from moving though still not entirely restraining the goat's obstinacy. The real breakthrough came a few days later when a bucket of crushed oats was fixed to the wall! While happily eating, Judy needed no restraint.

"What a difference," Jan's head shook in puzzlement as they discussed the total change some days later. "She even jumps up onto the bench herself now, without you lifting her. Do you think the woman we bought her from offered food regularly at milking times?"

"Probably. Seems like it - bribery will often succeed where all else fails. We tend to assume animals are stupid; Judy has more intelligence than we give credit for! I think that's what she wanted all along, why she wouldn't stand still; her way of telling us. We're the dumb ones, taking so long to understand."

* * *

Chris and his father stood in the office playing snooker. They played by candlelight since the oil lamp still hung in the dining room from where voices, sometimes raised in altercation, drifted through. Sharon, Stephen and their mother were deeply involved in a card game.

"Off the cushion and that red into the far corner pocket," Chris proposed hopefully. Two sides of the table lay hard against outer walls, causing many shots to be played off cushions. Piled temporarily in the adjoining lounge were four mahogany covers that converted the playing surface to a wooden table. Alongside lay a large sheet of blue Rexene, for protecting the baize below these wooden tops in case of spillage.

A forcing shot dropped the red ball in, white rolling back up the table but out of position; black was impossible, leaving a long blue.

"Jim says he played lots of snooker in the police," Chris commented, standing back to look at the shot with disappointment. "I liked the big full sized table he had at his old house. 'Hit it where it shines', he used to tell me, but it doesn't shine at all here. Pity we can't get electric." He got down, sighted along the cue and struck the white ball. The blue failed to fall, striking one side of the pocket, to roll off, ending against the far cushion.

"Good try. Hit it where it shines? Yes, Jim said that to me, to everyone I think," Gordon agreed. "On a normal table the lights are exactly overhead and symmetrical, he may be right then for some shots. Playing in this light could ruin our judgement in a proper game; the Tilley lamp would be no better, there's always a dark patch directly underneath." He struck the ball. The shot was too difficult, not really worth trying for but no one played safe on this table; to do so only spoiled an already slow game.

"Dad," Chris said tentatively.

Stepping back from the table, Gordon turned, curious at the inflection in his son's voice, seeking a hint of expression but the lad had his back to the candle, his face in deep shadow.

Chris continued. "If some of the boys at school were thinking of pulling down a bus stop, how bad would that be?"

Resting his cue against the wall and leaning back, Gordon gazed at the flickering light, thinking how to answer.

"When I was a teenager, about sixteen, I went each day from Amersham to London by train; the journey took about an hour. Sometimes I travelled with a friend. One day on the homeward journey something went wrong with the engine. We had to get off at Richmansworth station. It was late evening; there were only a few passengers. We all had to wait, the next train wasn't due for twenty minutes. My friend wanted to leave the station. He said, *'Come on, there's hardly anyone about, I'll show you something.'*

"I followed him and sure enough, outside the station we didn't see a soul. He led us maybe two hundred yards

368

on a path separated from the road by some bushes, or it might have been a hedge, with street lights all the way. They were different then, the lights; big glass globes with some sort of bulb inside, high up on tall concrete standards. My friend looked around, acting kind of furtively; I didn't understand why. Quite suddenly he bent down, picked up a stone and threw it. The nearest globe smashed with a great crash, then tinkling sounds as bits of glass hit the ground. He started to run; I must have been rooted to the spot because he came back, grabbed my arm and pulled. Near the station he stepped back into a recess, waiting in deep shadow. I stood with him. When the train pulled in, we ran through the station doorway and climbed aboard quickly. They were individual carriages then, we chose an empty one. He was excited, pleased with himself, felt big; expected me to be impressed. I pretended to be, maybe was... I didn't know what to think but knew he'd get off at the next stop.

"After that I was alone, wondering about the light, whether I could do it, how it would feel. Outside the window everything was black, nothing to see, so my mind wandered on. Who would make the repair? Those lamp standards were tall, someone must climb them. You seldom saw mechanical lifts in those days. I wondered how they reached; perhaps with a belt device like men who go up telegraph poles?"

Gordon paused, looking towards Chris but the face was still in shadow, candle flickering behind. The lad's reactions could not be gauged, standing quite still, waiting for the narrative to continue, making no attempt to play the next shot.

"I sat there, the carriages were fairly gloomy, bit better than our candle mark you, and the thought that came to me was this. My friend was not so brave; the brave one would be the chap that made the repair, not the one who broke it. Breaking it was easy. I began to think of other things that had been vandalised, the windows in empty buildings for instance. Smashing them, that was easy too, any fool could do it, nothing brave, nothing clever. The clever one would be the glazier who knew how to replace it.

369

"It formed in my mind on that journey that I was going to make things, learn how to build, be the man who could do it, whatever; the person people could turn to for help. I didn't say anything to my friend next day and I stopped copying him. My work got better, but not his. He seemed to have more friends but I wondered if they really liked the fellow; when they needed advice they never turned to him.

"I passed him years later, he was standing in a bus queue. We chatted briefly but had nothing in common. He hadn't done well, was poorly dressed and tried to borrow some money. He was bitter, said life had treated him hard, blamed other people. It may have been bad luck of course, that can happen but I remembered that street light and somehow I doubted it. His bus arrived and he climbed aboard; I was glad to get away. No spring to his step now, no daring, just a grey little man - not in size but little in spirit, in the sense of being useless, having no self-respect, nobody caring; sailing through life leaving nothing of use in his wake. When I hear of vandalism now, I think of him... of small destructive people, able to smash but without the flare to build, to create."

There was a pause before Gordon prompted, "Your shot."

Chris didn't reply. He leaned over, quietly cued up and put the red ball squarely in the far pocket.

* * *

"It's getting rather dark." Jan strained to peer through the office door, trying to see up the road as the twilight deepened. "I didn't expect her to stay this long."

Sharon was helping Audrey up at the bungalow. With Jan's agreement, she had arranged to stay to tea but that had been two hours since.

"What are they doing," Gordon asked, putting his book aside as the boys looked up from a game on the floor, shading their eyes against the oil lamp already hissing overhead. Seeing the raised hands, Jan wondered as she had so often before, how anything could be so bright when viewed directly, yet give so little light for reading. Maybe because the lamp shone outwards rather than down?

"She's learning to use the sewing machine. Audrey is making new curtains for the bungalow's back bedroom and offered Sharon the opportunity to help, but she wasn't supposed to stay this late."

"Why can't she bring the machine up here to learn," Chris asked grudgingly. "Bet she's watching Jim's television." His voice was a tinged of envy. Stephen's expression changed to deep resentment but he passed no comment.

"Our light is too poor to see the stitches," Jan reminded them.

"I'll go and meet her." Gordon disappeared into the hall but as he donned a coat, two headlights appeared; almost certainly Jim's car, for no other was likely to venture down the track out of season. The little Hillman Imp swung round in a circle, drawing to a halt. Sharon jumped out, turned to say something to Jim, then slammed the door and as the car drew away, she ran inside, eyes shining with excitement.

"You've been watching television!" Chris accused, not waiting for her to speak.

Shrugging off the coat, Sharon turned to her brothers, the irrepressible smile bursting from her cheeks confirming they were right.

"Like she's won first prize," Jan thought, watching her daughter's raised chin and the superior way the girl looked back at Chris and Stephen. "She knows they're upset, is enjoying rubbing it in, scoring her point as Gordon would say. Ah well, they do it to her often enough. Must teach her to be more subtle."

Later in the evening, the three children sat close together, Sharon talking animatedly while the others listened. Jan, a book in her hand, also found herself eavesdropping on the tale of adventure being related, wondering if all the children would gradually spend less time at home and find ways of watching with Audrey and Jim, or with friends from school.

Power remained the big unsolved problem. The price quoted for a mains supply looked ridiculous, totally out of reach, not really surprising with the nearest line half a mile away. Of course, they *were* managing without, but it was hard on the children when all their friends had power.

How could such a relatively recent invention so quickly become indispensable? A century ago nobody had electricity, and lived quite happily in its absence. For a short time it had been a toy of the very rich, a novelty showing their position in life, certainly not a necessity. Gradually, but with increasing speed, the supply had become more widespread. Now everyone expected it, except perhaps on holiday.

From time to time the children, and particularly Sharon, would pass comments about their friends' televisions or hair dryers, or music centres, with just that touch of envy at missing what was common to others. All of them felt it to some degree but were realistic, they knew the family could never afford the cost, and in general were uncomplaining. Only occasionally did those little wistful references slip out, for instance about a TV program all their friends had seen and were talking about, or even on one occasion that a teacher had asked them to watch.

Jan too, wished they could find a supply, particularly as days started to shorten and darkness fell earlier. She worried about it occasionally, most often in the daytime strangely enough, when sitting in the house on her own. Anything could trigger the thoughts, using a hand whisk, heating the ancient iron over the gas, or just the radio batteries running out. Sometimes after darkness had fallen, as she sat quietly watching the children sprawled together on the floor reading or playing games in the poor light, she wondered would things ever change?

In bed one night, restless and unable to sleep, Jan turned towards Gordon and snuggled near, unaware he remained awake. His hand slid under the short nightdress, up the back of one thigh, slowly on over the soft smoothly curving bottom, to rest finally in the middle of her back at waist level.

"I didn't mean to wake you," she whispered.

"I've been awake some time, knew you couldn't sleep.

What troubles you? Can I help?" He eased closer, kissing one cheek.

"You could probably take my mind off it." She pressed against him, inhaling deeply, the depression lifting, replaced by a new feeling that seemed to emanate from a delicious warmth spreading under that firm hand in the hollow of her back. Arching against him, writhing slightly, she sighed before forcing the sensations aside, making herself continue. "Solve the problem? Don't think you can. It's the oil lamp and candles again. I try to forget, but if sleep won't come the worries just drift back. I know we manage but it's not really bright enough for the children's homework. Will it damage their eyes do you think?"

"Unlikely. People never used to have electricity. Of course, fewer people used to read, or not so much anyway. I shouldn't think it would do any harm."

"You're probably right, but Sharon really envies her friends, they all have television. I miss it too, but not so much. The way some people look at me in spring and autumn when the days are shorter and they find we've no *proper* lights, it's embarrassing sometimes; as if I'm suddenly beneath them. Most are nice though - some even think it's an achievement to manage without. It would be so good to have, but what can we do?" She sighed again, the feeling of depression returning. He felt the fingers of her hand on his shoulder spread apart, recognising it as an unconscious copy of his own mannerism, an expression of hopelessness.

Her despondency was justified. After enquiries at the Electricity Board had drawn a blank, they had considered the possibility of a small generator. Apart from the initial expense, even the smallest model used a lot of petrol during a week; and there was the question of noise. Since visitors came for peace and quiet, a generator could turn out very expensive indeed. Sensing her unhappiness, Gordon ran a hand firmly up the smooth skin of her spine, massaging neck and shoulder muscles, knowing the sensitive places that responded to his touch. She moved slightly, twisting to loosen the flimsy material.

After a while he stopped, still worried how to make her happiness complete. He ought to be able to solve the problem. She was now flat on her tummy, nightdress thrown upwards, covering the pillow. He leaned forward over the warm body, kissing her skin, pensively brushing it with his lips. What could he say?

"There is another possibility. I thought about it a lot back in the early summer when things were a bit slack. I even wrote in June and got permission."

"For what? You never said anything to me!" Jan sat bolt upright in the darkness, the delectable lethargy leaving her body, surprise in her voice, other matters forgotten. "Got permission from whom? And why?"

"From the River Authority. I was toying with ideas of a waterwheel, but had second thoughts. Don't know enough about them."

He heard her sigh, sensed the sudden hope draining away as her grip on his arm went limp.

"A waterwheel? That would never work." She said it without force, listlessly, and lay down again.

"Don't be too sure." He leaned across, kissing her ear gently. "How often have I let you down in the past? Call at the library for me on your next trip to Penzance."

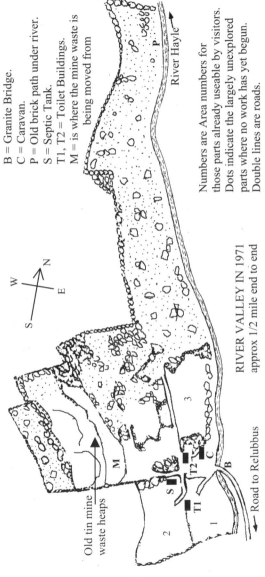

B = Granite Bridge.
C = Caravan.
P = Old brick path under river.
S = Septic Tank.
T1, T2 = Toilet Buildings.
M = is where the mine waste is
  being moved from

River Hayle

Numbers are Area numbers for
those parts already useable by visitors.
Dots indicate the largely unexplored
parts where no work has yet begun.
Double lines are roads.

Old tin mine waste heaps

RIVER VALLEY IN 1971
approx 1/2 mile end to end

Road to Relubbus

N
W   E
S

375

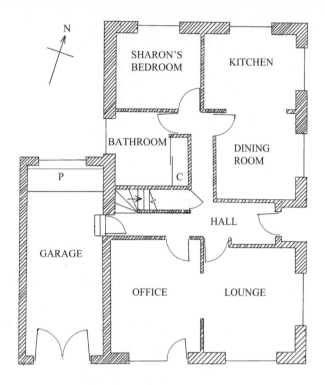

Plans of the House which the family hope to build for themselves - but will it ever be possible? Seeing the intended layout may make the story more real - which of course it is, for it all truely happened. This is the ground floor, but two more bedrooms are planned in the roof, reached by a flight of stairs from the garage end of the corridor. These are intended to be made in concrete; it's cheaper! The top two steps might be wooden.
In front of the office will be a large stony yard for visitors cars - that is, if any can be persuaded to come!
C indicates where the chimney will rise, and P is a pit in the garage where coal or perhaps logs might be stored.
The windows (shown by single lines) are arranged so that those in the kitchen, dining room, lounge and office, all face partly towards the river and bridge.

Chris with an orphan rabbit

Sharon gives a hand

Dangerous bird?

Stephen milking

The injured young swan

377

The Valley of Dreams Series.
by Gordon Channer

Village by the Ford	£6.95	0-9537009-1-7
House by the Stream	£7.95	0-9537009-2-5
Wheel on the Hayle	£7.95	0-9537009-0-9
A Buzzard to Lunch	£6.95	0-9537009-3-3
Follow that Caravan	£7.95	0-9537009-4-1

Book sizes:- 309   374   372   368   427 pages.
Best enjoyed if read in the order given above.

There is an experimental web page with photos:-
www.Cornishbooks.co.uk

The series is available through your local bookshop or can be ordered direct (post free in UK) from:- Cornish Books, 5 Tregembo Hill, Penzance, Cornwall, TR20 9EP Email Dreams@Cornishbooks.co.uk